More Raw Material

Work inspired by
Alan Sillitoe

Edited by
Neil Fulwood & David Sillitoe

With a preface by
Ruth Fainlight

First published 2015
by Lucifer Press

ISBN 978-0-9934241-0-6

Layout and design by
4 Sheets Design & Print Ltd
01773 836973

Printed and bound by
Russell Press Ltd, Nottingham
0115 9784505

Contents

	ACKNOWLEDGEMENTS	5
Ruth Fainlight	PREFACE	7
The Editors	INTRODUCTION	8
Viv Apple	The Plaque	9
Carl Fellstrom	Night and Day	10
Alan Baker	Whatever You Say We Are	13
Maria Taylor	Gangsters	14
Viv Apple	Feeler Gauge	15
Derrick Buttress	Love in Radford	16
Graham Mort	Midland Rail	18
Roy Marshall	The Horses	20
Mark Piggott	Picture This	21
Martin Figura	Paradise Street	23
Brett Evans	Big Women and Men of Imagination	28
Kevin Higgins	Things to do in Galway Before You Again Decide Not to Shoot Yourself	29
Kevin Higgins	Whataboutery, Ireland 2014	31
Sue Pace	Chant of Survival	33
Neil Astley	Blackened Blues	42
Roy Marshall	Carrying the Arrest Bleep	44
Bryce Wilson	Saturday Night Loneliness	46
Penelope Shuttle	London Road	50
Henry Normal	Did it Rain on the First Good Friday?	52
Kate O'Shea	Hell Poems	53
Jason Williamson	Fenlands	55
Bernard O'Donoghue	And Spoil the Child	57
Bernard O'Donoghue	Moths	57
Martin Knight	Alan Sillitoe — A Good Life	58
The Editors	An Unstarted Life	62
Alan Sillitoe	A Start in Life: screen treatment	63
David Cooke	Homeward	73
Ruth Fainlight	The Motorway	74
D.J. Taylor	Mapping the Territory	75
Neil Fulwood & David Sillitoe	Revisiting *Alan Sillitoe's Nottinghamshire*	78
Harry Paterson	Maybe Tomorrow	98
David Duncombe	Odds Against	103

Kate O'Shea	Black Hole	105
David Cooke	Drink	106
Tony Roe	From Gosling, R.	107
Brick	The Bar at the Trip to Jerusalem	118
Neil Fulwood	The Gospel According to Arthur Seaton	120
Ross Bradshaw	The Nottingham Issue	128
Ian Brookes	First Edition	133
David Constantine	Girl with a cello on the metro	135
Ruth Padel	A Trip to the Moon	136
Emma Claire Sweeney	The Taj Mahal of the North	137
Maria Taylor	Becoming Santa	145
Pippa Hennessy	The Certainty of Seagulls	146
Bethany W. Pope	Medical Records	148
Harry Gallagher	Steeltown	149
Derrick Buttress	By the River	150
Joanne Limburg	Swifts	152
Joanne Limburg	The View from Crieff	152
Andy Croft	Tomskaya Pisanitsa Park, Kemerovo	153
John King	See No Evil	160
Bethany W. Pope	When She Asks for Bread, Will You Give Her a Stone?	171
Paul McMahon	Shrouds	172
Mike Wilson	Gladly in Russia	174
Rosie Garland	Empty quarter	177
Rosie Garland	Asking for directions	178
Neil Astley	For Want of a Nail	179
Mel Fisher	My Mate Sid, and other Middle East memories	181
Keith Armstrong	In the Department of Poetry	190
Henry Normal	How Many Genii Does it Take to Change a Light Source?	191
Brett Evans	Wild Bill's Celestial Jazz	192
John Lucas	The Goods	193
Robert Kenchington	Solti in Nottingham	201
Jeremy Duffield	Sketching in Beeston	203
Cathy Grindrod	A Writer Visits	204
Michael Eaton	Lost Again: a Letter to Mr Sillitoe	206
Mark Patterson	No Further South is North	214
Nick Humphreys	Portrait of Alan Sillitoe	219
	CONTRIBUTORS' NOTES	220

Acknowledgements

Our thanks to Viv Apple for her efforts in securing many of the contributors featured in this volume; to Paula Fulwood for copy typing; to Liz Baugh and Amy Clarke for their assistance in proof reading.

Black Hole by Kate O'Shea was originally published in Prole, and *A Trip to the Moon* by Ruth Padel in Aeon.

The photograph of Ruth Fainlight on page 6 was taken by Hana Vályi and is used by kind permission of The Robert Graves Society. The photograph on page 181 is used by kind permission of Mel Fisher and any resemblance to Lawrence of Arabia is purely coincidental.

All other photographs are by David Sillitoe.

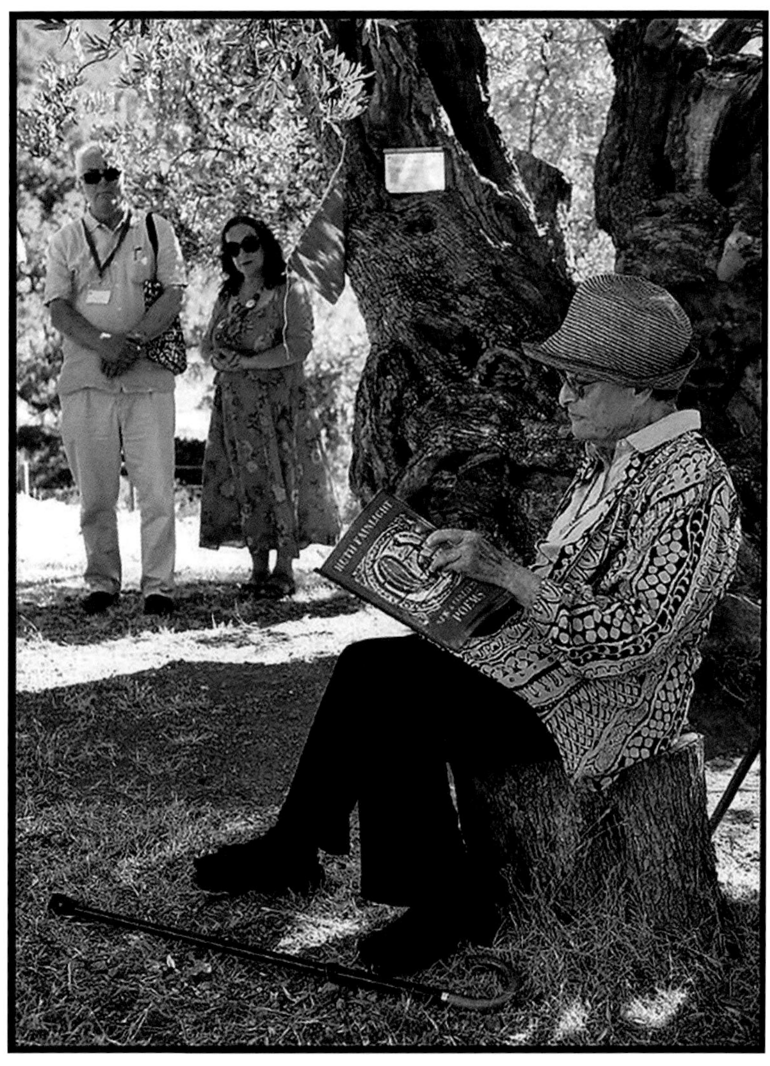

Preface

There must be something in the air — or in the water — of the city of Nottingham and the county of Nottinghamshire, to explain how it can produce, from one century, one decade, to the next, such excellent writers. Whether demonstrated in the vivid speech of marketplace and street, or the compelling images and narratives of its poets and prose writers, without doubt there is something special about the att-itude towards, and love of, language: its flexibility, its sounds and unexpected juxtapositions and shifts of meaning, which characterises almost every local inhabitant, writer or not.

Lord Byron, D.H. Lawrence and Alan Sillitoe are the first names which come to mind as examples of the literary genius of the region manifested through two centuries — although there are many others. The earliest writer I know about is the late eighteenth century poet Henry Kirke White; when Alan and I first met he told me about him and took me to Clifton Grove to show me what remained of the site of Kirke White's inspiration. We also visited Newstead Abbey, the Byron family seat, and on another day rode the bus to Eastwood, the small mining town where Lawrence was born. It seems almost unbelievable to remember now — but somehow we got into conversation on the street outside the Lawrence house with a man who did not seem that old (although he died the following year). When we told him we were writers and had come to see where Lawrence grew up, he revealed that he was Willie Hopkin, an important figure in local political and cultural life, and that his house had been one of the places the young Lawrence had gone to hear discussions and meet congenial people.

I can imagine that now, other young people might well go in search of the sites of Alan Sillitoe's youth — although the drastic slum clearance of the recent past has wiped out most of the places he lived and where he set his 'Nottingham' stories, and where much of the film of his novel *Saturday Night and Sunday Morning* was shot. There can be no doubt of Alan's lasting position in the canon of English literature and, particularly in Nottingham, I am sure that his influence will increase. This fine volume is testimony to that. I should like to thank all the contributors, as well as the editors for their discrimination and industry.

Introduction

"In the beginning was the word, and Adam was the Printer's Devil" — thus begins Alan Sillitoe's 1972 part novel, part autobiography hybrid *Raw Material.* For Alan there was no form of literary endeavour or discipline that was out of bounds, and his continual experimentation pushed himself, challenged his readers, and he didn't give a damn whether that put a dint in his popularity or not. "Go back to Nottingham, Mr Sillitoe" raged a reviewer perplexed by his existential novel *The General.* You have to wonder what that critic would have made of the anti-thrillers *The Lost Flying Boat* and *The German Numbers Woman*, the feminist character study *Her Victory,* or the deconstructive late-period masterpiece *The Broken Chariot.*

His output was prodigious: more than 60 volumes (many more if you count small press editions and limited printings) across six decades. Novels, short fiction, poetry, essays, travel writing, plays, film scripts, children's books, memoir. And letters; he corresponded enthusiastically, always writing in longhand: his fountain pen creating a beautiful, perfectly legible script. His literary output was typed, corrections, annotations and rearrangements made by hand. There was a brief experiment with word-processing; predictably, it ended badly.

In putting together *More Raw Material,* we not only wanted to pay tribute to Alan Sillitoe, but also to capture something of his spirit. And it's this that influences and infuses our contributors' personal reminiscences, short fiction, essays, travel writing, and of course poetry. We also hope that this volume stands as a corrective to the lazy, inaccurate 'Alan Sillitoe as angry young man' theorising that fixates on three or four volumes from the outset of his career. So, may we encourage the reader to explore more of Alan's writing, and find within it the richness and diversity of a long life's work.

We are honoured that such a roster of talented and important artists, both established and up-and-coming, agreed to be part of this project. And if they entertain, inspire and invigorate the reader, then we have done our job.

Alan left us in 2010. In assembling this anthology, it has felt like he's never been gone.

The Plaque

At 5.00pm on Thursday, 10 July 2014, an unveiling ceremony took place in the olive grove at Robert Graves' home and garden in Mallorca, Spain. The plaque, on an olive tree, is in memory of Alan Sillitoe and was unveiled by his widow, the poet Ruth Fainlight.

Robert Graves was a friend of Alan and Ruth for many years, and The Robert Graves Society (President, Charles Mundye), had arranged for the ceremony to be part of the Twelfth International Robert Graves Conference, a five-day event held in Palma and Deia.

Ruth Fainlight is shown in the photograph on page 6 in the foreground, reading a poem dedicated to Alan from her latest book, and in the background are Candida Ridler, former Curator of Visual Arts at the British Library (retired), and Jake Empson, son of the poet and critic William Empson. The plaque and inscription were the idea of Robert Graves' daughter, Lucia (a writer and translator), who first encountered Alan Sillitoe and Ruth Fainlight when they lived in Mallorca in the 1950s.

The brass plaque has the simple inscription:

In memoriam
ALAN SILLITOE
1928–2010

There is a last line in Morse Code: a fitting acknowledgement of his passion for that complex form which lasted from the time he served as a telegraphist and radio operator in Malaya just after the war, until the end of his life. The Morse message reads:

'WE MISS YOU'

Night and Day

The first literary encounter I remember with Mr Sillitoe was in a second-hand bookshop off Charing Cross Road in London around 1985 or 1986. It is difficult to be precise about the date but I was in London studying for a literature and philosophy degree at Thames Polytechnic, now University of Greenwich. As I recall I was mining the myriad of second hand bookshops for literature which would help familiarise me with an element of the BA course focused on the 'Angry Young Men' — an ill-advised, media-coined pigeon-hole into which various British writers including Alan Sillitoe and John Osborne had been wedged. *Saturday Night and Sunday Morning* was not part of the course but, feeling my way along the laden bookshelves with my eyes, a dog-eared copy seemed to edge its way out from among the other books alongside it and command my attention. I had seen the film and loved Albert Finney's performance. Yet, scandalously, I had never read the book. A mere 90 odd pence poorer I walked from the shop with a copy of *Saturday Night and Sunday Morning*, and instantly became richer for all the experience of reading it. I should digress and explain that at this point in time I knew nothing about Nottingham other than the legend which is Brian Clough. The text itself was a joy to read. As sparse and tight as anything written by Hemingway and with a wonderfully roguish, yet brutally honest anti-hero at the centre of its stage. There is an elemental force about the way the writing merges the unbridled passion of the night with the sobriety of the day. But enough about its narrative. Go and dig out a copy and read it if you haven't already and if you have read it already, well, read it again.

Years after I completed my degree and after a series of jobs on regional newspapers, Nottingham became my home — borne out of necessity and love — and once again, some ten years after I acquired that first paperback, I re-read the book and realised just how much Alan had captured an essence of Nottingham and bottled it for all time. Initially I was visiting a girlfriend in Nottingham at weekends, but within just a few trips I fell in love with the city. I was working down south and my squeeze at the time was working at the then broadsheet Nottingham Evening Post in a building where The Cornerhouse now stands on Forman Street.

At the weekends I travelled up to Nottingham and regularly frequented a trio of watering holes used at that time by Post journalists: Langtry's, The Turf Tavern and The Blue Bell. It was during these visits to the pubs, loud with chatter and pumped with good beer, that I began to have an overwhelming sense of *deja vu* and of familiarity with the many people who used these watering holes on Friday and Saturday evenings, albeit strangers to me. In those days people spilled out from the pubs at closing time and headed towards the Market Square in search of a cab ride home. It was all bonhomie and banter in the queues for the taxi. I realised where this sense of the familiar had sprung from, for within the tight confines of the packed bear pit pubs and in the queues for the taxi were the very real descendants of Arthur Seaton, raucously turning the night into their own show, swapping stories and philosophies on the meaning of life and seemingly fuelled by the very spirit of Arthur Seaton. Having familiarised myself with the city physically, I re-read *Saturday Night and Sunday Morning* once again and realised that Alan had, in the creation of Arthur Seaton, captured a great truth; the greatest hope any writer has when they put pen to paper.

So much has changed in the physical landscape of the city painted in *Saturday Night and Sunday Morning*. The demise of the Raleigh and John Player type of industry was coupled with the loss of vast tracts of terraced housing; the 'little palaces' of Radford, St Ann's and the Meadows. When I came to write *Hoods*, I guess part of me was mournful about the social changes which appear to have been ignited by the loss of those industries and undoubtedly ignited problems in other communities such as the mining satellites around Nottingham. Some of the grittiness I admired about Nottingham had somehow soured, turned in on itself, and become downright dangerous and I wondered what Arthur Seaton would have made of the gang violence and organised crime which had a grip on the city as it moved into the twenty-first century. Perhaps if Arthur Seaton hadn't been lucky enough to have a relatively well-paid job he would have been drawn into that world in his search for money to pay the bills. In Seaton's own words: "all I'm out for is a good time and all the rest is propaganda". It's a fantastically evocative turn of phrase, but I have never believed in it as a philosophy, any more than I believe Alan Sillitoe intended that Arthur Seaton should live by his own words. Arthur Seaton is, as we all are, a mass of contradictions searching for a fixed identity in the face of the cruel knowledge that we are only here for a short speck of time. But I have a sneaking suspicion that Arthur Seaton, grafter as he was, would have rather have gone off and done National Service or absconded abroad than contemplate becoming involved in serious criminality in order to survive. As a fictional character he even defied the pen of the man who had created him, as Alan had him vocalise these immortal words: "I'm me and nobody else; and whatever anyone says I am or thinks I am, that's what I am not, because they don't know a bloody thing about me."

One thing is for sure. In this age of mobile phones, PC gaming and social networking, we don't do nearly enough to encourage people to learn the value of writing and reading. Little symbols can help to counter that and I hope that at some time in the near future there is a lasting and fitting memorial to Alan Sillitoe, who, in my opinion, is a Nottingham legend. And if Brian Clough deserved a lasting memorial then Mr Sillitoe, whose words have launched, provoked and poked the thoughts of millions of people, most surely deserves a permanent pride of place in his home city.

Whatever You Say We Are

for Alan Sillitoe

To be here and nowhere else, what is that?
A question on the lips, the mind elsewhere

walking through the market square, with a dome,
sunshine, shoppers wrapped against the cold.

To be in your city, Saturday night city,
remembering a city of factories

sunset over Gregory Boulevard, men at dawn
cycling to Raleigh, women coughing

over the day's first cigarette outside Players
in this city of waking up famous

of coconuts and gold fish at Goose Fair,
of sitting in a Spanish sunset, under an olive tree

to write the city of coal and sandstone,
luddite city, city of narrow ways

city of Saint Ann's well, her mixed blessings,
the loneliness of the long distances

ghosts of framework knitters,
blocks of flats grey and crumbling

in grubby sunlight, to remind us we're in
the city of caves, of lace, city of the burning castle

a city trying to be remembered, dissenting city,
outlaw city, city of words.

Gangsters

Bassetlaw men always talked coal
behind closed doors, away from kids.
I imagined them in pin-stripes
and trilbys in Working Men's clubs,
smoking, playing seven card stud.

My father might be a gangster.
I had to check so stayed up late
to see him back from the club
with a pack of poppets for me,
a beery kiss, tell-tale trace of cigar.

He said coal had no future,
he drifted from place to place:
Cottam, High Marnham, West Burton,
like bad men did in movies,
whistling, coin-flipping in bars,
a tommy gun in our Cortina's boot.

I was too young to understand
why my father wanted out.
We were public enemies on the run.
I'd reach up to his blackbird face,
press my lips on soot. We'd scram,
split, not knowing our crime.

Feeler Gauge

My fingers freeze
with effort and the cold.
"Hold that light still!"

I bite my lip. I am.
I am holding it still,
but still it shakes.

Beneath the bonnet now
the engine glistens in the dark.
Oily corners, slippery as butter,
guide his blackened hands. He searches
to define the metal, finds a jagged edge —

"Give me the light! Now you can take the gauge!"

My hand relaxes for a second. Unlike him.
The light is steady now. I take the tool:
a fan of metal strips, each finely made
to measure tiny clearances we cannot see.
He slowly turns the starting handle
and the tappets move.

"Twelve thou! Now don't forget — twelve thou!"

I won't. I won't forget.

TWELVE THOU: twelve thousandths of an inch

Love in Radford

One day, because he had been sacked at the pit, our neighbour, Compton, went fishing in the Trent. It was spring. In the evening he came home with a live eel in a bucket. He blocked the grate to make a pool beneath the communal tap in the middle of Clayton Square and poured the eel into it. We saw a primitive, dangerous looking creature, with a slimy skin, probably hiding a set of fretsaw teeth. We watched in fear as it slithered at our feet. Then, as the girls squealed and we held our breath, Compton bashed its head with a lump hammer. He carried it to the fishmonger on Denman Street and swapped his prize for a piece of Scarborough cod for Liz and the kids.

***

Morris the myopic lived in the first house in the Square. He had terrible eyes. His horizon lay at his fingertips. When he reached out he could touch the edge of his world. Although he was more cunning than any of the boys, his teachers sent him to the dunces' school because he couldn't make words sit still when he had to read and write.

He went to work in the lace factory. There he fell in love with soft, warm Margaret, tried to tell her in jumping-bean words, scrawling out what he thought was her name which he copied from a packet of Stork margarine; '*der margarine I lov yu moris*'.

When Margaret tore the letter up in contempt and tossed it over his head like confetti, Morris decided that love was not for him, and turned to booze and serious brooding instead.

***

There was a boy in the Square so poor he never combed his hair or came out to play in shoes. He was so poor we could see his willy through the holes in his shorts. I couldn't understand how anybody could be as poor as that. Mam told me it was because there were ten kids in the house, but I heard her tell our neighbour that the boy's mam and dad were always at it, even though they were 'nowt to look at' and all of their kids scratched because of nits and fleas. She told the neighbour the rabbit-arsed dad should have had 'it' cut off years ago.

***

From the tallyman, Dad bought a snazzy double-breasted overcoat in herringbone tweed; he looked like the Duke of Windsor when he wore it to the domino school in the Smith's Arms on Sundays. He loved that coat. He would rather have been married to that coat than to Mam. On Sunday night he would lock it away in the closet before he went to bed. He thought he had the only key. On Monday morning, Mam made a lovely pledge at the pawnshop.

***

Compton was off work for a long time. Living without a wage coming in made something die in Liz's heart. She turned to Harry the tallyman because all her prayers were ignored. Harry the tallyman took her from hearth and home to a flat in an out-of-luck part of town where she saw rain clouds, even on the sunniest day. Harry was generous. He never left her short, and there was a shilling or two in her purse every day. But she went back to Clayton Square because she missed her kids, and even Compton's selfish little ways, for love bites deep, and will never let you go.

Midland Rail

Crows over stubble like a Dutch painting;
a bandage of mist, everything wounded —

the red clay, seeping sky, burnt trees
charred by dream-flamed hours of night.

It's been a year since she went home to
patch its remnant of childish time. Her

book's forgotten now instead of this: a
freight train's rapid admonition on rails

smeared with dawn, cattle stooped at
the treeline, anointed by hefted sun.

A trinity of cooling towers coughs out
clouds; birch leaves blaze yellow slag;

flat rivers carry away light. Her face at
the window, pressed between glass; her

eye-pits brimming over a white house,
grazing horses, the canal's printout.

Wheels sing it: *you were never here, never
here, never here* where blind factories

fall, bulrushes spike the mill lodge and
an old man casts a line, waist deep in

reflections. Two herons stagger — stage
drunks faltering on scooped wings:

she sees them lifting mythically scented
feet, flying to locations their shadows

announce, like the next town and the
next. Around her they pull down bags,

check cellphones, search platforms for
those they have loved or may have

loved or love still; now doors open,
recursive, repeating dawn's chill.

The Horses

In the first bright slew of laughter and bedclothes
we hear them, and cars slowing to pass,
the drifting talk of their riders.
They clop through gathering dark
as lights come on and the baby kicks
and dreams inside you. Hooves break
the skin of our sleep, wake us to green shoots
or rusted leaves, to shoe prints in early frost,
a puddled road and soft scatterings.
The boy grows tall and oversleeps
as we lie tangled or back to back,
while the phone brings news
of a slipping away, a collapse
into nearly nothing. Blossom is blown
to blizzard, blackbirds return
to build in clematis. But always,
we hear horses; though we never know
their barrelled flanks, the sway
and tilt of a saddled back,
as they trot through the days
of promise, arrival, exit.

Picture This

This city was foreign to him, and for the first few weeks he wandered as if lost in the dusty old streets near the apartment where he had taken lodgings. One afternoon, just as loneliness threatened to overpower him (as if he were being annihilated by the sky) he passed a shop window and saw a portrait. His heart chilled, his eyes watered, and he pressed his nose to the dirty glass. Mouth vapour obscured his view, and impatiently he wiped with a cold hand and stared at a small framed portrait of a young woman, carelessly leaning at the back of the display. She was the image of beauty, and now his heart pumped, bleeding warmth through his body like good whiskey. Never had he seen those eyes, and yet he knew them, knew her, those perfect cheeks, such tender lips (stained a little with ink). He knew that as long as the picture stared solemnly out from the window, he would never be alone in the world.

Every day for many years he passed by the window, and no matter how he tried he could never keep from looking therein. Deep down he had a deep terror that someone would come along, purchase his picture even though it bore no price and take it away from him forever. Each time he saw its ever-changing gaze (its shifting meanings and moods) his breathing slowed a fraction, then his blood would boil again in fury.

When wine got the better of him he would come late at night, his eyes imploring those eyes to pity him and his loneliness, yet knowing within his sober soul how futile were his hopes. When he awoke with a tender head he would be embarrassed and ashamed, wondering why this unobtainable image held such power over him.

He came to know and love many women over those years, and sometimes he was rich and sometimes he was poor. Occasionally, reeling over the defeat of yet another hapless affair and crazed with desire for the picture, he would work all hours in a desperate attempt to save enough money to make her his forever. But every time he went into the shop, no matter how much money he had managed to save, it was never quite enough. In a fury he would purchase a cheaper picture and spend what was left on alcohol, often smashing the cheap substitute to matchwood before the night was done.

After a dozen years his work beckoned him away to another city, filling him with a shared relief and sorrow at leaving the portrait behind. On his final night he tried to stay away from the window, as if to prove something to himself, but failed. It was late as he walked up the narrow street, and the old city was still.

As he drew nearer the window he realised that something was amiss: the very glass which had separated him from his beloved image for all those years had been shattered by some robber, disturbed, who had fled. Although some other pictures had been taken, his own beloved lay unharmed in a pool of glass.

With unnatural care he picked up the portrait and held it to the street lamp, overcome: here was an object of more wondrous beauty than he had ever believed. Secreting the painting beneath his great coat he made his way to his meagre lodgings, his heart a vortex of extreme emotion.

As he drew near to his lodgings, a large ruffian with red hair held him against the wall and demanded his money. When he protested that he had none, the scoundrel demanded to know what was beneath his coat. Seeing the picture, the thief scowled with delight. Kicking him in the belly, the ruffian ran away with his portrait of wonder. The man went home and wept, not for pain, but at his loss.

The next day the man was passing a place which sold cheap replicas, and to his surprise saw an exact copy of his beloved picture. Buying it with cheap, unwanted coins, he took it away to the foreign city. When framed, it was impossible to tell that this was not the original upon which he had poured so much love. Friends admired the copy, and he accepted their praise, but secretly he was sad, knowing in his heart as he did that this was not the picture of his dreams, the one he had for so long dreamed of holding only for it to be snatched away.

He grew old, and looked back sagely, ruefully. The copy had long gone to a pawn-broker and he was drinking himself to death. It seemed that sadness had been in his make-up for so long he did not know how to live without it; until now, as death called him near, and that sadness finally gave way to a warm joy, and the realisation came upon him that for one fleeting moment, a fraction of time, she of the infinite beauty had been his.

Paradise Street

Out of the Strong Came Forth Sweetness.
JUDGES 14:14

1941 Blitz*

The Mersey is a hungry mouth, her dark city night
torn down by bombers, her fearful people
in cellars. In the blood-red after-fire of the docks

SS Malakand's munition belly swells and explodes,
her tonnage of anchor hurled through the trembling sky
to the hospital steps. A fireman lies at the gates,

his coming of age watch stopped on his wrist. A lad
surfaces through diesel and puke, hands slapping
at the water, teeth chattering in his skull, the burnt

toffee stench of molasses at his throat, the burning shore
so far away. A mother stumbles from the shelter,
hurries pale along Paradise Street, its pavement of rats,

flinches in the sudden blast and clutches her Maggie,
her sweet baby's eyes wheels of flame. Across Bootle, Kirkdale
and Walton, the thin wail of sirens strung out for the loss.

1953 Shallcross Street: Red, White and Blue.*

Men smoke buttoned up and slick as if Sunday.
Women load shrouded trestle tables, the cake's
top tier askew on Doric columns. Fancy dress kids

pose dead dog still for the Echo's photographer.
Maggie, eye-patched and one scabby knee bent, leans
on the worn head of a cut down broom, calls to her uncle:

aargh Jim Lad. Jim's Bantam splutters about, kids
bouncing in its sidecar, like eggs loose
in a box. At night fall, someone's upright piano

is lugged from their parlour out to the street.
Who wouldn't feel sentimental under such bunting,
under such stars, and fill their lungs

for *O Waly, Waly,* for *Liverpool Lullaby:*

Although you have no silver spoon
Better days are coming soon.

*1834 * Young Barker*

falls to his bony knees, sings
Miss Dobson a lullaby:

A-gath'ring flowers both red and blue,
I little thought of what love can do.

A tiny shop on Paradise Street
from their union, something sweet.

*1963 * Barker and Dobson Sweet Factory*

Girls pour through the gates, dipper hands sticky
from putting the twist into buttered brazils. Arm
-in-arm they sway, a necklace of misshapes strung

the width of Whitefield Road, singing themselves
home for Friday tea, sifting out to Everton's
furrowed brow of terraces. Below, the docks

loose flat-hatted men with thirsts more than equal
to a ten bob note. Bizzies brace for the Blue
and the Red, the Taig and the Prod. Jim has a joke,

digs deep in his pocket, puts off the stagger
up the hill until his belligerence is tight enough,
the kids asleep in bed. Maggie scrubs herself squeaky,

puts on the lippy, promises her da she'll be on
that last bus. Once safe round the corner
she hitches her skirt, lets the Devil walk her

to the top of Breck Road, show her the city
spread out brightly below. And look
at the gob on it! This Mersey mouth will spill

from transistors and Dansettes, cross oceans,
set girls screaming with a shake of its moppy head,
write a new history in sweat on cellar walls.

Maggie steadies herself at the Necropolis gates.
Is this the love everyone's singing about
or just a Tate and Lyle lorry trundling past.

*1981 * Cantril Farm*

Slum-cleared here in the Summer of Love.
One road in, no road out, no buses or pubs
or goats or pigs come to that. At night

you can hear the 'Mancs' in the safari park or maybe
it's just the motorway roaring past. And now
Love Lane Refinery's gone, there's no sugar

to sweeten the pill. The Devil watches
the burning city from his tower block
and Maggie falls out of love with her name.

*1807 * Kitty Amelia*

Captain 'Mind your Eye' Crow sets the last slaver
against the current, her three hundred tons of burden
cleaves rough water not healing in her wake.

*2008 * European City of Culture*

The Albert Dock all done up and Maggie's lad
Michael visiting from London — *I know the shame, the shame.*
He walks her quietly through the Maritime Museum:

the old docks handmade bricks, wartime heroes
lost at sea, the shackles of the slave ship's hold,
the masters' commemoration, cast in iron:

Rodney Street,
Ashton Street,
Sir Thomas Street
Penny Lane.

She saw them *loads of times* down the Cavern
where her mother clutched her the night
the sky blazed and where his father told her

the first lie, a good one too, that he was
Billy Liddell's son and had a trial at Anfield, which
was almost true; the trial was not at Anfield though.

They're making over Paradise Street: Liverpool One,
Liverpool's Mayfair: apartments, leisure
facilities, bronzey goose-pimple girls

and retail outlets. John Lewis's for a treat.
He opts for the healthy option, Maggie stirs
three sugars into her tea and enjoys the view.

*2012 * Stockbridge Village (formerly Cantril Farm)*

Tarzan returns, silver maned in a long
camel coat, *Maggie* she says, shaking his hand —
after the robbing prossie in the song, not Thatcher,

me da had some pride and they both laugh
till it hurts. Lord and Lady Heseltine
are presented with a framed aerial photograph

and a jar of Stockbridge Village honey.

Although you have no silver spoon
Better days are coming soon

Big Women and Men of Imagination

The man of imagination needs to know he has mapped
territory worthy of report, a skinny isthmus
is only ever of slight importance; his preferred
expedition is of the vaster plains. Zaftig sculptures
whose beauty was appreciated in a more
civilised age reaffirms he has not been duped
by fickle fashions, and that where women
are concerned, the maxim *less is more* proves
a fallacy. The man of imagination drops anchor
at port between sizable thighs.
Without leaving the covers he wants to feel
he has circumnavigated the globe,
held the world in both hands.

Things to do in Galway Before You Again Decide Not to Shoot Yourself

Take up smoking other people's cigarettes and wear
a beret you found on the Ballybane bus.
Write a Last Will and Testament in which you bequeath
your lungs to your least favourite busker.
Get given a banjo on someone else's
fifty first birthday and fully intend
to learn how to play it.

Launch an online petition angrily calling
for more of the same.
Organise a fundraising concert in aid
of yourself, headlined by a guy who once met Peter, Paul
& Mary. Carry a concealed photo of a young Lord Haw Haw
in the breast pocket of the shabby three piece
you wear at weekends and consider

a career in broadcasting. If male, nickname
that thing in your underpants
the late Bishop Browne; if female,
erect a sign officially
re-naming your equal and opposite bits
John F. Kennedy Square.

Become an elderly crank in pyjama pants
who once owned a craft shop.
Try our range of face creams
Druid's Semen Number One, Two & Three.
Wake up shouting about homeopathy,
El Salvador, Palestine.

Skulk up back streets face down-
beat as a bad turn out
at a charity event for athlete's
foot. Visit the Abbey and buy a Mass card.
Send it to yourself by registered post,
so tomorrow at least
the world will have some sympathy.

Whataboutery, Ireland 2014

Government policy is a disgrace and [I] have written so several times.
But there are more important things to march about, and we've never done it.
FERGUS FINLAY

If I showed you
the enormity of my compassion,
you'd go roaring
back into your houses
never again to emerge
until the last day. That crowd,
their mouths full of
the wrong question, don't get that
most things are inevitable,
especially me. Each time I have to
argue in favour of keeping things as they
intolerably are, I need help carrying
my excessive heart from the room.
Last night the abuse
from the trolls on Twitter was such,
I had to be rushed
to an emergency dinner party.

Against your monosyllable: no,
I counter pose
the disabled children on whose behalf
you never marched in the rain;
the old woman tied to her chair and shouted at
regularly in a state run home
about which your crayoned sign
has nothing to say; refugees
of too many horrible situations to mention,
who I'm so busy loving in abstract,

I've no time to join you through the streets
saying that one simplistic word
you appear to actually mean.
To your blank refusal, I prefer
the conference on ethics
at the university of Exeter
I'll be attending next week.

Today, I'm dreaming up *viable*
alternatives to the current paradigm
and having my hair cut for charity,
while you waste your time
overthrowing the government.

We can't have the country being run
by people not familiar with the effect
blue cheese washed down with
the right dessert wine has on the taste buds;
both know it typically results
in the likes of me being pulled
apart by horses.

Chant of Survival

MAC

"I understand that you want to do this on your own," Mandy said, "but we're going to have a baby and, when the time comes, I need you absolutely clean and clear."

"I know."

"Not just for now, either, but for the rest of our lives."

Mac nodded and finished screwing on his leg.

She reached for the gold framed wedding picture of the two of them; Mandy in her flowing white dress and Mac in his uniform. "I love you," she said, "no matter what." She tucked the picture into the gym bag's side pocket, kissed him and went downstairs to unlock the door and flip the switch to the open-for-business beer sign of her father's tavern. Mac blinked away the sting of tears and finished packing his gear in the battered and stained Navy duffel.

RALPH

The VA Hospital waiting room was filled with demons and aliens. That's how Ralph thought of them. Hell, that's how he thought of himself. It wasn't just the fact that he no longer needed to shave the half of his face that was pocked and scarred with skin as pink and shiny as half-chewed bubblegum. It wasn't the shrapnel-dimpled torso. It was the lost leg, chopped off six inches above an absent knee. When it came right down to it, he was just one more partial person sitting next to half a squadron of partial people.

The man sitting across from Ralph had the body of a long distance runner and wore blue camouflage pants and a t-shirt with a Navy insignia and the letters EOD stenciled on the front. Ralph knew Explosive Ordinance Disposal would be stenciled on the back. It was a job that demanded steady hands and nerves of steel but Ralph could see that one of those hands only had three fingers. Ralph noticed that because the vet was reading one of the slick advertisements piled on the floor. The colorful brochure said a bionic prosthetic leg system (with a chrome socket design) could be ramped up for hard duty road work but the plastic ball-bearing prosthesis was cheaper and nearly unnoticeable in a pair of long pants.

Ralph was going back into rehab because he needed to sweat off too many months of hard drinking. Plus, half a year ago he'd gone into debt to buy the prosthetic upgrade and he was still learning how to navigate the titanium spring-loaded-stilt. The money for the metal leg was eating away at him because, after all this time, he was still trying to master the skillset of a daily run — which, some days, was the only thing that kept him from putting the barrel of his 9mm Glock in his mouth and pulling the trigger.

The navy guy looked up. "Stop grinding your teeth. It's fucking annoying."

Ralph nodded and shrugged. "Sorry."

"Where were you stationed?"

"1st Battalion. 75th Regiment."

The Navy guy nodded. "You were a Ranger."

"I can kill you seventeen different ways with a toothbrush and a rubber band."

"Don't think that will get you to see the doctors any quicker."

The room smelled of sweat and fear with an overtone of urine. "I'd suggest we go for a run but that piece of pink plastic you're looking at won't stand up to the pounding," Ralph said.

"In case you haven't noticed, I'm wearing a training blade. This cheap shit would be for Christmas with the in-laws." The shiny brochure in the thick, freckled hands sagged like an upside down pup tent. "I don't need them making nice to the family cripple. My wife doesn't need it either."

"You don't look old enough to be married."

The sailor pulled out his cell phone and flipped it open to show a series of pictures featuring a clear-eyed redhead with the face that could stop traffic.

"Wow."

"I need to keep clean for my wife and for the little angel that's coming."

"You don't want to keep clean for yourself?"

"Right now, I'm willing to do it for them."

"Whatever works, I guess."

The sailor's hands were shaky as he flipped through the brochure's pages. "I've got most my fingers and an opposable thumb. And I still got my dick. I'm partial owner of a pub and I need those parts."

"It takes a dick to operate a tavern?"

"You bet. That and a baseball bat. You would not believe what assholes some drunks can be."

"I might."

The sailor put down his magazine. "Sometimes life hands you a peach and sometimes it hands you a lemon."

"If you tell me that life is learning how to turn lemons into lemonade, I'm going home to get my gun."

"I sold all my guns. I'm done with explosives. Especially the point and shoot kind."

"Thus the baseball bat."

"And the need for a dick."

Ralph found himself smiling. "What's the name of your place?"

"The Office."

"You're shittin' me."

"Nope. Mandy and I live upstairs and we're buying it from my father-in-law."

Somewhere there was a shout and then laughter echoed down the long linoleum floor. The two men were silent, watching a young woman wheel across the room, down the hallway and through the sliding glass doors that had slowly opened. The chair was automatic because both her feet and her left hand were missing but her smile was brilliant and the toddler on her lap was laughing and saying, "Faster, Mommy! Faster!"

"How the fuck can she smile?" Ralph's voice was filled with awe. "You think it's easier on women?"

"No."

Ralph wiped his face. He hoped it was sweat and not tears. "I just lost a leg and I'm furious most of the time. I don't know what I'd do without both my hands."

"I think having a kid helps. It gives you something to live for. You got kids?"

"No." Ralph cleared his throat. "I'm one of those drunk assholes you were talking about."

"Yeah, that's what I figured."

"It's that obvious?"

"The old brewski aroma gave you away."

"I'm just getting back into rehab," Ralph said. "I've got an AA meeting later."

"Day at a time."

Sounds of a door slamming and shouts echoed through the waiting room. The receptionist and the nurse behind the desk didn't even bother to look up as a loud angry baritone damned the Lord God straight to hell and all the fucking congressional assholes, too.

Ralph sucked in a breath and the sailor across from him squinted, hard, at the floor. After the room relaxed back into murmurs and groans, Ralph cleared his throat and whispered. "I met someone. Is that making lemonade?"

"Maybe." The sailor stuck out his hand. "My name's Leonard MacDougal. You can call me Mac."

MAC

The VA doc didn't look at Mac. He looked at the computer. "You know that I can't give you anything for the phantom pain."

"It doesn't feel phantom."

"I'm sure it doesn't but it comes with the territory. Just be glad you look normal and people don't stare when you walk into a room."

"I don't mind my wife staring," Mac said. "Especially when I'm doing my male stripper routine."

The doc quit tapping on the keyboard and smiled. "Get outta here. And no script for Oxycodone. I don't care if it feels like the devil has set your foot on fire."

"I didn't ask for Oxy," Mac said. "I'm done with that. I asked if there was any medicine that wasn't addicting that I could take instead."

The doc's face was sad. "Not that I know of."

Mac hated running but was good at it. It kept him clear. It kept him clean. Mac didn't do the marathons because he mostly liked to run alone, at night. The VA didn't allow that so he ran with a partner. His old partner was discharged so he grabbed onto the new guy, Ralph, who was horrible at keeping his balance and also abysmal at setting a reasonable pace.

"Fuck," Mac said. "Do you want to be dead by the end of the first mile?"

"Yes, I do," Ralph said. "I truly do."

After two miles Ralph had fallen fifteen times and Mac was losing patience. "You're going about this all wrong," he said. "You can't try to run like you did before."

"So, how am I supposed to run?"

"Not like you're dragging a log."

"But it *feels* like a fucking log."

"Pretend like it's a motorcycle," Mac said. "The engineers knew what they were doing. Let the spring loaded thingamajig do its job. Don't fight the mechanism. Just trust it and let the damn thing push you forward. Your job is to keep up."

"Fuck," Ralph said.

They ran daily for a week while Mac coached and Ralph swore. Then, something clicked and Ralph made a mile without falling and then he was pushing three miles at a time.

MAC

The rehab group was celebrating Mac's discharge by taking him out for dinner. He picked the Thai restaurant six blocks from the base and the whole crew walked there. They celebrated with sparkling water and four-star hot sauces and laughed their respective asses off. They especially laughed at the VA counselor's suggestion that they start every morning with the chant, "Keeping straight! We'll be great!"

After dinner, Mac headed for the restroom but the hallway was dark and he bumped into a six foot tall woman wearing a long black coat, three inch heels and not much else. "Mac?" she said in voice that was more *basso profondo* than *contralto*. "Is it really you?"

"It might be. Who are you?"

"Georgette Finelli."

"George? From my unit?"

"Georgette." The baritone was firm. "I'm my own true self now."

"Wow. You look ... uh ... nice boots."

"Don't be a prick, Mac."

"Give me a minute. I might need a little time to adjust."

Mac hugged her, then, in a purely comradely fashion. George Finelli had saved his life — pulled him from flaming oil-slick water and into a lifeboat and he was pretty sure his folks and Mandy were grateful for that.

"How you doing?" George a.k.a. Georgette asked.

"Good. And you?"

"Day at a time."

Mac nodded.

"The booze never called your name, did it." It wasn't a question.

Mac shrugged.

"You still juicing?"

"I never juiced, George...ette."

"Right. I forgot. You were the Ox-hound."

"Was."

"You quit?"

"Yes."

"I got some nice stuff in my bra and I don't mean boobs."

"I quit!" Mac's voice was fierce. "I quit Oxy, Cotton, Kicker, Hillbilly Heroin. Whatever the hell you want to call it! I *quit*, dammit!"

Mac didn't realize he was shouting until he turned and saw that Ralph was suddenly standing beside him.

"I have you recorded." Ralph held up his cell phone to the woman in the shadowed hallway. "You were trying to sell an illegal substance. If you don't get the hell out of my man's face, I'm turning this evidence over to the authorities."

The boots and the wigged figure wearing them pushed out the EXIT at the end of the hallway and melted into the shadows. Mac would have thought it was another hallucination except for Ralph's hand on his shoulder. The rest of the group had headed back to the dorm but Ralph stayed.

"You got to expect that kind of thing." Ralph's eyes were on the streetlamp and anyone watching would think he was talking to himself but Mac was listening hard. "It creeps up on you and *blam*, there you are."

Mac shrugged.

"But you handled it," Ralph said.

Mac shrugged and Ralph pushed on: "Damn straight, you did fucking great."

"No stupid fucking poetry," Mac muttered.

"Poetry?" Ralph stared at Mac.

"Straight. Great." Then they were both laughing and it was okay, really okay, again.

RALPH

The Saturday after Mac finished his oxy rehab and told everyone good-bye, Ralph entered his first Hero's Half —also known on base as an open-to-anyone 10-K. He came in tenth from last (behind a pregnant stroller-pushing mom but ahead of the three hundred pound grandfather). Ralph only fell twice so he considered it a personal best.

He called Mac at The Office. "I finished it."

"Glad to hear it." Over the phone, the buzz of the tavern was tinny but familiar and Ralph felt the longing start up — longing for booze, longing for a whole body and —under it all —the longing for the bullet.

"A beer right now would taste pretty damn good."

"Stop it," Mac said sharply.

Ralph's hand was sweaty and he almost dropped his cell phone onto the sidewalk where he was still sprawled by the finish line. His voice shook. "You talking to me?"

"You know I am."

"Doper."

"Drunk."

It was a supposed to be funny but it held the sour aftertaste of truth. At the VA, they had started every run and workout with it. It was their own chant for survival.

"Call your sponsor," Mac said roughly.

"Is that what you'd do?"

Mac snorted.

"I'm asking," Ralph said. "*Is* that what you'd do?"

"I'd call my wife but you don't have one of those."

"Your wife can't be much good," Ralph said. "You went to rehab."

"And I'm keeping clean. Now quit bothering me at work." Mac cradled his cell phone between his shoulder and chin while filling two steins with the house dark ale. Mac looked at the customers lined up along the bar and clotted in the rough wooden booths surrounding the small dance floor. "You still there?" he asked into the phone.

Ralph started to cry, sobs wracked his lean body like a series of seizures. They were so loud that Mac almost dropped the phone. "Where are you?" he asked again.

"F-finished. At the finish line."

"Don't leave."

Mac shoved the cell into his pocket. "Garret!" He handed his brother-in-law the keys. "The bar's yours for the night. Don't steal anything but beer." Then he limped out the door.

The Hero's Half organizers were taking down the flags, folding up the tables, and loading the pickup parked at the curb. Mac's missing fingers had never bothered him but the stump, where fire and the devil with a pitchfork lived, always ached. Booze had never helped but the Oxycodone had. And, he reminded himself, the running helped, too. He figured he would log a million miles before he died.

Mac handed Ralph a Gatorade. "What's going on?"

"I gotta have something to work for. My friend explained that to me. At least I think he's my friend."

Mac sighed. "Of course I'm your friend."

Ralph finished the liter and a half and let loose a rumbling burp. "Maybe I'll get married."

"Do you have anyone in mind?"

"Sort of. A woman in my last rehab group." Tears gathered in Ralph's eyes and rolled down a face pink and pitted with scar tissue. "Maybe, if I keep clean and work hard, she'll notice me and not because of my face and leg. Because of who I'm trying to be."

The wind had picked up and a cold rain soaked his jacket. Mac cracked the plastic lid of another Gatorade and handed it to Ralph. "And who's this person you want to be?"

"Somebody with a future. I've been thinking that I'll go back to college."

"*Back* to college?"

"I'm sorta working on my doctorate. In science."

"We've run a couple hundred miles together and you neglected to tell me this."

Ralph's head was down. "It's like you said," he mumbled. "I'm trying to make lemonade."

"Fuck lemonade," Mac said. "And fuck life ever handing out peaches but do you remember that woman in a wheelchair, back when we first met? The one with the kid in her lap?"

"Can't forget her," Ralph said. "I keep hearing their laughter."

Mac put a steady hand on Ralph's shoulder. "If a woman in a wheelchair can laugh her way to the door, maybe we can, too."

Ralph nodded and stood up. "Okay. Maybe I can't laugh but I can run and I can go back to college ..."

"And you can call me," Mac said. "Anytime."

"It's a start," Ralph said.

"One without that stupid fucking chant of survival," Mac said. And they both laughed.

Blackened Blues

A body bag unzipped itself
and slipped a no good body loose.
It toasted its own blackened health,
fired off a triage of abuse,
death cries, its blackened body blues:

"Let cockerels crow the firestorm glow
when missiles cruise your streets at night.
Let heads and tails spin round with rounds
of red and yellow tracer light.
Death dances to the blackened blues."

"When gunships home in on your homes
a crowded shelter's your best bet:
its infra red is easy meat
for a heat-seeking exocet.
Death cries your blackened body blues."

"The curfew wakes at crack of dawn
when guns are chattering like cold teeth.
Let bullets sign out in the trees.
The convoy sighs without relief.
Death dances to the blackened blues."

"Nowhere to run on a death march
when mortars pound the town ahead.
Children are slow. They're first to go
when snipers earn a pound a head.
Death cries their blackened body blues."

"My fighters are all irregulars,
their semtex breath's like marzipan.
The safe areas are never safe
except to death's militiaman.
Death dances to the blackened blues."

"The clampdown brings on a seizure,
the ceasefire holds in its breath.
The bread queue's panned with hot crossfire.
The unmarked van delivers death,
death cries, those blackened body blues."

Carrying the Arrest Bleep

It's cool, at first, to feel it
weighting my pocket, to be wired to a voice
swathed in static,

to run through empty corridors
past a gallery of night-blacked windows,
to fly down stairwells

that smell of the dust
drifting in the hospital's
concrete heart. To be joined

by junior doctors, going hell for leather
over walkways, the city below
sunk in 3am quiet, our feet

skidding in corners, bursting through doors
into the light of a ward
where I'll slap pads

to a chest, get busy with compressions
and the drawing up of drugs.
The buzz wears off

with each heart pumped or shocked;
paper thin skin over prominent ribs,
grey chest hair and deflated breasts

all our futures laid bare
in a strip-lit bay, the whole scene
lasting far too long

and when the registrar asks
if we agree to stop, I meet
his eye, and nod.

Saturday Night Loneliness

Questioning a text's 'relevance' is one of the sneakiest, most unworthy ways to avoid engaging with it. As though how a book aligns with the political sensibilities, social realities and stylistic fads of our brief blip of an era is the only measure of its worth.

Yet there is no denying that there is something a bit funny in our post-Great Recession/Austerity era about going back and reading the literature basted in the years of post-war fat. It occurred to me that if Arthur Seaton has an American equivalent it's probably John Updike's Rabbit Angstrom whose first run was published two years after Arthur's. Both are mediocre non-conformists unable to articulate an alternative to the discontent they're rebelling against (though in both cases that seems too active a verb), too dim to understand the damage they do to others, and too cowardly to take responsibility for it. It's not a perfect match: Arthur is four years younger, a more forceful, glamorous character and lacks any trace of Rabbit's religious angst, but it's not hard to extrapolate a little and see Rabbit as a peek at Arthur's future, older, married and ground down by the bastards more than he expected. Anyway, spiritual ennui is all well and good, but when the protagonist's main complaint against society is, 'I am being paid a living wage,' it might be hard for a college graduate earning $7.25 at McDonalds (and only getting 30 hours a week so that their employer doesn't have to give them health insurance) to give much of a shit.

Still, whatever the milieu, the central engine of *Saturday Night and Sunday Morning* is sound. The tension between Arthur's admirable individualism and callow selfishness; said tension compounded by Alan Sillitoe's understanding that the two traits are intrinsically linked. We sympathize with Arthur's determination not to be "dead from the neck up" while simultaneously being made uneasy with the havoc he wrecks in the lives of those close to him. "Don't let the bastards grind you down" is a fine enough philosophy, but Sillitoe never lets the reader forget that Arthur is himself a bastard doing his own share of grinding.

The problem with the adaptation of *Saturday Night and Sunday Morning* is that it wrecks this fundamental balance. Arthur is never interrogated in the film the way he is in Sillitoe's novel. In the context of the film, rooting against him is as unthinkable as rooting for the Texas Rangers in *Bonnie and Clyde*.

This comes down to two factors. The first, most obvious being the major narrative change from novel to film, the downgrading of the grisly DIY abortion in the book to a contemplated abortion which is then shrugged off in favor of having the child. In doing so the film nullifies any consequences of Arthur's actions. The worst he faces for his reckless behavior is a good kicking which, let's face it, would be less than a blip in Arthur's life (he admits as much). It's not only a disastrous decision thematically but narratively as well: the abortion is a load-bearing plot point and without it, Arthur's eventual turning towards the straight and narrow feels perfunctory and unmotivated as the twenty-first chapter of *A Clockwork Orange*. His promises that he will retain his rebel rock-throwing spirit ring hollow.

Ironically this problem is exacerbated by the film's best element, the casting of the impossibly young Albert Finney as Arthur. Bull necked, with a barrel chest, lantern jaw, hair in a wave and rocking a sharp suit and working class flannels with equal ease, Finney has the swagger of an archetypical English rogue. There's more than a touch of Tom Jones to his Arthur, and any ambivalence that may have remained about the character goes right out the window when he enters the frame. He is simply too glamorous for the story's own good. Like Paul Newman in *Hud* or James Cagney in *Public Enemy*, he's just too damn cool to ever serve as a cautionary tale.

The film around him is not without merit. Karel Reisz shoots the industrial cityscapes with a suitably grim skill, taking care to capture the remnants of pastoral country that they've spoiled. The camera work is impressively ahead of its time with subjective framing and hand held shots that are very new wave adjacent. But none of this changes the fact that when one of the key characters snarls at Arthur, "You're getting off light, aren't you?", it's hard not to agree. For a film about a character who despises compromise and half measures *Saturday Night and Sunday Morning* is surprisingly full of them.

The Loneliness of the Long Distance Runner survives the adaptation better, if only because the central conflict between personal integrity and the ruthless imperatives of an impersonal system is a sturdier theme than 'The Working Classes: How Miserable Should They Be?' This is not of course to say that class does not factor into *The Loneliness of the Long Distance Runner*; to claim so would be obtuse bordering on perverse. But the metaphor at the heart of the story is broader than the specifics of its sociology, and the act of defiance at its centre is more archetypical still.

Crucially *The Loneliness of the Long Distance Runner* maintains the complexity that *Saturday Night and Sunday Morning* jettisons. While the borstal system is depicted as a grim pit of misery that plays off its inmates against one another for scraps of self-respect, crucially the people who run it aren't seen as sadistic martinets. This isn't *Scum*. Michael Redgrave's nameless governor is certainly an autocrat and his behavior grows progressively worse over the course of the film, but in his own queer way he's a fair one. He's so obsessed with besting the boys from the public school because he clearly does believe on some basic level that his charges *are* their equals — an opinion I'm willing to bet wasn't the dominant one in the English reform system of the early Sixties. Said public school kids could easily be depicted as snobbish nitwits but instead are shown genuinely trying to relate with their counterparts, commiserating over corporal punishment and bad food. They may be patronizing but that's because the situation they're in leaves them no other way to behave, the system they participate in is rotten, which is not to say that they are as well. (The one time the film does indulge in the grotesque is in the rather ghastly Entertainment Program the boys are given, and frankly that's a clean hit.)

This all makes its central thesis more powerful, that you cannot allow what you love to be co-opted even if what is trying to co-opt it isn't out-and-out evil and thus easier to cheer against. What running becomes for Colin Smith (Tom Courtenay) is too pure to become the tool of a bad system, even if the leader of said bad system is arguably well meaning.

Which does lead to the problem for director Tony Richardson of conveying running so that it looks like it's worth martyring oneself in a machine shop for. Running long distances being one of those things that is perversely uncinematic. Richardson's main technique is to break it down into abstraction, using elliptical editing and off centre camera work to turn Colin's private runs into fragmentary sensual experiences. It works well enough, but it feels like playing to tie. (Also, as a long distance runner myself, it's worth noting that the little pedantic man inside my head can't stop from heckling everyone in the film for their terrible form.)

Richardson's new waveish tendencies also manifest in the film's non-linear structure, and here we have a bit of a problem because for a film that goes to such great lengths to cultivate the soul deadening air of the borstal, *Loneliness* lets us out of it an awful lot. Not just into the woods with Colin where our relief of escape would nearly match his, but into his past which is hardly better than the borstal with his harridan mother, dying father and generally terrible life, but which at least offers moments of respite in camaraderie and romance.

But as with Sillitoe's novella the crux of *Loneliness* is in the climax and Richardson nails it, from the build up to the race to the wordless epilogue. Simply put, it's one of the great moral victories in cinema. And Richardson's direction, Sillitoe's script, Tom Courteney and Michael Redgrave's performances all come together to sell it like a crescendo. As someone once said, "It's a fine life if you don't weaken."

London Road

London Road pelts along
from Pontes
Here's the brand-new
Staines Union Workhouse
the Orphan Boys Home
the Isolation Hospital —
so it must be 1913

Blink —
now on this fevered site
Tesco 2014 squats
with its good cheer of three for two
and its brave-new-world
of every little helps

On the hard corner
where Long Lane meets London Road —
the cemetery where my grandparents
and my great-aunt stay
under a length of green chippings
their stone book
open at the same page forever

Long ago Auntie led pre-school me
across the common
and along the path by the pits
and through a gate
to her sister Kate's grave —
she tended that single grave well

I trotted to the dripping tap
Auntie put fresh flowers in the metal container

Graves surrounded us
far and wide
Quiet Death leaning weary head
on work- and world-weary hand
as a few noisy planes
from the pre-cheap-flight era
plied the heavy sky over Heathrow

and I played in the necropolis

and the London Road
scurries on for dear life
past the bare-knuckle fighters gone
from The Crooked Billet

across ghost meadows and lost orchards
towards Stanwell
the keys to the Heath
still rattling in its dirty old pocket
all the way to London Wall

(from Heath *a book-length sequence about Hounslow Heath and environs in collaboration with John Greening)*

Did it Rain on the First Good Friday?

A downpour of hailstones
On the way to the park
At any other time of year
Would deter

It's Easter and the weatherman has egg on his face

Only kidding says the big guy with the white beard
His hazy grin
Flashing like the amber
Declaring all fools day everyday

April is the time for prospecting illusions

For damp patches
Getting the wind in your sails
Constructing plans
Two by two

For coming back from the dead

For fair weather friends to eat and run as

The umbrella and the parasol see saw out and in doors
Like neighbours trying to have the last word

Drizzle half cocked
Spring loaded
God with an itchy trigger finger

Noah must have been a nervous wreck by the end
Of April

Hell Poems

1.

Your love is Toca torture, a cloth inserted into my mouth
and I am dumb with only the impression of drowning.
My limbs still without the sex appeal of treading water,
legs opening and closing. It's you all over.
I am suffocating. You are good at impressions.
That doesn't mean I would hang you up.
You are flat, lacking in perspective
like an old religious painting
on my beige wall
stained by the smoke of too many cigarettes,
and wine splatter from another glass,
as I try to make sense of love and you,
day in, day out, my idea of hell.

2.

He's growing his hair long,
thinks it will give him gravitas,
take away from his V-neck jumper,
paunch and scraggy ass.
No jawbone here or heroic feats.
He leaves his clapped-out bicycle
locked to lampposts on Dublin Streets —
scarcely born to be a Nazarite,
she decides to wear her dress too tight.

3.

My temper is everywhere, licks the air like petrol.
You like the smell but know it is bad for you.
The colours are slimy-shiny, a dark rainbow
with nothing at the end of it, maybe a heart attack,
no love lost, if you're lucky it will take you suddenly.
Anthropologists claim fire is man's greatest invention.
I bet they pray for rain in hell.

Fenlands

The worst bit was the initiation ceremony. The initiation ceremony wasn't exactly a single event; it kind of lasted for about 6 months and it basically involved a series of terrifyingly hatched plots by the blokes who worked around the butcher's table. The factory was brand spanking new and built for the sole purpose of supplying ready cooked meals to Marks n Spencer's. I worked in the butchery and, as a school leaver, I was given all the shit jobs. I say shit —the fucking best jobs were shit but my daily tasks were fucking road kill, mate, 6am ventures into the undead, the torture of wage labour, and I fucking hated them for it.

"She has the baby in 4 weeks, I'll wait a bit then she can go to fucking work, I'll fuck this off and stay at home, I'll look after the fucker." —Steve on the loading bay.

The first part of the initiation involved me being dragged onto the butcher's table by about 4 blokes, being pinned down and given a series of Love Bites around my neck. This greatly amused them, it made their shit lives better and my shit life worse. It made the long haul until first break quicker, it made the shit sex they had with their partners better, it made the fury of existence, the endless end, better. Years later I found out that one of them contracted throat cancer; I fucking laughed.

"No working man votes Tory," he said in the canteen whilst chewing on a fucking Hamlet cigar, 'may death be thy destiny' tattooed into his forearm. The working man might not vote Tory but the working man is controlled by such forces, it doesn't matter what fucking tick goes in what fucking box, the worker is doomed, the worker is a bastard with manic senselessness and a small area that holds his or her second hand belongings. A fucking orange and a shit train set. An immaculate car that's 15 fucking years old, a second hand Kawasaki that replaces the erectile problem, and fucking divorces. I come from there, from the generic houses and the varnished bar in the social club. But don't get me wrong, I've no love for Social Mobility either; it's the legal way in which to betray yourself, isn't it? But my working class: well that can fucking kiss my arse, too.

The second stage of the initiation ceremony was called 'The Jockey' which involved being ambushed by The Lads again and having my boxer shorts hoisted up so far they would rip. I couldn't take it this time. I calmly walked to the personnel dept with the intention of getting the cunts bollocked, maybe sacked. A tug on my overalls as I turned round to see one of them almost in tears, white faced and deadly serious

"I've got a family, mate. It was just a laugh. Don't tell them, mate, I can't afford to get the sack."

I turned back, got my apron on and then my wellies and went back down into the work chamber, the long staircase, the hand wash, the bin overflowing with used hand towels and the smeared window in the middle of the hard plastic door that led us into the cutting room.

And Spoil the Child

A tall, strong man — a man I learned things from:
a man I even in many ways admired —
swung a stick high in the air, to bring it down
after one or two preparatory swishes
and a light upward tip on the finger-ends
of the right hand supported at the wrist
of Barty, a hopeless speller — with such force
and rage that the boy's bare feet danced a tattoo
and jiggled on the floor as if he stood
on the red-hot pavement of Hell's judgement.

Moths

Soft butterflies of night, we've learned of late
to share the bedroom with you and react
with horror only to the smeared glaze
you mutate to when, so unmajestical,
you're offered any show of violence.
What used to make us shudder, I see now,
was your pure vulnerability: the threat
your frailty posed by demonstrating
our species' programmed disposition
to kill anything that can't resist us
or fight back: to concede existence only
to creatures which are strong. You are so near
the dead end of the fly-by-night continuum
of strength and wealth and contest in the world.

Alan Sillitoe — A Good Life

I was lucky that my Mum and Dad had both worked in public libraries and had indeed met in one. Their shared love of books and knowledge was passed on to us children from a very early age. Before, as five-year-olds, we were introduced to the school curriculum and the *Janet and John* series, Dad in particular (Mum was operating the house) sunk us into his lap and read from a collection of big red encyclopaedias — *Pictorial Knowledge*. He loved these volumes as they had informed his childhood and had defiantly survived the Second World War bombing of his family home. The information contained therein was phenomenal and was brought to life by hundreds of black and white plates. Some of these images remain imprinted in my brain to this day, as do countless random facts and slivers of obscure knowledge.

Each week Dad would walk to the shops and pick up two magazines which moved us on from the black-and-white pre-war world of *Pictorial Knowledge* to the glorious colour of *Look and Learn* and *Treasure*. My older brother and sister were fixated on *Look and Learn*, while I, being that bit younger, gobbled up the lighter, more cartoony *Treasure*.

At infant school, they were moving us through *Janet and John* books One, Two, Three and Four and some *Noddy and Big Ears* by Enid Blyton, but I was already ahead of this — impatient for the teacher to catch up. I was certainly reading the *Dandy*, *Beano*, *Beezer* and *Topper* long before many of my peers. Even though, considering they were called comics, they never made me or anybody I knew laugh. We adored them none the less. I started to feel a pull towards Rodger the Dodger, Dennis the Menace and Minnie the Minx — characters who exasperated their parents and teachers. An ambition was forming to become a Bash Street Kid.

When I moved up to the junior school aged seven my reading world opened up further. My classroom in the second year housed a large bookcase and I sat in front of it so I soon knew the spines and geography of every shelf. I discovered a dusty row of red-covered *William* books by Richmal Crompton and the rebel inside me was fully awakened. Here was a boy of about my age who deliberately rolled down his socks, carried catapults, had enemies, wound up his parents and knew his older brother was an idiot and his sister deluded. It wasn't until I re-read them as an adult that I realised the stories were shot through with humour. I would say that William Brown was my first literary hero. It would be interesting to know how he fared as an adult. If he was alive today he'd be 105. *Billy Bunter* and *Jennings* soon usurped William Brown in my affections, however, even though life in a public school with its majors and minors, hampers and "wizard" capers should have been as remote to me as caviar and cocktails.

Around 1971, aged 13, my literary appetite careered off in a whole new direction and changed the course of my life — I'm sure of that. My Mum was still an avid reader and sometimes I dipped into the novels that sat next to her chair, on her side-table, in the space that in later years would accommodate a TV remote control. I recall dipping into Howard Spring's *Shabby Tiger*, Leslie Thomas's *Tropic of Ruislip* and *The Good Companions* by J.B. Priestly. But it was a hardback book with an image-free, fairly plain cover that captured me. *A Start In Life* was by Alan Sillitoe, an author previously unknown to me, and told the story of a young man who comes down to London from Nottingham and encounters various crooks, characters and pretty girls along the way. It was written in the picaresque style although I would not have had any idea what that was at the time. I fell in love with the adventure, the rebellion, the irreverence and the sex. Most probably it was mainly the latter as reading the book coincided with high levels of unexpected hormone-driven activity.

"You really enjoyed that, didn't you?" said Mum. "I haven't really got started, but if you like him you should read *Saturday Night and Sunday Morning* and *The Loneliness of the Long-Distance Runner*. They are his most famous books." I was soon library-bound.

If *Just William* triggered the rebel in me, those two books transformed me into one. I didn't work in a factory, I never went short of food and I hadn't been to borstal. But, boy, did I now want to. I found an identity. I was working class, resentful of the rich and powerful and up for the revolution. I felt an affinity with the grime and struggle of the North, even though I lived in Surrey, suffocated by stockbrokers and belts. When I swaggeringly told a careers teacher my ambition was to be a dustman — I was Arthur Seaton. The careers advisor was a pratt. I sneered at the rest of the class as the English teacher took them through curriculum books like *Moonfleet* and *No Boats on Bannermere.*

The Loneliness of the Long-Distance Runner chimed the most. I was transfixed from when the rain washed hidden bank notes down the drainpipe while the police questioned Smith — the young hero of the short story. I relished the way he allowed the borstal's head and others to become excited by his running skill and his ultimate act of rebellion by throwing away his ability to triumph in the race. A subtle fist in the face of authority. As I worked my way through Sillitoe's catalogue as it was then in the early 1970s it was a heady time for me. By the age of fifteen I had exhausted what there was and moved on to George Orwell, Aldous Huxley and others, eventually being seduced by real life adventures to those on the printed page. I had no idea for some years as I got on with the hectic business of living that Alan never laid down his pen. Never opted for the easy life and allowing the money that would have flowed from iconic books and films to smooth his edges. Insisted on highlighting injustice, exposing inequality, puncturing pomposity and capturing the lives of real people to the day he died.

It is one of the highlights of my life that Alan Sillitoe became a personal friend. In the late 1990s I saw a letter he had written to a national newspaper, which included his home address. I felt the urge to write to him and let him know just how much his work had influenced and formed me as a boy, and I did. A shared appreciation of all things Alan had also helped bring myself and fellow author John King together and he wrote to Alan also. We both received attentive replies and one thing led to another culminating in the three of us meeting up at a pub of his choice — The Lamb and Flag in Covent Garden. We continued to meet there regularly for the last decade of his life.

What a delight to sit in that pub and chat with Alan. He always preferred to talk about us and what we were doing rather than himself. He did not dwell on the past and was focused always on his next book. Alan believed that if he had been bestowed the gift of being able to write it was his duty to do so. He always said that a committed author will need to find his voice and when he or she has done that should then devote their lives to writing.

I once mentioned to Alan that my father was a lover of maps and the next time we met he brought a string-tied bundle of pre-war maps he owned for areas where I had said my Dad had been stationed during World War Two. My old man was thrilled with the maps and the thought that Alan Sillitoe was thinking of him. Alan took us to his house to break bread and cheese with him and Ruth, and I was excited to join in the celebrations in Nottingham when he was awarded the freedom of his home city. He looked forward to driving sheep across Trent Bridge.

We took the actor Sean Bean to meet him. Sean had narrated *Saturday Night and Sunday Morning* for a Radio 2 production some years earlier and was a true admirer of his work. It was memorable to see Sean, at the time riding high on his Hollywood horse, humble, respectful and awestruck as he drank in Alan's words.

John and I formed London Books, a niche publishing house, and were delighted and honoured to republish *A Start in Life* — 35 years on. This issue marked Alan's 80th birthday. Not long before, Alan had written and released *A Man of His Time* — one of his finest novels, which draws on his family's social history. It is in my all-time top ten of novels. I recommend it to all and sundry. This should give hope and motivation to those who fret over their creative juices running dry in mid and later life. Alan was bang-on to the end.

Alan Sillitoe was a gentle man and a gentleman. Wise and witty. Generous with his time and spirit. Encouraging to others. Calm and collected. I only ever saw him angry once and that was when he was explaining how the literary establishment insisted on pigeon-holing him as one of the so-called "angry young men". He had no time for labels. No time for praise. He believed in life and learning.

He would have poured his pint of bitter over my head if he heard me say it — but he was my hero.

An Unstarted Life

Alan Sillitoe's first two books, *Saturday Night and Sunday Morning* and *The Loneliness of the Long Distance Runner*, not only firmly cemented his literary reputation, but were adapted for the big screen, to make what became classics of British cinema.

Elsewhere, however, he wasn't particularly well served by the medium. Ralph Nelson's *Counterpoint* was ostensibly based on *The General* but drifts away from its source material, and towards war movie clichés. The scenery-chewing performances by Charlton Heston and Maximilian Schell seem disconnected from Alan's story. Harold Becker's *The Ragman's Daughter* struggles for a directorial style analogous to Alan's melancholy but unsentimental script. A television drama based on the short story 'Pit Strike' (from the collection *Men, Women and Children*) was the only other film adaptation that made it into production.

Alan's essay 'Che Guevara' (published in *Mountains and Caverns*) tantalisingly recounts the year he spent researching the life of the Argentinean revolutionary, and crafting a screenplay for director Tony Richardson. However, the film was never made, and the 'what if' factor still remains, leading any self-respecting movie buff to wonder at the results of a post-*Long Distance Runner* Sillitoe/Richardson re-teaming and a Guevara biopic 40 years before Steven Soderbergh's roadshow two-parter …

This draft of a screen treatment for *A Start in Life* presents us not only with another 'what if' story but a literary work in its own right. It reads as miles removed from the bland summary of set pieces and selling points that usually comprise a screen treatment. The narrative itself truncates, and yet stays faithful to the book. In the interests of keeping things spoiler-free for those who haven't read the novel (do: it's hilarious), what follows is the first half of Alan Sillitoe's outline for a rollicking and politically incorrect blend of road movie, social satire and crime thriller. It's presented in Alan's original typescript, including his hand-written corrections and annotations, and is a fascinating insight into this particular creative process.

Call us biased, but we reckon this would still make a cracking movie, and there's plenty of British filmmaking talent out there, so … over to you!

A Start in Life — Screen Treatment

A START IN LIFE screen treatment

GILBERT BLASKIN - a large, loose-lipped, bald man - author, philanderer, narrator of this film. Wearing a wine-dark smoking jacket and smoking a cigar, he sits in his ornate and opulent London flat - in his study, with his back towards us. He turns, and says:

"This is the story of a bastard - a real, twenty-two carat working-class bastard. It shows what happens in his native city, and what befalls him when his lucky star takes him to London and sundry places beyond. A tale of his infamous follies and foolish mistakes. Believe me. The sort that can happen to any of us."

During this narration Blaskin's wife, a haggard forty year old, has been snatching things off his desk, pictures from the wall etc., because she is leaving him.

"Michael Cullen remembers childhood as an intense and wonderful love affair that was stamped out by the wilful circumstance of growing up. So you can be sure we won't spend long on it."

He turns to his typewriter, to begin the tale. His wife snatches it away. "Well get out then, you bitch," Blaskin snarls. "You've plagued me long enough. We'll have a divorce, then."

A street in Nottingham. It slopes steeply. MICHAEL CULLEN, as a boy of four, scruffy and unprepossessing, comes out

2

of his house and gets into a small van parked by the kerb. The van begins to roll down the street. Screams from inside. It goes across another road, and is stopped by a tall hedge.

A MAN runs after it - the OWNER. Shouting, he pulls the boy out and cuffs him, calling him a little bastard.

Michael's mother MAVIS CULLEN, a slim pretty and jaunty woman in factory overalls, pulls the man back and hits him, telling him to leave her son alone, and that if she had a husband he'd get his face squashed in. Michael's GRANDMOTHER comes out and also gives him a thump. A quarrel ensues, and Michael bursts into tears.

Blaskin in his study. Apart from his desk and chair it is empty. A WORKMAN comes in with an armchair. Another with a picture. "As far as we know," Blaskin says, "those were the last tears Michael Cullen shed." A gorgeous brunette comes into the room and sits on his knee.

A secondhand car yard in Nottingham. Twenty year old Michael cullen pays DEALER £130, gets into a beaten-up old car, and drives into the centre of Nottingham. He sees GWEN BOLSOVER, the secretary at an estate agents' where he used to work. Michael is a very smart young man. He gives her a lift to her small bungalow in Wollaton. She reminds him of the cheating he did over buying and selling houses, and supposes that he has bought the car on his proceeds. He says

3

he has a better job now, managing an estate agents' office in Loughborough. Gwen is a somewhat impressionable woman, and Michael goes to bed with her. He promises to marry her, and she takes him half seriously. She says she loves him because he is so simple and straightforward.

Michael goes home. The house is empty, for his mother is at work. There is a knock at the door. Tired and scruffy, he lets in his girlfriend CLAUDINE. She tells him she is pregnant. Michael asks her whose the baby is. It might be Alfie Bottesford's, he says. She says she has never made love to Alfie. They quarrel: she hits him on the forehead with a sauce-bottle. They make love, and he promises to marry her. He says he will come to see her parents tomorrow night. She believes him, and leaves.

Blaskin, at the wheel of an Aston Martin, with his girl friend: "He's learning quickly where women are concerned. Reminds me of someone I know!" He puts his arm around his girlfriend, and goes off the road - over a grass verge and down a bank.

Michael is in bed. It is dark, and the alarm clock goes. He gets up, and packs a suitcase. He fries his breakfast, tells his mother he is leaving: "North, east, south and west. I'll be back, though."

4

"Don't lie to me," she says. "But look after yourself."

He goes to his car on the street. It won't start.

Elaskin's flat. He is underneath a girl, his arm in plaster. "Don't worry. Michael's car has to start. His life has only just begun. He won't get off so lightly."

Nottingham street: Michael dries the contacts, and drives along Castle Boulevard, over Trent Bridge.

Michael goes, head bent forward, along the Great North Road, towards London, in heavy rain and lorry-traffic. A lonely drenched figure is standing by the side of the road, thumbing a lift. Michael picks him up.

BILL STRAW is a man of thirty-odd on his way to London, he says, to find work. The headlights begin to smoke when Michael turns them on in worsening visibility. Bill Straw gets out, twists the offending light off, and throws it away. "If it don't work," he says, "get rid of it. Otherwise it'll be nothing but trouble."

The radiator is boiling and steaming, and with a loud bang blows its top. Michael gets the car into the forecourt of a filling station. "Leave it to me," says efficient Bill, who fixes the radiator with sticky tape and chewing gum.

5

On the road Bill talks: "I hopped it to London a few years ago, and started knocking off cars for a bloke called Moggerhanger, the biggest racketeer in London. Then I do a wages job, driving the getaway car. They get away. I don't. But I decoy the police. I get five years hard. So after four I'm out, and going back to collect my share of the loot. I'll be rich, Michael, beyond the dreams of bloody avarice!"

They stop at a transport cafe. Bill is invited to eat, and while Michael has a cake and some tea, Bill loads up with soup, liver, sausages, bacon, eggs, and a pudding.

A young woman JUNE, is sitting at their table. Bill charms her, and she is on her way to London, so offers her a lift. There isn't much Michael can say, but he is learning.

Outside the cafe: a heavy lorry backs into the car. Michael and Bill run out to see the lorry going up the road. Bill, unfazed, fixes on the spare wheel, rolling the other towards some wasteground. He pulls the mudguard straight.

Back in the car, June and Bill make themselves comfortable in the back. June works at a cabaret in Soho. "You mean strip-club," says Bill.

The engine coughs and bangs, but they get along.

June talks: "I had a perfect childhood. My parents wanted a girl, and they got me. They loaded me with dolls houses and sewing machines. But then they thought they should have had

6

a son, so to make up for it they gave me guns and toy soldiers. It got so's I didn't know who I was."

Bill has to get out to dry the contacts when the car stops. They are almost crushed by an enormous lorry. Bill suggests they stop for a drink at a roadhouse. Michael pulls up. A man comes out of the door marked 'RESTAURANT' - spewing his guts up. A tribute to English cooking.

They go inside for a drink. Bill buys cigarettes and whisky, and gets the respect of the publican, while Michael is not able to, though he is the one with money and car.

Sitting at the end of the bar is a writer: GILBERT BLASKIN - our narrator - whom June recognises. He talks to June, and says he's going to give a lecture on Novels - in Leeds. He shakes Michael's hands.

Blaskin in his refurnished study, trying to type. A whisky bottle is by his hand, and he is half-drunk. "That was the first time I met our hero - or so I thought."

PERAL HARBY, one of his admirers, brings some sandwiches. He snarls: "There's no mustard, you trollop! -- Anyway, let's get back to Michael -"

Pearl kneels by the desk, and bites his hand savagely.

Rain. Sodium lights. On the road. Bill and June necking in

7

the back. Michael straining his nerves to keep the car on the road. He puts on the windscreen wipers, and they fly off. Bill asks him to pass the map so that they can find out where they are. It is sucked out of the window.

The front wheel falls off: they fix it. They wobble. The horn no longer works. At a traffic light near London a man in a souped-up big car shouts that Michael should buy a new car. Michael tells him to bollocks. Bill recognises the man as CLAUD MOGGERHANGER - the London gangster who has the police in his pocket. Moggerhanger bashes into the side of their car, pursues them sportively for a while, then veers off.

Michael pulls up by Hendon tube station, and the engine drops out. Bill suggests he either sells it for a quid, or abandons it. When Bill gets out, the door falls off. "This journey to London's cost me £150," Michael moans. "I could have done it for half the price in a chauffeur-driven Rolls Royce, eating smoked salmon and drinking champagne!"

Bill cadges a pound from him, and goes off with June.

Michael stays on his own.

The reception desk of a seedy hotel in Bloomsbury. The MANAGER is an overworked ulcerous looking man, with a dislike of people. Michael is shown to a tiny room.

Michael at breakfast in the hotel, sitting with Kundt, a

8

Swedish journalist doing the vice dens of London. Kundt isn't hungry, due to his exertions, and Michael wolfs his leftovers.

Crossing Russell Square, Michael is stopped by a bearded Almanack Seller. Michael says they only contain bad news, but ALMANACK JACK (a middle-aged drop out) insists that if they didn't he wouldn't sell any.

Standing on the pavement in Leicester Square Michael sees a goodlooking young blonde girl coming towards him, and asks the way to Adam Street. She is BRIDGITTE APPLEDORE, a Dutch au pair girl. Michael invites her to a place for coffee. He tells her is a student of English literature, and that he is from a rich landowning family in Nottinghamshire.

Blaskin's flat. Pearl asks him to marry her. Blaskin says he can't he's already married. "You told me you weren't!" she weeps. "You foul liar!"

He turns in despair. "That makes two of us, Michael. It's time we met again - but not yet. I hope you have better luck than me."

Dr. Anderson's place, where Bridgitte works. A six-year old boy called Smog shits on the floor so as to see her wiping it up. Michael tells him there is money in it, and when Smog looks close he pushes his face in it - thus curing the habit. Michael helps himself to Havana cigars. He and Bridgitte make

9

love. Out of the last clinch, Smog is looking at them.

Michael is greeted in a friendly way by the hotel manager. Michael gives him a cigar. He is told that he owes a bill for ten days. Michael says he'll settle it after he's been to the banks.

Next morning Michael stands in his room, naked. Puts on a set of underwear, then another. He dons one shirt, and a second one. Same with everything. When he stands he realises he hasn't yet put his shoes on.

There is a knock, and Kundt walks in. Michael gets him to put his shoes on. Kundt borrows a razorblade, and goes out. Michael puts on two jackets, and fills his overcoat pockets with toothbrush, razor etc.

He falls down, and gets up by using the sink - though pulls it off the wall. His gloves are still on the floor, but he decides to forget them.

Michael walks stiffly down the stairs. "Just off to the bank," he calls. His newspaper falls, and he kicks it away.

The UNDER-MANAGER runs down the stairs: "Kundt has tried to kill himself. He's slashed his wrists."

Blaskin - at his typewriter: "Oh, Michael, will you never learn! Giving a razorblade to a madman! You've killed him with kindness."

IO

Coming out of Leicester Square toilet with a parcel, Michael is noticably thinner and easier in his walk.

The Fig-Leaf Club in Soho. Michael pays his money and goes downstairs to the show. One girl is undressing another, and he recognises June, who came with him to London. After her act Michael calls her over, and they talk.

A burly man in an undersized mackintosh makes a disturbance, and knocks the MANAGER down. Michael floors the heckler. Makes him pay ten pounds for damages. The manager gives Michael a job as the club 'bouncer'. "Mr Moggerhanger will have to comfirm the appointment," he says.

Hampstead Heath. Michael is with Bridgitte. Smog is up a tree and can't get down. Dr. Anderson is bullying Bridgitte because he's having trouble with his wife. Michael says he'll go back with her then. "Anderson might rape you," he says, "and cut you up. England's full of Jack-the-Rippers."

In Bridgitte's room Michael tells her about his job, saying his family have stopped his income. He says that she should get a tube of lipstick that Anderson's wife doesn't use and put it under his pillow . She'll find it, and they'll fight ~~smog~~ about ~~themselves~~ it, so he won't bother her then. They make love.

The Club. Michael standing importantly outside. Moggerhanger drives up in his Bentley. He pushes by Michael: "Follow me in," he says.

Homeward

The slow haul back you think of little else
but a stamping ground less bleak than Faroes,
Fair Isle, Viking, but still have work to do.
Scouring, swabbing and sluicing down
the gangways, decks and quarters,
you grease moving parts, while all things
that shift and roll are stowed away,
until there's nothing out of place
to snag the agent's curmudgeonly gaze,
or give him scope to knock back your wages …

With a lathering of cheap carbolic soap,
some aftershave and a slap of Brylcreem
you'll scrub up yourself, good enough at least,
with cash on hip and a clean shirt,
for the tarts that shoal in shadows
around Riby Square or come across for trade
in the warm lee of certain boozers —
The Kent Arms, The Humber, the fractious
dives where ale flows freely
and mind-numbing gregariousness
absorbs the wad you've slaved for;
and while you're flush you'll pull her in,
some girl that's caught your eye —
her hands softer than braiders' hands,
but in their way as skilful.

The Motorway

I was born in the motorway era:
we both were. He used to say it made him
happy to see me writing in the car,
in the passenger seat.

We drove the motorways — going north on
the M1, all the routes through France heading south,
west from Nashville to San Diego, then
east again across the continent
to Montauk Point before returning the car:
you driving, me writing.

Sometimes I'd be aware you'd quickly turned
your head sideways, only for a moment
shifting your gaze from the road — one flick
of your eyes, to watch me making notes.
I laughed and said: "It's perfect — you driving,
me writing, let's go on like this forever",
and you laughed and agreed.

But we didn't. There were other things to do.
And now it's impossible. You're dead.
And I'm driving with another person,
with someone else.

I stare through the windscreen into the distance
as the pylons draw their lines of power
across the green and brown and yellow fields,
the landscape of small hills, hedges and streams
you taught me to understand — stare into
the distance — as if by looking hard enough
I'll find that place where the two sides
of the road merge and unite.

Mapping the Territory

Without wanting to sound like the worst kind of literary luvvie, I first met Alan Sillitoe at a Sunday lunch party given by A.S. Byatt at her house in Putney in the spring of 1992: a benign-looking, grey-haired character (he would then have been in late middle age) smoking a pipe — you could still smoke in people's houses in 1992 — and wearing a curious garment around his midriff which memory insists was a black leather waistcoat. At that age, I had only one technique when introduced to a writer whose work I especially admired, which was to babble ingratiatingly away. Alan listened affably to this breathless account of how I had picked up a copy of *Saturday Night and Sunday Morning* in a second-hand bookshop in Oxford and never looked back, indeed was courtesy itself, but I got the impression that beneath the benignity lay a steely core, a refusal to be drawn, an absolute determination to be his own man.

Later sightings tended to bear out this early judgment. Asked by the organiser of a literary festival or an over-zealous interviewer to do something he didn't fancy, Alan never made any bones about the not fancying. There was something bracing about this intransigence — it put you in mind of Evelyn Waugh's small creature of the field, cornered in its lair but liable to turn nasty — and also faintly disconcerting. Certainly, echoes of it can be found in several of the literary memoirs of the 1960s and 1970s in which he plays a supporting role. One might note, for example, the entry in Rayner Heppenstall's diary for 24 January 1973 [Jonathan Goodman, ed. *The Master Eccentric: The Journals of Rayner Heppenstall 1969–1981*] in which the diarist, then occupying a flat in the same West London property as the Sillitoes, goes downstairs to complain about the TV aerial which, at his neighbours' instigation, is being installed on the Heppenstalls' flat roof. Alan, according to Heppenstall, greeted him with the words "Why are you making trouble?" When told that he "was behaving like an imperialist and trying to take the whole house over", he agreed to try to get the wires which had been slung over the Heppenstalls' roof removed, and then slammed the door in Heppenstall's face.

There is no way of verifying any of this, or of establishing the rights and wrongs of the case. Heppenstall's write-up of an incident in the 1930s in which George Orwell attacked him with a shooting stick suggests that he was not always a reliable witness. On the other hand, it is difficult to imagine Anthony Powell or Malcolm Bradbury behaving in quite the same way. For myself, I quite liked the faint air of purpose — an underlying resolve not to be mucked about or unnecessarily inconvenienced — that Alan brought to the literary festivals or the Royal Society of Literature bun-fights where we used most often to meet. If there was a connection between us, over and above literature, it lay in the fact that my father, like Alan, and only a few years before him, had been a wireless operator in the RAF. A large brown-paper envelope sent to me not long before he died turned out to contain a map of Northern Ireland with what are presumably flight-paths marked up in red ink.

The determination to be his own man undoubtedly extended to the books he wrote. Here he was a long-term victim of the tendency — identified by Harry Ritchie his excellent study *Success Stories* (1988) — of sensation-hungry newspapers to promote and sometimes misrepresent the novels of the later 1950s for reasons that had little to do with literature. The 'working-class novelist' tag, so instrumental in establishing his reputation in the days when the Great Pan paperback of *Saturday Night and Sunday Morning* sold a million copies, hung round his neck like a millstone towards the end of the career, to the point where several of his later novels almost seem bent on subverting it. My particular favourite is *The Broken Chariot* (1998), a kind of skit on the whole idea of being a 'working-class writer' in which an upper-class boy named Thurgarton-Strang breaks out of his boarding school and re-invents himself as the Seaton-esque 'Bert Gedling', an aspiring proletarian novelist employed by the Nottingham Royal Ordnance factory.

I last saw him in the autumn of 2008 in what, to me at least, were peculiarly memorable circumstances. An early morning phone call announced that he had stayed the night in Norwich, in the aftermath of an appearance at the UEA: was I free? Of course I was free. No trumpery piece of journalism or finely-wrought paragraph of the work in progress was going to take precedence over Alan Sillitoe. We arranged to meet outside Norwich Cathedral, outside whose West Door, where I stood waiting, a bearded figure eventually came in sight trundling a wheeled suitcase. We walked up to the cathedral coffee shop as the blue-blazered pupils from the nearby

Norwich School swarmed around us. My eldest son's English master, Mr James, caught my eye and nodded, and I winked back, gripped by a sudden vainglorious urge to tell him who I was with. *That's right, Mr James, Alan Sillitoe. Author of* The Loneliness of the Long Distance Runner. *The very same. That's who I'm just off to have coffee with, don't you know? Shame you can't join us.* As for a final judgment, no-one sitting down to compile a mini-library of post-war English fiction could decently omit two or three of his novels and the *Collected Stories*. Equally, no-one should be allowed to get away with the lazy categorisations that have sometimes undermined proper considerations of his work. Born into an age of tendencies, movements and writerly alliances — both real and imagined — Alan represented no one but himself.

Revisiting *Alan Sillitoe's Nottinghamshire*

Alan Sillitoe's Nottinghamshire was a late addition to my collection, a good quality hardback bought on the internet, which I read in December 2014. The book charts Alan's walking tour through a city and a county he stamped on the literary map more definitively than anyone since D.H. Lawrence. A city and a county that he left before even starting to write about them. It's this that gives *Alan Sillitoe's Nottinghamshire* its flavour; what makes it a compelling read, as he re-engages with a contemporary Nottingham, whilst filtering it through the memories of his youth.

It struck me immediately that the contemporaneous Nottingham of the book was the Nottingham of *my* youth. A Nottingham that had a Home Ales pub in its flagship Victoria Centre shopping arcade (virtually every pub was a Home Ales or Shipstones tied house); where a snooker hall was tucked behind some industrial buildings a stone's throw from where I lived in Bulwell; where catching the bus or getting a lift off your mam and dad were alien concepts if you owned a bike. We cycled everywhere, no skid-lid, knee pads or epilepsy-inducing blinking lights. Now, watching parents swaddle their kids in everything short of an industrial-sized roll of bubble wrap, I can't decide whether we were thoroughly irresponsible then, or just knew how to take our bumps and grazes without whining.

David Sillitoe's photographs for the book compounded the dynamic. Some show a Nottingham unchanged after thirty years: a disgruntled crowd of football supporters exiting Meadow Lane, flanked by police; the looming buildings and narrow streets of the Lace Market; the monolithic entrance to the Royal Concert Hall. Some show a Nottingham nominally changed: Goose Fair thronged with skinheads rather than chavs; Slab Square with flowerbeds instead of a water feature, the Council House unchanged in the background. Some show a Nottingham that's gone; evoke memories. The Maid Marian Way underpass: a newspaper vendor ran his stall from there. I remember litter and a pervasive smell of urine. It occurs to me that I should have been more sympathetic to his vocation; bought the odd paper or magazine.

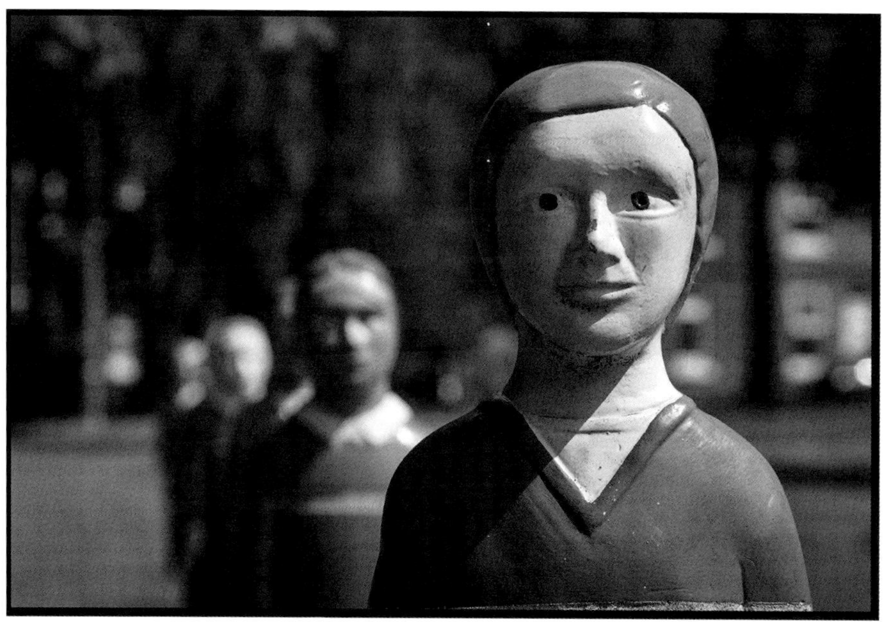

Child bollards, Newstead Village

New housing, Annesley

Another picture of what's been lost: a mournful study of Newstead Colliery, a goat staring up from the bottom right of the frame, its expression an admixture of challenge and defeat. The pit was closed in 1987, the year *Alan Sillitoe's Nottinghamshire* was published. Newstead Village was goat-free when I visited on an overcast bank holiday weekend, just a few days before the 2015 General Election. The village was silent; disconcertingly so. The child-shaped bollards added to the feeling of unease. God knows who thought them up, but they only resemble children if your touchstone is *Village of the Damned.* I drove past the school and the Miners' Welfare, down towards the station. More of a halt, really: a short stretch of platform, a sign, a couple of litter bins and a grubby yellow container of reinforced plastic: presumably grit, kept in readiness for bad weather. Opposite, the once-grand Station Hotel stood empty, chipboard covering its windows. A building that ought to have a second life as a heritage centre, library, youth club or meeting hall, but has been left empty. Tragic.

In 2010, Newstead played host to the inaugural Headstock Festival. The organisers announced it would be an annual extravaganza. Financed by £120,000 of Lottery money and promoted as not-for-profit, it was headlined by indie band Ash. The media were enthusiastic; thousands of music fans descended. It seemed to promise the rejuvenation Newstead desperately needed. The following year, Echo and the Bunnymen were the main attraction in a weekend-long series of acts and events. By 2012, Headstock was either taking a break or the plug had been pulled, depending which news report you read. The organisers promised it would return in 2013; it didn't. The Headstock Festival website has disappeared and their Facebook page is little more than a listing for occasional gigs at the Newstead Centre. A post dated April 2014 asks *is the festival ever going to happen again?* Nobody's responded.

Leaving Newstead, I drove a few yards up the road to Annesley, where my grandfather put in his time at the coalface. The headstocks were unmissable, displayed prominently in a section of well-tended ground. They dwarfed the cottage on the other side of the road. I wondered, if granddad could see the place now, whether they'd be the only thing he would recognise. He'd probably do a double-take at the Jasmine Gardens housing development and the huge banner outside the now-closed site office inviting

Station halt, Newstead Village

Miners welfare, Newstead Village

the nascent home-owner to enquire about a government equity loan. It didn't sit well with the surroundings. I took a couple of pictures of the head-stocks, got back in the car and carried on.

Emerging from Annesley Cutting, a boarded-up pub was decorated with a UKIP flyer. Someone had thoroughly defaced it. Nodding my approval, I turned right and followed the A611 up to the turn off for Ravenshead. A stark name for a village that's actually an enclave of privilege in an otherwise hardscrabble part of the county. "Millionaire's row," I muttered, surveying the various detached properties, all set back from the road; styles ranging from mock-Tudor to hacienda. Properties I couldn't afford if I worked half a dozen lifetimes.

Vote Labour signs popped up a few miles later and I was in Blidworth. In May 1984, striking miners who had opened their doors to pickets from Yorkshire found themselves under siege by the police. The village was effectively under martial law for the day and a half duration of the siege. In an example of the police's thuggish ministrations that is all too typical of that time, officers kicked down the door of the village hall and threatened women and children who were assisting at a soup kitchen.

The headstocks are displayed in front of the Blidworth Community Leisure Centre, sunk so deep into the earth it's as if quicksand is pulling them down. On the ground, an eye-catching mosaic spells out the village's name, the intricate pattern of tiles depicting its natural and industrial heritage. I took the obligatory snap and drove home thinking about how little is left of the pits that used to define these — and two dozen other — Nottinghamshire villages; and how, despite these few remnants, there is still a palpable, even tactile, sense that these are communities which remain ravaged; unhealed. It might always be like this. Feelings run high, even thirty years on. Later that day, when I shared the Blidworth picture on a mining heritage page on Facebook, the first comment was "Notts scabs!!!"

If you didn't work down the pit, it was Players, Raleigh or Boots you'd clock in at — back in the day, at least. The current face of Nottingham employment is the likes of Experian and Capital One. I've worked at one and shunned the other and further musings are probably best kept to myself. Boots is now a subsidiary of American retail chain Walgreens, and a major

Headstocks, Annesley

John Player & Sons, Triumph Road

commercial and residential redevelopment is in the offing at their Beeston HQ. How this will sit alongside the Grade I and II listed buildings remains to be seen. I temped there for a while: the scale of the site was absurd; the offices were like something out of Terry Gilliam's *Brazil*. From leaving your desk to clambering into your car could entail a 15 minute walk — and that was before you'd even exited the site. I'm convinced that some third world border crossings are easier.

Cigarette manufacturers John Player & Sons moved from Radford to the airily named 'Horizon' factory adjacent to the Boots site long before *Alan Sillitoe's Nottinghamshire* appeared. The Radford complex originally comprised four factory buildings and a personnel block. All that's left now is the clockface from No. 2 Factory. Mounted on a plinth that wouldn't look out of place as a war memorial, it's positioned awkwardly in a corner of the Castle Retail Park in front of a goods inwards section. The clockface is damaged. The hands are stopped at twelve o'clock. There isn't even a plaque to contextualise its history. On the other side of Radford Boulevard, there's student accommodation where Factory No. 1 stood, much of it now awaiting demolition after a fire in March 2015 that robbed Nottingham of a piece of its architectural history.

Still, trace elements of Players remain on Triumph Road, a location that was once a nexus of the city's manufacturing heritage. Not, sadly, that the same can be said of Raleigh: the factory was demolished in 2003. New premises in Calverton were mooted, but the preferred business model for outsourcing to the Far East prevailed; the business model, in other words, that set Raleigh on its steady decline in the first place. Triumph Road is now home to a thrown-together University of Nottingham campus comprising some of the most outlandishly designed buildings in the county. Buildings I gaze out at from the Medilink bus as it ferries me to work every morning, shaking my head in despair: the dull grey Geospatial Building that looks like an Amazon fulfilment centre; the Institute of Mental Health, fronted by a sculpture resembling a nervous breakdown in 3-D; the Amenities Building and International House (shortlisted for the 2009 Carbuncle Cup for ugliness in architecture) panelled in blotchy shades of red, pink and puce that suggest less a seat of learning than a severe dermatological condition; the Sir Colin Campbell Building, resembling nothing more than a crashed

No. 2 Factory clockface, Castle Retail Park

Demolition, Radford Boulevard

spaceship. Its extermination by a Dalek fleet would be a huge aesthetic favour to the city.

But these oddities were only half the story, as I discovered when I wandered down Triumph Road with David Sillitoe, one glum Sunday morning. We started at the Wollaton Road end where Players' Bonded Warehouse dominates the skyline as imposingly as it must have done in the firm's heyday. Built in 1939, it represents Nottingham brutalism at its finest. Huge and unwelcoming, its bleakness almost shades into beauty. Getting a decent shot of it from street level was frustrating.

"We need access to one of those second storey windows," David mused, glancing across the road at a row of terraced houses. Picking the one that faced the Bonded Warehouse most directly, we knocked at the door. Waited. Exchanged glances as the door swung open of its own accord and revealed a shadowy and decidedly empty hallway.

"Well, that was a bit Amityville," I quipped, a lame attempt at levity.

"Anyone home?" David called.

Silence answered us. Glancing round, I noticed that two women were watching us with the suspicious regard of residents who have returned to their accommodation only to find a couple of strange blokes standing at the threshold debating whether to enter. Which, as it turned out, was exactly what they (and we) were. David explained our intentions and they seemed to downgrade their assessment of us from murderous housebreakers to mere simpletons. In heavily accented English, they asked us to wait while they spoke with someone. Minutes later, we were talking to John, an eminently personable fellow to whom the prospect of two complete strangers requesting access to his bedsit for the purposes of architectural photography seemed an everyday event.

A steep and narrow staircase took us up to his domicile. The conversation flowed as David tested the furthest extent to which the window opened, perching himself on John's windowsill and performing a kind of acrobatic routine by which his camera found itself dangled in mortal peril above a sheer drop. John told us that the warehouse was used for drying out cigarettes. That rumour had it demolition was on the cards. Another link to Nottingham's past under threat. David did the pictures, I jotted notes. John

Players Bonded Warehouse, Wollaton Road

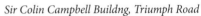

Sir Colin Campbell Buildng, Triumph Road

spoke poignantly of the landmarks he'd seen disappear over the years, just from that one window.

Back on the street, we thanked John for his hospitality and bade him farewell. Something about the confines of his bedsit juxtaposed with the Reichstag-like expanse of the Bonded Warehouse seemed characteristic of the city in a way that I was still trying to get my head round when, five minutes later, we found ourselves amidst the unreality of the university buildings. On foot, they seemed even gaudier than from the bus. A sign announced the crashed spaceship as "the Gateway to the Innovation Park", reinforcing the sci-fi analogy. Vaguely intrigued, we wandered past a stagnant water feature and the vista opened up to reveal … hmm, how to describe it? Imagine an episode of *The Prisoner* filmed at IKEA's head offices instead of Portmeiron. But even that doesn't do it justice. Just when you've rationalised a mental imagine of a teenage Patrick McGoohan yelling "I am not a student, I am a free-thinker", you catch a glimpse of the Learning Resource Centre and realise that a whole new frame of reference is required.

The Learning Resource Centre sits in the middle of an artificial lake, accessed by the kind of jetty-like walkway so popular on inspirational posters. It's an octagonal building whose sides slant downwards in what was doubtless intended, on the drawing board, as a diamond shape. It actually looks more like the half-drowned nose cone of a rocket, albeit one with a nicely inoffensive *faux* wooden finish. Maybe that's why the campus seems so wonky despite its desperately futuristic attention-seeking: everything looks like it came in a flatpack. It's as if the Swedes had made *Blake's 7* on a set assembled with an allen key.

A set, moreover, that's been configured for a surreal episode where the few remaining inhabitants of some soullessly homogenized community awake to find that everyone else has disappeared. University campus as ghost town, me and David — the two unlikeliest candidates for students in the East Midlands — wandering around like we owned the place. Nobody challenged us as we went clanking up and down circular fire escapes in search of a more expansive shot, a different aspect that might encourage a description of the locale less sarcastic than the above paragraphs. Some hope!

Little hope, either, of uncovering trace elements of Raleigh. A locked construction of the same bland Scandinavian style announced itself as a

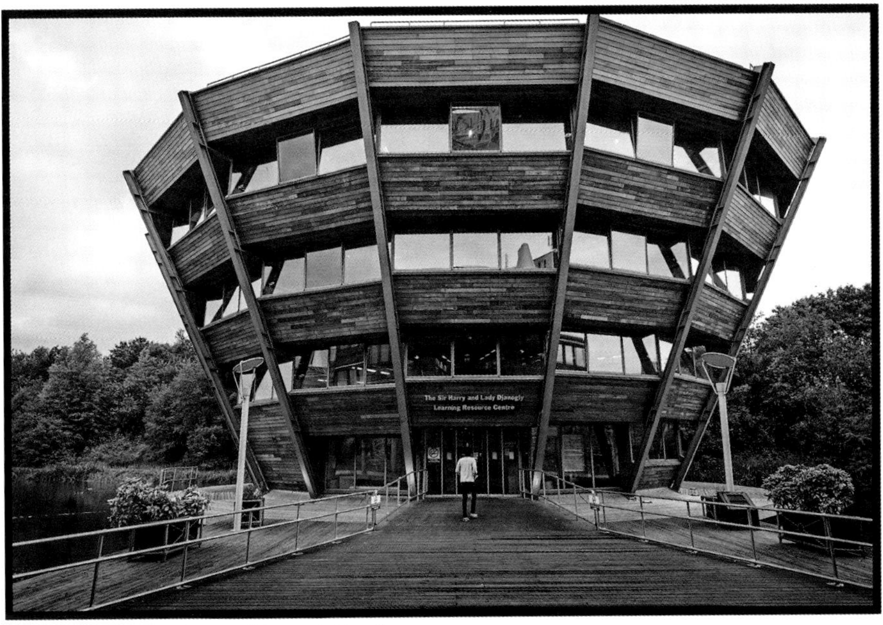

Learning Resource Centre, Triumph Road

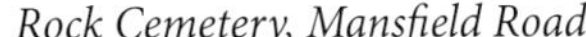

Rock Cemetery, Mansfield Road

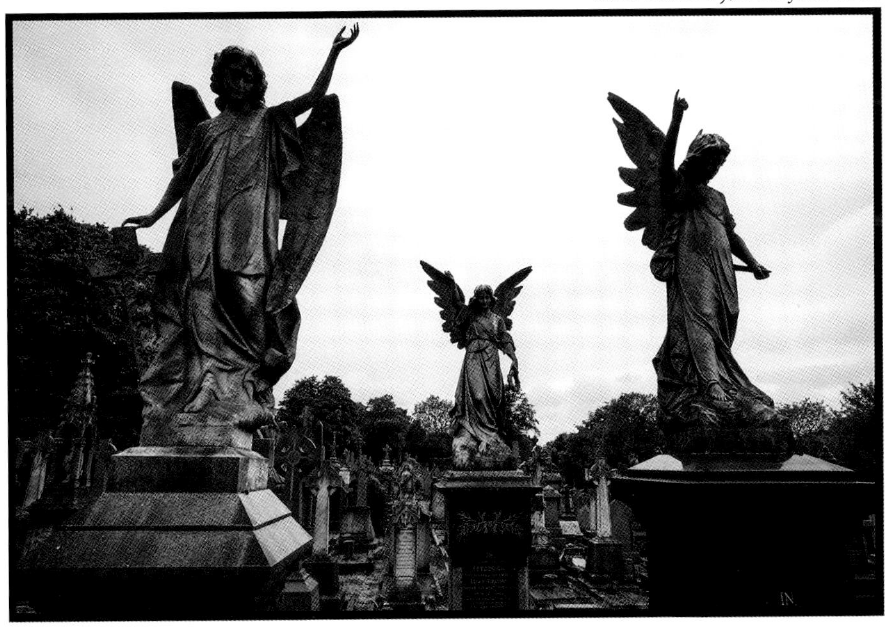

cycle store. It was tucked away out of sight of the road. Maybe it was filled with lovingly maintained Raleigh Choppers and Superbes. Or maybe not. In front of the Institute of Mental Health we found a bike chained to one of those extruded posts that look like a u-nail on steroids. It was a Claud Butler.

"If that'd been a Raleigh, it would have been perfect," David observed.

My thoughts exactly: the perfect shot; the perfect note on which to end this section. But this is Nottingham, and the city is nothing if not belligerent. Whatever you think it is, that's what it's not (to paraphrase one of *Saturday Night and Sunday Morning*'s key lines). So we adopted a 'work with what you've got' philosophy, David shooting with the no-nonsense efficiency of the seasoned press photographer while I sauntered down Triumph Road, hands in my pockets, head in the clouds, imagining the factory back in place, its shimmering phantom outline discharging a flotilla of ghost bikes, a working-class *tour de Nottingham* pedalling full tilt for the nearest boozer, a week's pay packet in every rider's back pocket and the world at their cycle-clipped feet. That's the great thing about imagination: it beats reality hands down.

The Bavarian filmmaker Werner Herzog once said "tourism is sin and travel on foot virtue". Walking into Nottingham — the proliferation of parking meters render the car a dead loss — I fantasised about a Herzog adaptation of a Sillitoe novel. Imagine it! The visionary director of *Aguirre, Wrath of God* and *Fitzcarraldo* tackling *A Tree on Fire* or *The Lost Flying Boat*.

Tourism is sin. I decided to steer clear of the obvious sites. Particularly the Castle, which is easily the most embarrassing example of a castle in the UK, if not the world. It's more like a mansion house on a rock and I can fully understand why Arthur Seaton, in *Saturday Night and Sunday Morning*, daydreamed about packing Mortimer's Hole full of TNT and blowing the lot to kingdom come.

The temptation to map out a pub-based geography was strong, even though dismal acknowledgement would have to be given to The White Horse's unceremonious fate. Made famous by Arthur Seaton's drinking contest with a mouthy sailor in what remains one of the greatest opening chapters of any novel, The White Horse is now a takeaway. The Five Ways, scene of the poignant finale to *Birthday* — the nominal sequel to *Saturday*

Closed shop, Mansfield Road

Clumber Street

Night and Sunday Morning — closed in 2015. Fortunately, the real ale aficionado in search of the authentic Sillitoe experience can still rely on a quality pint and friendly service at the Plough Inn, the Nottingham Brewery taphouse, on St Peter's Street.

Just walking into Nottingham along Mansfield Road is a drinker's paradise. In the mid-90s, me and my mate Alex were made redundant at the same time. We collected our giro on the same day, cashed it, met at the cemetery gates and wandered along to the Arboretum Manor. A plate of fish and chips, a couple of pints, a few frames on the pool table, then we'd head towards the city centre and call in at every boozer we passed. By nightfall, the better part of our dole money was gone and we were happily insensate.

I decided to indulge in a little nostalgia for those beer-soaked, responsibility-free days and begin my walk at the cemetery gates. A pint at the Arboretum Manor would have set me off on my peregrinations in even finer mettle, but I was stuck for borrowing a time machine that day. The Arbo, as we called it, burned down in 2006: arson. Reality prodding the sharp tip of itself against the helium balloon of nostalgia, I put my back to the cemetery and its avenues of canted headstones and alabaster angels, and started walking down Mansfield Road.

Back in the day, bantering with Alex, the Lincolnshire Poacher would have beckoned, one of a number of pubs on either side of the road. We'd bounce between them, eschewing pedestrian crossings in favour of reckless sprints between gaps in the traffic, yelling "keep death on the roads" to the accompaniment of car horns, upraised fingers or window-flung swear words from the motorists who'd narrowly avoided us. We'd laugh it off and dive into the Nag's Head, the Golden Fleece, the Rose of England, the Peacock.

We got thrown out of the Nag's Head once, though I'm buggered if I can remember why. And when did I twig — or bother to read the claim to fame on its ornately lettered signboard — that the Peacock was a favourite watering hole of novelist John Harvey? How many of the Inspector Resnick novels had I read before I realised I'd sat in the good detective's seat, got in his way at the bar, been no bloody help at all solving the crime?

What I *do* know is that Mansfield Road had a buzz back then: the shops were eclectic, as open-doored and inviting as the pubs. Would I go as far as

Market Square

Lace Market, Broadway

saying bohemian? Maybe, maybe not; but there was a different vibe back then. Returning to the here and now, Mansfield Road still boasted a few quirky independent shops, but there were just as many properties boarded up, to let, their erstwhile signs faded, paint flaking away. These were the emporiums that I remembered most keenly, crammed with second hand desirables. They beckoned the collector, the completist, the connoisseur in from off the street in a way that the commercial expanse of the Victoria Centre never could.

Speaking of which, the Vicky Centre was undergoing a redevelopment that was working wonders internally but left the exterior looking like the West Bank only without the Banksy mural. The same cluster of generic retail outlets that can be found in any UK city formed a join-the-dots invitation to overspend. I gave them the cold shoulder and headed for the more eclectic environs of Hockley.

Although Nottingham doesn't (yet) have a "cultural quarter" the way some other cities do, Hockley gives the impression of checking its watch while it awaits the appellation. Few would argue. Hockley's cards are on the table, a royal flush of youthful vibrancy and creative energy that includes independent arthouse cinema The Broadway, headline-grabbing free art gallery the Nottingham Contemporary, the headquarters of culture magazine LeftLion, and a cluster of trendy coffee shops, restaurants and bars.

It's also a bit pretentious, a bit too sure of itself. The Contemporary (or the Tempreh, as it's increasingly become known) opened in 2009 and got off to a cracking start with a Hockney retrospective and *Star City*, an exhibition featuring Soviet propaganda about the space race, but it's never quite hit those heights since. The Broadway remains the cineaste's first choice in the city, but it's been two decades since former director Adrian Wootton decamped to the South Bank and took the *Shots in the Dark* crime movie festival with him. I used to book annual leave around *Shots in the Dark* and drop a couple of week's wages on seeing as many films as possible: there were premieres, workshops, introductions. James Ellroy curated a season of *film noir*. Quentin Tarantino was guest of honour the year he won the Palm d'Or at Cannes for *Pulp Fiction*. I bumped into Tarantino randomly on my way to the Broadway for a screening of Terence Malick's *Badlands*. No entourage, no security, no ego. I offered my congratulations on the award;

Station Street tram stop

The Old Angel Inn

he shook my hand. I mentioned the film I was going to see; he gave me a fifteen-minute masterclass in '70s cinema. I staggered away, head reeling, trying to memorise all the movies he'd recommended.

Yeah, Hockley fancies itself; but the likelihood of bumping into a zeitgeist-defining film director nowadays? Don't hold your breath.

On Stoney Street, the Old Angel Inn boasts a portrait of Alan Sillitoe bearing a quote from *Saturday Night and Sunday Morning*: "Once a rebel, always a rebel, and it's best to be a rebel..." Continue along the street and university buildings, offices and an ugly great car park are the order of the day. A thoroughfare called Broadway connects Stoney Street with St Mary's Gate, which puts you out near the tram stop and the Tempreh. Broadway remains a showcase of traditional Lace Market architecture — grandiose, patriarchal, slightly threatening — and again past and present marshal themselves into a blunt contrast. Way back when, workers would have filed out of these buildings, knackered, slouching into the evening air after a back-breaking shift. Today, the city's confident and affluent young things queue up at nightfall for the clubs and bars which have come to define this now trendy area. Again, industry has been replaced.

I decide that I'll stay where I am, thank you very much. The Old Angel is a refreshingly down-to-earth pub, the kind of place you could describe as 'spit and sawdust' and feel confident the management would take it as a compliment. It's good to see that, despite the self-conscious posturing, there's a small corner of Hockley that's still in touch with its inner Arthur Seaton.

Time, maybe, for that long-delayed pint? The walk back into the city centre can wait. There'll be time aplenty to kick my heels in Slab Square where couples mooch and smooch in front of the left lion, the more socialist and socially-engaged of the two stone lions guarding the council house (guarding them from us, or us from them? who knows? who cares?); where trams rumble past the grubby chain pubs and up towards the Theatre Royal.

The tram system is Nottingham's white elephant, a *fait accompli* upon which hundreds of millions in public funds have been haemorrhaged. The spiralling budget for its extension out to Wilford, Clifton and Toton has necessitated workplace parking levies. The civil engineering scheme proved only moderately less divisive than the Berlin Wall, turning the Queens Medical Centre campus into a building site, disrupting the Medilink service and rendering Beeston practically inaccessible, to the chagrin of residents and local businesses. Still, a bit of PR can work wonders and the trams smartly play up to a sense of civic pride, each of them named after a famous son or daughter of Nottingham: Byron, Clough, Torvill and Dean, Bendigo. In November 2014, in conjunction with Nottingham's bid to be recognised as an UNESCO city of literature, tram n° 219 was officially named Alan Sillitoe. A nice enough gesture, but one that misses the point. Alan Sillitoe defined Nottingham and not *vice versa*; he is part of the city's identity, but he was never constrained by it.

It can wait, that walk back to Slab Square. Right now I can do without the Kremlinesque dome of the Council House, somehow symbolic of all the conflicted thoughts that define my relationship with my home town. I came looking for the remnants of *Alan Sillitoe's Nottinghamshire*, those areas with one foot in the past, and one just testing the waters of our brave (or buggered) new world. Right now I'm looking up at a portrait of Alan, stuck on the front of a pub where some Arthur Seaton of today is probably downing his eleventh pint. I'm still hanging around outside, so I stop wasting time, and go in.

Maybe Tomorrow

"Ey up, youth! Over 'ere!"

I'd spotted Big Vinnie straight away. The wince-inducing roar was entirely redundant.

'Friday night, dressed to kill, down at Dino's Bar 'n' Grill' we weren't and it wasn't. Not a hope in hell Phil Lynott had had the 'Spoons' in Stabbo in mind when he'd penned some of the most famous lyrics in rock 'n' roll. Still less that our regular quartet could ever be the sharp-dressed rakish vagabonds Phil had brought to life in *that* song.

I sighed and mentally braced myself. Tonight was going to be tougher than usual.

I collected my usual half of Guinness and single measure of Laphroaig — the traditional 'haulf and haulf' — from the bar. I might have been resident in Stapleford, a small typically working-class town about seven miles from Nottingham since 1984, but some habits died harder than others. And in Tullibody, an equally working-class suburb in my native Scotland, that was the way a man took his drink.

I made my way to our usual table, in a small book-lined nook to the left of the main entrance, and awaited the onslaught. It commenced immediately.

"Look at the face on it!" jeered Vinnie. "I fucking *knew* you'd look like a wet weekend in Skeggy, ya soft twat."

"Evening, Vinnie," I replied stonily and lifted my glass. "Lads." I toasted the other two. Ali smiled and winked at me over his pint of Stella.

"Donald," he returned my greeting. A slim, even at forty-four, fighting-fit kick-boxing Pakistani and, his words not mine, a "culturally-devout Muslim." A line he usually delivered slyly whenever someone questioned a Muslim who drank alcohol.

The fourth member of our wee band of brothers, Vinnie's literal brother Patrick, chimed in: "Ignore the cock, Donnie. Tek no notice of 'im."

The two, members of a notorious Irish family numbering dozens in and around Nottingham, were Nottinghamshire born and sounded it. Which was about all they had in common. Where Big Vinnie was a loud, outgoing, shaven-headed man-mountain and looking like a *Daily Mail* editor's stereotype of a football hooligan, the more cerebral Patrick was five foot six with a movie-star smile and a way with the ladies that had been the envy of the rest of us since we'd been friends, which was thirty years now.

"Come on, then, youth," invited Vinnie. "Let's hear the prophet of doom."

"Not biting tonight, Vinnie. You can fuck off."

He laughed. "Ah but you will, 'comrade.' You won't be able to help yourself."

It hurt. Another General Election and the fucking Tories had done it again. Against all the predictions of the pollsters, bookies and pundits alike, the fuckers had actually won a *majority*. What the fuck was *wrong* with the frigging English?

Vinnie read my mind, almost. "Still, at least your lot, your Bannockburn re-enactment society, stuffed it to 'em, eh, mate?"

"If you mean the SNP, you plank, then aye; they certainly did. Much good it does the rest of us, mind. Stuck in Tory fucking England for another five years and *this* time they'll..." I broke off. He'd done it again. He crowed in delight.

"Ha! Fucking gotcha! You just can't help yourself, can you?"

He was right. I couldn't. Ever since we'd met during the miners' strike I'd been fighting the good fight, the class war. And what had I got out of it? A divorce from Debbie, two estranged kids and, at fifty-eight, more chance of prostrate cancer than any sort of revolution occurring on Britain's — sorry, *England's* — increasingly right wing-drifting shores.

I'd come down from my pit at Polmaise in the summer of '84, to help out the tiny band of Notts strikers with picketing. That's where me and Vinnie came in. He'd been at Hucknall pit and had been sacked a mere three weeks into the strike. For the crime of defending himself when jumped by two scabs in the Welfare car park. It hadn't, as we say in Tullibody, put his gas at a peep, mind. He'd stayed solid to the end. A very bitter end, as it turned out.

I'd been sacked for a similar crime. A copper from the Met had had it in for me from the day I arrived in Scab Land. There'd been about a hundred of us from Scotland who'd come down and our convoy had been stopped and turned back as we tried to leave the M1 at junction 26. This copper had given me a hard time then and on the subsequent occasions we'd made it through their lines and onto a picket, he always seemed to be there. Gedling, Bevercotes, Blidworth, didn't matter; the fucker was always there. He'd marked my card and despite two arrests and a pure mental battering in the cells at Hucknall, I'd managed to hang on to my job. Until the big Mansfield rally.

Arthur had come to preach the gospel and we were lapping it up. About 50,000 of us. A braw summer's day. Wives, bairns and supporters from all over the UK. And then the polis got stuck in. As we were making our way back to the coaches and cars at the end, they'd just appeared. Hundreds of the bastards out for blood. Bludgeoning, punching, kicking and I found myself — of all the polis in all the world — face-to-face with this bastard who'd been plaguing me from day one.

I'd just had time to get my arm up as his truncheon came flying towards my face. The crack was like a gun-shot. My arm just went and I knew it was broken. Still, I managed to pit the heid on the cunt and the sound his nose made when my head connected with it made a very satisfying noise of its own.

If ever a victory was pyrrhic, though, that was it. Three of his pals waded in and I took the battering of my life. I was in the hospital for a week and then on sticks for a month. I'd narrowly avoided the big house when a wifey fae a nearby shop testified on my behalf and two polis who gave evidence against me turned out not to have even been in Mansfield at all on the day.

Didnae save my job, however. Summoned back to Polmaise and the manager gave me my cards.

We didn't care, though. We were gonnae win, see? And then there'd be the amnesty and we'd all get oor jobs back. Aye, and that'll be right, as my auld man cynically remarked at the time. Turned out he was right and I was wrong. Not for the first time. Nor the last.

I drifted back down to Notts and stayed there. I was winching Debbie by then and her sister, Julie, was married to Vinnie so I stayed with Vinnie and Julie.

At the end of it I was luckier than a lot of the boys, blacklisted and broken, some hastened to early graves in poverty and despair; I'd got a job in a textile plant in Long Eaton, working in the dyehouse. Brutal and backbreaking it was and on a bad day — and there were more of them than good days — even worse than the pit. But it was a job and it paid.

Vinnie went a different road. He'd always been a canny lad and he set up for himself, a wee building firm. Started out from his garage, just him and another boy fae Gedling pit, and now, thirty years later, he was pushing sixty, retired, nae mortgage and his two laddies running McGraw's Building Services.

That wasn't the only area in which we differed. After the strike I'd become even more militant. I ended up in the Communist Party and then, eventually, in the Labour Party I'd come to despise for its betrayal of not just the miners but the entire working class.

I figured that it needed winning back to its socialist roots and that that was an easier task than starting from scratch wi' the new party the ultra-left nutters were always proclaiming had been born, with each disastrous new initiative.

Vinnie washed his hands of the lot. His philosophy had become brutally simple.

"What have I been telling you for nigh on thirty years, mate?" he asked. "Eh? You can't change the world. It's too big. It'll break your heart or you'll die trying. Probably both, state of you."

I'd heard it all before. More times than I could even begin to count. Vinnie was remorseless, though.

"Look after your own small corner, mate. You and yours. First, last and always. If you can do someone a good turn, at no cost to you or your family, then fine; do it. But otherwise? Fuck 'em, youth. There will never be a revolution in this country. The strike showed us that. And last night should've proved it to you beyond doubt. The great unwashed don't *want* what you're trying to give them. Another Tory government, mate. That's what you've got. Waste of time. They're all as bad as each other."

And so on and so on. Big Vinnie's mantra. I'd always thought it was defeatist, cynical bollocks. Still did, in fact. Just that with every passing year it was getting a little bit harder to keep myself convinced …

Ali and Patrick finished their pints. "Into town then, chaps?" enquired Ali.

I shook my head and Vinnie jumped in again. "Nah, he'll be off home crying into his whisky and whining on Facebook till brekker with his lefty mates."

"Piss off, Vinnie. You're a fucking broken record, you are."

"Ah, but that's because the song remains the same, Donnie." He softened and reached across the table and slapped a meaty paw on the back on my neck, pulling me in close until our foreheads were touching. "Get laid, get a hobby, get a *life*, kid. Before it's too late. And if you can't do that, get yer arse round our's for Sunday dinner, right?"

"Aye, mebbe. We'll see."

We all trooped across Derby Road to the bus stop where the Warren Arms had once stood. Now more bloody flats and tat shops underneath.

The 4A pulled in. Packed with dolled-up lassies off into Notts for the big Friday night piss-up. As the doors opened a blast of perfume and sweat hit me. Once it would've have smelled like opportunity and the possibility of delights to come. Now it smelled like despair. Denial and escape. But what the fuck did I know? They all looked happier than me.

Vinnie, Ali and Patrick climbed aboard. As the bus pulled away, they were hauling themselves down the aisle grinning and flicking the vees at me. Ranging in age from early forties to nearly sixty, they were still acting like fucking wains. I smiled despite myself and started walking.

Up to the crossroads at the Roach, a left onto Church Street, past the Feathers or rather what used to be the boozer. More fucking flats, these days. The library had resisted the cuts, though, and was still there. To my mind a tiny beacon of resistance to the austerity bandits now back in office for another five fucking years.

As I drew level with St. Helen's Church, the doors of the Cross, over the road, exploded open and bunch of Forest lads spilled out down the steps, chanting and singing. They hadn't much to sing about this season as far as I could see but maybe Derby County's narrow failure to gain promotion was reason enough.

For some reason Springsteen's voice echoed in my mind. I couldn't quite place the song but I could hear the tune, loud and clear. Something about needing a reason to believe. At the end of every shitty day we always find a reason to believe. At least that's what the Boss reckoned.

Not tonight, though. Not for me.

Maybe tomorrow.

Odds Against

After a backward glance, like a petty crook
or a jockey in the lead, swish through
the plastic strips into the betting shop,
eyes stinging at the smoke. Step over
the thin mongrel with a rope threaded
through the handles of two fat Kwiksave bags.

Four of eight screens show the same steak-fed
greyhounds springing from six traps at Catford.
The mongrel ignores them, but sniffs the bags
and the greasy owner raps his snout,
crooning "Number Five." Number Four wins.
The punter accepts a polystyrene cup,
tea, from a sad-lipped woman in mock mink.
A poster shows Ascot, gold, champagne.

Edge past Jed, he's always here, face webbed
with a spider tattoo. If he could win
enough, he'd have it removed and never
be noticed. He's helping short-tongued Brian
to read the runner's names from the pages
of today's *Racing Post* pinned to the walls
and to fashion an each-way treble
with one of the stub-sized ball-points half-
generously provided. A mug's bet,
hopeless as Joe and Brian, odds well against.

Best to reduce risk, so avoid Yankees,
through-the-card accumulators, triple
forecasts. Stay off handicaps, sellers,
claimers and amateurs — and don't risk the rent.

It's enough perhaps to avoid losing,
to be in this shabby place, feeling slightly
disreputable, to have a system,
form against course and distance, pass the slip
and a couple of coins with expertise
to Sheila or Jean and most days get some
back, standing shoulder to shoulder with Lee
from Mr Wong's thumbing a wad of tens
over a horse's name you can't quite read.

Wet outside and no raincoat. Just your luck.

Black Hole

I have to avoid pubs and spiritualists,
dirty rhododendrons and uptight gardens.
My route home via Manor Street
is riddled with temptation and a dead poet
with his black herds grazing.

I am more intent on lazing in the rain
than getting soaked to the skin.
Raindrops big as Brazil nuts
crack the skull if you are not careful
or get too full of yourself.

That picture of God like all the wise kings
is older than myself, probably knows more,
but I don't buy magicians or fairytales
since burying two friends in three weeks,
beardless and young, not even fifty.

The room for hope is in a public house, except,
too obsessed with goodness and anti-matter,
the many worlds of parallel universes,
and that conviction that a continued life
is as pointless as black holes and singularities.

Drink

He has a way with a pint that hints
at who he is. It starts as the ale is drawn,
his eyes moving from the barmaid's chest

to her grip on the polished wood
of the pump. Along the tilted side
of the glass, the liquid rises

as if spelling danger, or re-establishing
an equilibrium, while the over-lively froth
gushes forth like loose talk

before it drains into the slops;
and when the measure's attained,
with a small headspace left,

she sets it up on the counter
for him to assay. He pauses briefly,
holds it up, then gives it a quarter turn,

staring into it like a talisman,
or the dark mirror that shows him
what he needs to see.

From Gosling, R.

From 2004 until his death in 2013 Ray Gosling communicated with his BBC producer in Nottingham, Tony Roe, through letters and postcards. These are extracts from a small selection, and the stories behind them. Ray's correspondence has been presented verbatim.

> *From Gosling R.*
>
> *7 xii 04*
>
> *I suppose all is shut down until AFTER the Dreadful Xmas but I am about — and do call us if you wish. No news of a contract yet ?*

We took Ray on by chance. We were thinking about making a film to counter a programme which showed Nottingham as the boozy capital of Britain. I began by searching through the BBC's own archives and stumbled upon some great drinking and pub shots from a film made in 1963. I was struck by the style of it. The simplicity. The people it featured. The young presenter who spoke in his own verse and his own accent. And the fabulous archive footage of Nottingham and Leicester in the film which was called *Two Town Mad.*

The day I watched the footage I went home wondering how I could use it. And in those channel hopping moments before bed I saw Ray on the telly: a BBC Four documentary called *Bankrupt*. That same presenter. Older now. But that same style… and he was in Nottingham.

It didn't take long to find him. His house had after all been featured in *Bankrupt*. I prefer to go and see people if I can rather than sit in the confines of an office and phone… or email. Ray was out. So I stuffed a note through the letterbox.

That night Ray rang. Abrupt. He was always abrupt. Straight to the point as uncomfortable as that might be. We met. And we decided to remake *Two Town Mad* forty years on.

The format of *Inside Out* is three films over half an hour which goes out on BBC One against *Coronation Street*. Ray's work on our first film was so good we made it the whole programme without seeking permission from above. The viewing figures rocketed. The feedback from viewers was astonishing in the quantity and the praise for Ray. From above came the words "Next time ask."

25 May 05

The success of INSIDE OUT TWO TOWN MAD was the ease of having a classy, populist 1962 half hour
& me still alive.
So it was made with an ease (the new one)
We can not expect again.

There followed several years of new ideas. Always ideas. People he wanted to listen to. Places and things popular in our lives. To be honest the kind of films you wouldn't do without a "Ray" to do them.

23rd July 2005

I'm fine and have been in North Wales-but heading back now.
Mobile should be charged.

I can understand due to recent events — the bombs in London — there may be among some of thee a doubt as to going ahead with at this time THE BUS.

Well for any reasons like that —I think strongly it would be very wrong.

And if anyone has doubts over ME — as it'd be known I'm not a beloved of Our system — no way at all do I condone the indiscriminate murder of common people who ride on public transport. It's absolutely wholly abhorrent to me even more so than was the bombing of just an ordinary pub by Birmimgham New Street, or Warrington Town Centre.

But but Tony I THINK WE MUST PAY A NOD THAT WE KNOW. And then a tribute in the section where brave bus driveresses leave for their duties.

31st July 2005

I shall soon maybe have a landline — but not much use really as I'm away so much and don't necessarily answer any phones even if it rings/bleeps beside me.

Making Ray's film *Bus* that summer was a delight. We were surprised at the number of people who would stop and talk to him in the street. He was a distraction to shoppers in Sleaford. And at the bus station demonstrated his ability to ad lib as he directed cameraman Darren to "mind the vomit" as he stepped around the bus shelter which was apparently the town's bus station.

Later in Nottingham we borrowed an old Bartons bus to take a party of Radio Nottingham listeners on a tour. First to Incinerator Road in Nottingham and then to Top Valley because Ray had always wanted to go on a bus trip to the estate which for some reason had been left off the tourist map. Somehow we managed to lose a passenger.

Friday 9th December 2005

I like v much the STATUES film we've done v.much. You of course will have your opinion — and I'll ask you merely not to muck about with it without talking to me.

I am right proud like very much its content and its style.

Statues was the film in which Ray urged us all to "look up, look up" at the buildings which surround us. It's a pretty good motto.

6th February 2006

Hoping your teaching in Sneinton happened and fine as could.
These things like that are so worth doing a bit of.
I get worried at more than a bit of — but a bit of and if we all did a bit of —
...what a wonderful world..

if only...!!

I've had loads of lovely reactions from STATUES — from friends, acquaintances and folk as let on to me in the streets.

One of the joys for me being in direction by Tracy and Neil was I felt they "carried" me a bit and that was lovely.
Now — I feel on every corner of my life — I've got to be /am expected to be "the leading thought".

Thank you for the work and encouragement
Every good wish respects, regards

Ray

Tu.14 xi 06

I owe you £20 still.

After you left today the day just went. It does teaching. They said it was THE best class I ever done. All I know was it was VERY hairy for me.

Ray took what he did do well on TV and Radio to the classroom with "University of the Third Age" talks to the retired and semi-retired who like him wanted to continue to learn; and continue to be active. I witnessed one of his talks and walks once. He was like the pied piper leading his party around Sneinton in Nottingham finding the interesting in what most of us take for granted. Stopping off in pubs on the way.

We.17 i0 07

There are some really wicked myths about homeless people you see in shop doorways & church porches. That they're alcoholics — well I drink too much. That they're scroungers — well so are some politicians. That they won't do a proper days work — nor will some gaffers. Homelessness happens — a complex of reasons and can happen to anyone. Twice in my life — it's happened oh that close to me. So I been past few months listening to the homeless — those who recently have been and some as still is. And thinking what can they do about it — and what can we.

Friday 27th October 06

Thanks for walking up to see me today —and your much appreciated kindness with my technology deficiency. My DERBY LEICESTER homeless filming day is scheduled as Tuesday 7th November.

Ray was busy again. In demand. Award winning programmes for BBC Four, and on Radio 4.

31st January 2007

Tone
is we forgot GRAVES
for a future ?
Ray

Friday 23rd February 2007

For coffee bars.
We need 3, 4, or 5 local owners who tell us they can carry on, love being local, and can "beat" McDonalds.

I do know Michael Brucciani of Leicester who famous as a young man asked the young David Attenborough to drink up and leave as he'd been sitting in their then Horsefair Street branch a gabbing with his mates too long.

1st March 2007

Talking of BBC South...
There was a "lad" there then in Southampton days — journalist making / editing his film about the police v hippies at Stonehenge. I got on with him well in pub though he was a very senior copper's son — hence his "project" — as he had — via his Dad — the access. He later went on this and that and eventually to be elevated up to be boss of BBC World Service and for a short time after Greg Dyke was acting D.G.

He used to watch over my shoulder as I was scripting LEWES and say "You'll not get away with saying that Ray." And I would smirk and reply —"Half a pint in pub at lunch time." — I forgotten his name [Mark Byford]. *I've always had a certain fondness for coppers, and copper's sons.*

They have to be both close to "what you'll not get away with" and an understanding that some of us do,

They were lovely days — for me — out of Southampton.

Sunday 25 xi 07

I had to go to London Friday — another of them do's and I won a Grierson Award for the Available Light OAP film. No money in it — again !! So ta for your £40.

I know it's just a Nottingham thing But Kenneth Alan Taylor is Dame in Whittington at Playhouse. I know he says it's his last year after year. But I'd love to see him "done" — he's written and staged and played so much both Nottingham and my beloved Oldham and is so reclusive.

Yours — remaining wretchedly broke.

7th October 2007

Ta the money — again. With no ITV I'd say for ever, and no BBC FOUR I'm really grateful — for the work and the money.

As we know I'm a known character as is approachable on the street and in the bus/train — so I collect a fair dash of comment after I do anything on the telly and the "feedback" I had direct after the Joe Orton was quite interesting — several middle aged men took me aside for a "private" word with me — one an airline pilot, one a soccer referee, one an Irish labourer — None I'd say was gay, nor interested particularly in art or theatre. They all said my/our piece on Joe was "very sensitively done" : "you were very careful not to criticise Ray" — and they liked that.

Ray did a film for us on Leicester's Joe Orton. Interviewing Joe's sister, Leonie, as part of it. Including the library on what's known as Pork Pie Island where Joe stole his first library books. Joe, who was gay when it was against the law, had once told a lie to a newspaper that he had married young and divorced in Leicester. No one bothered to check it out. When Joe was murdered by his lover, Kenneth Halliwell, in 1967, his divorce was a passing fact in the obituaries. By using newspapers as source material a lie had become an apparent truth. It was that easy.

28 May 08

£ ?!

Ray was always short of cash. You always had to carry a spare tenner for the end of a lunchtime meal or a drink.

12th August 2008

WINDMILLS
I don't want to get too Eco do I ?
Are we planning still to go to Skegness on the sand with a sandcastle windmill of little plastic sails.
I want to be naive?

I like them because the wind blows free...don't it.
So why are so many facing east when our best winds are from the west?
Why are so many windmills in the Eastern Counties?

As part of Ray's film on windmills we took him out on a boat to the huge wind farm off the Lincolnshire coast. Ray was the one who coped best with the choppy seas. Producer and picture Editor Matt didn't do too well at sea.

11th September 2008

It was very exciting at sea — you and Stuart and Luke would have loved it and looked very manly. Ship fit. Not sure about Darren — but poor Matt... ah ah he was so brave. On the prow of the heaving ship, with two hefty minders to pin him down with their weight — plus — plus being strapped by a harness

to the railings as the weather and the waves tossed and swung and upped and downed and fair lashed us.
Ah — for art's sake we did our best.
Of course in the "rushes" it may not LOOK like this. Just me as an aged frightened scarecrow quivering for little visible reason !!
However nothing can take away that we know as we were there-
Matt was v v v brave.

PSS ta your postcard advertising brain food for seafarers. Is that made of brains? Anyway ta but that was not what was needed. What was was standing upright embrocation — ie glue.
You ask Matt — he was so brave.
regards and respects

Ray

The watery theme continued. A film on fishing. Fishing in the canal. By now we made sure we did all the filming in the morning and kept Ray away from the pub as long as possible. He was at his lyrical best in the mornings. Not so good after lunch.

091108

Just mind meanderings re
Angling
I see a chance of doing a romantic watery little intro piece we could collect as Daz goes hither and thither — or we/you might have already.

I like fish and chips — but that's not what I'm doing is it ?
Please don't go away — this is to be a film about fishing.
Please don't go away.

Th 15 i 09

Matt was lovely yesterday.
V. Nice Derby people. Normal. No grumpy "side" to them like here.

Mo 19 Jan '09

Re angling — after your phone call
with Matt. Suggest I dress. Not sure it's dress up.

MARIE
All over the world people'd love the job I do.
Being elegant and meeting great people while you're presenting t.v.
But on a muddy day on banks of the Erewash we find Ray Gosling —
the reluctant presenter.

RAY TO TONY
Do I have to do this ?

You are going to pay me ?

You know in my heyday I did St George's Hall in Liverpool live : Buckingham Palace for Floella Benjamin. I done Singapore : Calcutta : the top of the Woolworth Building in New York City. I interviewed Harold Wilson — live — and the Mayor of Barcelona, Paris, Istanbul.

But now alright — for Inside Out East Midlands I sit on the banks of the Erewash near Ilkeston, waiting to interview a fish.

Ray's love of the "University of the Third Age" was used as a platform for a film on people wanting to stay active beyond the bus pass years. At one point in the film there's a touching reunion with Michael Parkinson whom he'd worked briefly with at Granada in the sixties.

15th April 09

Dear Tony and Rob

I have been worried at the U3A film as to how to make it potentially watchable by young people.

A day at the races:
Yes — lovely.
I'm not sure either of you know how the races work. But I do.
Me and my sister book a second class table at a course like Southwell — we done Stratford/ Huntingdon. That size of track.

And second class is important, to my mind — because the first class dining is full of swanks and more money than senses. It costs us about £100 — but you get light lunch, and a bottle of wine, and thermos flasks of coffee and teas. And whatever the weather you've got your dry, table with a first class view — which is yours all afternoon. We usually make up a party of about 6 — or two tables would be 12.

So we'd need to know does Clement fancy that.
Is he staying/are we staying the afternoon ?
Will Clement be bringing friends with him ? How many ? in his party ?

I quite fancy trying to bring about 4 of my younger friends — in their 20s because I like young people and get on well, and they with me — and it adds an element beyond just a film of all oldies.

16th April 2009

Dear Each and Both

Have heard Dear Clement Freud has died — oh dear, but so soon after speaking with Rob probably means not much pain. Does it scupper our plans? Well, a bit — but shouldn't scupper the project. I'm pretty sure you Both and Each will have ideas — and by Monday I shall too. We didn't "sell it" on Clement alone.

Ray had always hankered on doing a film on the one certainty in life: death. We had an idea for him to do his own obituary one day.

8th Sept 2009

Pretty hard up at the moment. I COULD DO DEATH. I have a grave paid for at Wilford Hill. And any other bits of dosh around. I'm pretty very hard up really!!
With DEATH me and ROB did a Leicester U3A afternoon where the subject was EUTHANASIA and several members had "put me down" cards which they carry around.

With DEATH we could combine graves — we have some lovely ones Byron: Mary Potter : the flowers on lampposts to roadside death.
Anyway we could lunch out on that one ?

This was the lunch where, with producer Rob Whitehouse, we talked about how to do 'death'. We met, as was often the case, at the Hard to Find Café on Mansfield Road in Nottingham near Ray's home. I remember it well. We kept being addressed loudly by a shouty woman who clearly had a problem. Ray was very civil with the interruptions. This was the meeting which would later in the BBC hating newspapers be called a "boozy lunch". Far from it. Rob was driving, and I don't drink. Ray was on good form. He told us "I killed a man once…." Rob and I exchanged a look.

The film which went out on death in February 2010 ended Ray's career. The confession that he'd smothered a dying friend was made up. But it was a lie he had told so often he probably felt he couldn't say anything else. He did it on the telly because he said he felt for the people who had lived with the dying. Like he had with his partner Bryn, who he'd nursed through pancreatic cancer until his death in 1999.

Ray told me later he had a pact with the man who had died an AIDs related death but he hadn't carried it out. And he had been berated for that. By himself or another, I don't know the truth of that.

1:10

FROM GOSLING R.

Tony
have I been paid for DYING ?
I think I have but would you check please ?
Ray.

The postcards continued until Ray's death in 2013. He didn't phone much. But he did call me out of the blue from the QMC. "Tone. I've had a heart attack".

Ray Gosling died on 19 November 2013

TONE'S

The Bar at the Trip to Jerusalem

The Gospel According to Arthur Seaton

i.m. Alan Sillitoe

1.

The gospel according to Arthur Seaton:
don't let the bastards grind you down. Words
to live by. It's a great life if you don't weaken,
so stay strong. Study the three Bs: birds,
booze and brawling. Drink that mouthy sod
under the table, leave him with the bar bill
as you stagger off for a piss. You're a god
and the White Horse is Paradise. Your will
be done. The only Fall is the one you take
down a painless flight of stairs (though
something tells you it'll hurt like mad
tomorrow morning, make no mistake).
Sober up. She's waiting at the bar, you know.
Her fella's a fool. You're on a promise, lad.

2.

Go on: foolish not to. You're on a promise, lad,
and that bit of loving snatched between
the full-throttle of Saturday night and the sad
grey hangover of Sunday morning — the mean
reminder of what you spent and how long
till the next pay packet — that bit of loving
is the best you can hope for. It's the Song
of Solomon, if Solomon were ready to swing
for a slice of hearthrug pie with his mate's wife.
It's grand Italian opera, Verdi or his like,
the orchestra steaming away like an express train.
It's the only thing that makes sense of a life
spent at a lathe, turning parts for bikes.
It's a sure thing. Your track record's unbeaten.

3.

One thing for sure: your track record's unbeaten
when it comes to living on your own terms.
That's what rules are made for — to be broken
by blokes like me. Said with a grin, but folded arms
reinforce the fact: you bloody well mean it.
The world's your oyster and Nottingham the pearl
(which makes the back streets of Lenton the grit)
and your main priorities are a pint and a girl.
All you're out for is a good time; all the rest
is propaganda (your *raison d'ëtre*: a great motto,
it'll be on a tee-shirt one day). A passing fad,
your parents think; callow youth, your bosses attest;
something to be paid for, others declare. Are you
worried it'll all catch up with you, even a tad?

4.

Worried it'll all catch up with you? Not a tad!
Worst you'll cop is a black eye from a jealous
husband. The days of being called a cad
and slapped round the chops with a white glove
are over. None of that meeting at dawn, appointing
seconds, choice of weapons, taking ten paces,
three-volume novel bullshit; just a swift pasting
down some dark alleyway. If he's got the face
to do it himself, that is, and not chicken out
and leave the rough stuff to a brother or a mate,
a couple of squaddies thumping seven bells
out of you. No real victory: it was chucking out
time, you were pissed. They'd have lost a straight
fight, let's be honest. Fuck it. What the hell?

5.

Let's be honest: sometimes you lose. What the hell?
You got a good few punches in, you took
your lumps. They're no different from that little
Hitler at the factory, that pencil-neck fuck-
face of a foreman who gives it the "yes sir, no sir,
three bags full sir" to management, that brown-
tongued sad-sack no better than a whipped cur.
Your *don't let the bastards grind you down*
philosophy is validated by a single glance at
the alternative: marriage, mortgage, pension,
fitted kitchen, car, foreign holiday, some rammel
about giving your kids a start in life. Stuff that!
Deny the past, rail at the present until the tension
between the two resolves. The future's decision is final.

6.

Time erases, rebuilds; the future's decision is final,
though you'd protest to you find yourself sixty years
down the line and everything changed: vinyl,
Brylcreem and teddy boy suits old hat, the gears
and repetition turned parts you used to produce
for Raleigh bikes outsourced abroad, the factory
demolished and Triumph Road reduced
to a cluster of outlandishly designed university
buildings. This is what the city has become:
an edifice stripped of industry. At Calverton,
Annesley, Cinderhill, silent headstocks tell
a grim story. This is where you came from,
unrecognisable now. This is Nottingham, or what
passes for it. This might not sit with you too well.

7.

Nottingham might not sit with you too well
and I can imagine you sneering at the current crop
of Saturday night revellers: lager, aftershave; all
talk, no action. The White Horse is a kebab shop
(whoa! ease up, mate — don't shoot the messenger)
and the fleapits where you sat at the back
and made your moves are trade counters now or
carpet remnant stores, or boarded up for lack
of tenants. Recession, austerity, the credit crunch.
The sense of an ending. The kind of guff
your well-read brother would probably call
a *fin de siècle* or a *götterdämmerung*.
Big words, but the truth of it's clear enough:
every generation's lost, every age is autumnal.

8.

Every generation's lost, every age is autumnal,
every politician spouts the usual propaganda
before he u-turns like an atheist in a foxhole
and sells the voters out to the highest bidder.
The revolution? Sorry, mate; the country
never managed to get off its arse and howl
for blood. There was summat on the telly
or it was karaoke night down the local,
some talent-deficient yawper with a yen
to be the next big thing prancing on the stage
while the audience embrace banality.
Fame as yesterday's forgotten headline.
Bernstein's Age of Anxiety ebbs to an age
of false idols, magazine covers, celebrity.

9.

False idols on magazine covers. Celebrity
culture grins idiotically from a surface sheen.
You used to rib your dad about how much TV
he watched. He was glued to the screen
back then; now, he'd overdose on freeview:
endless reruns, the +1 con of watch-it-again,
lifestyle, movies, news, sport. No need to
spring for a season ticket to Meadow Lane,
go out in the cold and watch it live. The idiot
box drains your existence to indentation:
the shape of your arse on a threadbare sofa.
Be vigilant. Know the signs. If it's got
a screen and scart lead, treat with suspicion;
back away from the remote controller.

10.

Back away from the remote controller,
or 'remote' in the argot of constant truncation
(and you'd hate what text-speak has done for
language: even the lubricated inflections
of slang sound poorer), hit the off switch, fight
your way to your own hard-won opinion.
Know the signs. The ad-man talks shite,
the spin-doctor lies, the tie-wearing minion
tows the company line. There's nowt
in the way of integrity. Take the workplace:
team meetings replace hard graft; some clown
shows his profile, tosses a few buzzwords out.
Fuck it. Tell 'em to shove it up their arse,
log off, exit without saving, head into town.

11.

Log off, exit without saving, head into town,
get hammered. So you didn't last the morning,
so what? No job, no boss, no problem.
The pubs are open: they were serving
breakfast from 8AM, a huddle of old blokes
queuing up for their first pint at nine.
Pissheads but good company, their jokes
and stories a throwback to a still-recent time
when PC meant the bastard in uniform
who moved you on from that doorway snooze,
and not political correctness. Rough and ready
colloquy, factory talk: it was the norm
back then. Birds, brawling and booze:
the three Bs. All that you were out for, really.

12.

The three Bs: all you're out for, really,
the great saga of life lived for the moment,
fully and without regret. As it should be.
Education, work, authority, commitment,
taxes, the shackles of mortgage and loans:
life's a prison cell if you fall into the trap
of obeying orders. Once the millstone
of blind obedience has been draped
around your neck, you're theirs for life,
a cotter pin holding a cog in the machine.
Take their pay, sure, but don't pander
to the hierarchy. You'll never get rich,
but you can spend your wages having
a good time. All the rest is propaganda.

13.

Good times. Saturday nights. All the rest
is propaganda compared to the buzz
as you walk into a pub, the sharp taste
of your first pint, the clatter of pool balls
as someone shoots the break, the grin
on your face as a favourite song comes on
or the barmaid catches your eye. You were in
a foul mood yesterday, thoughts of revolution,
your bastard bosses up against the wall.
But that was then. This is Saturday
night and you own this low-rent town;
this is the feeling that makes palatable
the drudge of the working week; this is why
you don't let the bastards grind you down.

14.

Don't let the bastards grind you down
with the millstone or the carborundum wheel,
or their repertoire of petty rules. Be a thorn
in their side. Adopt the bolshy, belligerent spiel
of the barrack-room lawyer. Don't forget
how many different types of bastard there are,
don't let them blindside you, don't put
on the mask they expect you to wear:
drone, working class pleb, regular Joe.
Your credo: *I'm me and nobody else*
and whatever people think I am or say I am,
that's what I'm not, because they don't know
a bloody thing about me. Amen! Here's
to the gospel according to Arthur Seaton.

15.

The gospel according to Arthur Seaton:
take what's offered. You're on a promise, lad,
a sure thing. Your track record's unbeaten,
but it'll all catch up with you. Worried? A tad,
if you're being honest, but what the hell!
Live for now. The future's decision is final
and the results might not sit with you too well.
Every generation's lost, every age is autumnal,
studded with false idols, photoshoots, celebrity.
Back away from the remote controller,
log off, exit without saving, go to town
on the three Bs. All you're out for, really,
is a good time — all the rest is propaganda.
Don't let the bastards grind you down.

The Nottingham Issue

In his review of Alan Sillitoe's *Key to the Door* in the December 1961 issue of *Anarchy*, Nicolas Walter wrote: "I began reading Alan Sillitoe's new novel a few hours after hearing he joined us in the big [anti-nuclear] sit-down [organised by the Committee of 100] while I was lying on a police-cell floor during the long night of September 17th. I can think of no more suitable time and place, for Sillitoe has a voice of pure dissent, like Seán O'Casey or John Osborne; there are no concessions to his total commitment. He offers no comforting message like Forster or Wesker, no prophetic cure like Shaw or Behan, no escape into art like Wilde or Behan, no indulgent affection like Orwell or MacInnes. He is just *for* the ordinary people and against their bosses and rulers, without question or quarter." This paragraph is interesting in so many ways, especially the comparison, by an intellectual of the time, to those – all male – writers considered important in the wake of *Saturday Night and Sunday Morning* (1958) and the collection of short stories *The Loneliness of the Long Distance Runner* of the following year. Walter asks "Who read this book?" [*Saturday Night*] and Alan replies "Ordinary working class people." Of which more later.

That particular issue of *Anarchy* included essays by Colin MacInnes and the artist Augustus John, indicating the importance of the journal. Later, in the April 1964 issue, Alan himself wrote an essay, 'Poor People'. He begins: "I once knew an American writer in Majorca who, over a bottle of gin and a dish of spiced snails, smoking a two-peseta cigar, would lean back contentedly in his chair after finishing his work for the evening, and exclaim: 'Ah! I wonder what the poor are doing tonight?' I didn't try to tell him, because I was poor myself." Pointing out the real poverty people in which people were living, Sillitoe continued: "The gap between the very poor and the very rich is wider than it has ever been." Ah — 1964, how this country has changed in the years inbetween ...

This later edition of *Anarchy* was the "Nottingham issue". Other contributors included journalist Ray Gosling, novelist and D.H. Lawrence biographer Philip Callow, planner Paul Ritter examining how "man and motor" can live together in this metropolis, and climbing writer Harold Drasdo looking at culture in the city. All had something to say about this era — a time which, for most of us, is just out of reach but almost close enough to touch.

Sillitoe is not the only novelist to write of working class Nottingham in that period. Shoestring Press recently re-issued *The Hosanna Man* by Philip Callow, whose main characters were a small group of Nottingham working class autodidacts. Originally published in 1956, it was quickly withdrawn following a libel claim by a local bookseller. Scarred, Callow would never allow the book to be reprinted but, posthumously, it has appeared in an unexpurgated form.

Stanley Middleton, the only Nottingham writer to have won the Booker Prize, wrote largely about middle-class life but in 1960 published perhaps his best book, *Harris's Requiem* (now available in a scholarly edition and a mass market version from Trent Editions and Vintage respectively) about classical music culture within the Nottingham mining community. What unites these novels is the relative absence of anyone other than the working class, as is the case with those early Sillitoe books. It is not until the mid-60s that things start to break down. Michael Standen in *Start Somewhere* (another recent Shoestring re-issue) catches the moment when the previously sharp division in class starts to fall apart. His novel describes a teenage romance. Mr Griffin — a grocer! — warns his son: "You be careful. Their station isn't ours. They have a different road of going on. Her father's someone in the Town Hall; I've seen his name in the *Post* ... If you think I'm complaining because you're mixing with a good class of people, I'm not. Miss Cooper's got real breeding... So don't start treating her like the girls round here." But has any such plaint stopped a romance?

Ray Gosling in *Personal Copy* (available as a Five Leaves e-book) describes our working class city in non-fiction. Saturday afternoons down the Kardomah looking out over the city: "'Just waiting for a friend,' you'd say to the nippie." Sundays down the Market Square, Sally Bash at one end and the Communist John Peck on his stand at the other. Peck later held the balance of power in the City as a Communist councillor. Labour would rarely support anything he proposed, but he did save the Bulwell allotments.

And women writers? There was Ruth Adam in the 1930s writing about the Depression era — though she was of middle-class background, and Hilda Lewis, best known for her mainstream historical fiction, first published *Penny*

Lace in 1942. In this novel the Mr Penny of the story is as angry with society as Sillitoe's Arthur Seaton but takes a different route, to become a "master" himself. It's a fine portrayal of Nottingham working class life in the previous century, within the lace trade. In modern times only Nicola Monaghan hits the mark with *The Killing Jar* (2007), set, like so much of the output of the older working class writer Derrick Buttress, on the Broxtowe Estate. Alan Sillitoe gave Nicola a lot of encouragement, as he did with the less successful young author Pat McGrath whose one immature novel *The Green Leaves of Nottingham* came out in 1970 when he was fourteen. Whatever happened to him? Apart from Nicola, the only other significant recent working class woman novelist I can think of is the playwright Jenny McLeod who published one title with Virago, *Stuck Up a Tree* (1998), an unfairly forgotten novel set in her own black community in St Anns.

Other art forms contributed to the record of working class Nottingham. I'm thinking primarily of Paul Waplington, initially a factory worker who painted miners, union parades, allotments and street scenes. Paul now lives in Portugal but Nottingham Castle did him proud with a retrospective of his local paintings in 2013, but less proud in not producing any catalogue or even a couple of postcards for keepsake. In the theatre world there is Amanda Whittington, Nottingham born, whose credits include the play of *Saturday Night and Sunday Morning.* And, coming up to date, we have the Sleaford Mods to remind us that, though we might not have the factories of the past, Nottingham is still, at heart, a working class city. But the nature of the working class has changed — Kev Fegan noticed this in *Let Your Left Hand Sing, stories of migration* (2003) when, in verse, he described a typical street, with the stories of the migrant people who now contribute to our city.

There's never been another Alan Sillitoe in the sense of someone whose work has national significance but also speaks for the people of this city. Perhaps there never will be, or perhaps the next Alan Sillitoe is currently seventeen, female, and has parents who came from Kashmir or Kurdistan ...

I can't recall exactly when I first met Alan. I would not claim to be a close or even long-standing friend, but I felt some kind of connection. Mostly we met at events in Nottinghamshire. He was the guest speaker at a day festival I'd organised at the Adams Building in the Lace Market and I can recall him talking about his illiterate father (something I knew, but hearing the story first hand made it fresh); there were book launches, talks, the odd interview, a meal out. Alan always refused a fee or travel expenses —"anything for Nottingham". Five Leaves republished the odd story of his and a set of poems in a Nottingham poetry collection. At Southwell Poetry Festival, Alan was asked to speak about the poetry of the King James Bible and, to the amusement of his audience and my consternation as chair, talked about anything but that. He kept making what I thought would be his farewell appearance as health reduced his ability — the audiences must have thought that too as the attendance at every reading seemed bigger than the last. And more people than is possible turned up saying they had been at school with him.

We didn't always agree. Alan said he was not a working class writer but a writer — but most of Nottingham's working class are with me on that one. To them, and not solely people of his generation, he was the one who told *their* story, or that of their father or their uncle. I've just read James Rebanks' memoir *The Shepherd's Life* in which he, the son of a hardscrabble farmer, wrote of W.H. Hudson's classic *A Shepherd's Life* (Rebanks' own title, presumably, in homage): "Until I read this book, I thought books were always about other people, other places, other lives. This book, in all its glory, was about us." I've heard dozens, hundreds of Nottinghamians use similar phrases about *Saturday Night and Sunday Morning.*

Nobody minded that Alan moved to London. His best books were always the Nottingham ones. He represented our class, whether he wanted to or not. We also disagreed about Zionism. Alan had, like many other writers, properly supported the Russian Jewish refuseniks. He had been fêted in the Soviet Union as a working class, socialist writer and his books sold by the bucket load. Soviet royalties could only be spent in the Soviet Union so Alan went there, and publicly raised the cases of political prisoners with the Soviet regime. His sympathy for the refuseniks spurred him to support Israel — he became a Zionist and was outspoken in defence of Israel. Some suggested this was at the behest of his Jewish wife, Ruth Fainlight, but the reverse was true. In 2004 Ruth was one of twelve poets who gave a public reading in protest against the invasion of Iraq while Alan was one of only a handful of writers who defended the invasion, writing in *Authors Take Sides on Iraq and the Gulf War* (Cecil Woolf, 2004): "One can only congratulate the United States forces, and the soldiers of Great Britain. And as for settling things in the Middle East, if this won't help the process nothing will. Israel and the West must stick together." Thankfully Israel stayed out of that war, despite being hit by Scud missiles fired from Iraq.

Few people around Nottingham noticed or cared that Alan had taken these positions, although a friend rang up to ask me if I could arrange for Alan to speak at the local Israel Independence Day celebration, suggesting I could fix the speaker then picket the event! I did arrange for Alan to speak, and did not picket, though joined many marches against the Gulf War, organising a couple of them locally. To some, however, Alan's support for the War was a step too far, especially Alexis Lykiard who wrote a sharp piece 'Vanishing Hero, Vanished Place' in Iain Sinclair's monumental *London: City of Disappearances* (2006). Much as I disagreed with Alan, I would not have included Lykiard's piece if I'd been editing the book. It would, however, be fair to say that the Alan Sillitoe of these times had changed from the Sillitoe of *Pit Strike* in 1977.

But life moved on. There were more readings and interviews, a health scare, a remission, another huge event at Lowdham Book Festival. And then Ruth rang to say that when I was next in London I might want to call round, Alan would like to see me. Sure, I go to London a lot — except I didn't, or if I did I was too busy with meetings. Ruth rang a second time: would I see Alan? I should have listened — not to what she said but to what she did not say. I should have got on a train straightaway. I never saw Alan again.

All I could do was pull together a memorial meeting. The City Council provided the premises, and everyone came. John Harvey spoke, representative of Nottingham writers; D.J. Taylor spoke of Alan's importance as one of a phalanx of regional writers; Frank Abbot showed in slo-mo the part of Karl Reisz's *Saturday Night* film which reveals just how Shirley Ann Field as Doreen wins the catch of Albert Finney as Arthur Seaton. It is Doreen who triumphs. There was a display of Alan's books, first editions and translations, other Nottingham writers performed, there was music and there, look, was his famous Morse code machine. And here we are, still celebrating Alan.

The "Nottingham issue" of Anarchy was reprinted as a Five Leaves Bookshop Occasional Paper in spring 2015.

First Edition

In the late summer of 2006, while teaching at Nottingham University, I started doing some research on *Saturday Night and Sunday Morning*. I was especially interested in the critical reception of the first hardback edition, published by W.H. Allen in 1958, and the popular paperback published by Pan in 1960 as a film tie-in to coincide with the release of the film adaptation the same year.

I wanted to look closely at the covers of these two editions and particularly at the kind of paraphernalia surrounding the text itself — that is, the blurb, the illustrations, the advertising, and so on — all instances of what the French literary theorist Gérard Genette has termed the 'paratext'. Sillitoe's text remains the same, of course, but I was interested in how these paratexts of the respective editions worked to 'frame' that text in markedly different ways.

In order to proceed with this research I needed, obviously, a copy of each edition. The familiar Pan edition was easy as I already had my own battered copy from years earlier. Getting hold of the first edition, though, was a different story altogether. With no copy available from Nottingham Public Library, nor the University's Hallward Library, I requested it through the Hallward's inter-library loan service where it would be obtained from any British library in possession of it. A copy duly arrived but without the necessary cover. Subsequent enquiries revealed that it would be most unlikely that any such copy would be available, it being routine practice in university libraries to discard a book's dust jacket before putting it on the shelves.

I mentioned the problem to one of the librarians, Alison Stevens, whom I'd known for many years and who had an uncanny flair for obtaining requested material, however impossible that request might be. Alison mentioned it in turn to her colleague, John Turner, another resourceful librarian. John had known Alan Sillitoe previously when their paths had crossed through their work at the Workers' Educational Association (WEA) and Adult Education in the East Midlands. Quite fortuitously, John had got Alan's home address (he was then living in London, seemingly without email) and wrote to him.

Alan replied to John in a letter dated 31 May 2007. He said that he did, of course, have a copy of the first edition. However, as it was his only copy he would be dreadfully anxious to part with what was obviously a highly valued possession (this being, of course, his first book). “I hear they occasionally change hands at quite a high price,” he said.

Nevertheless, he put it in the post straightaway — although, quite alarmingly, in a flimsy envelope and by standard mail — and it arrived a few days later at the library where it was given to me.

I was then able at long last to get on with my research and I must say that it was a rare pleasure as a researcher to work with Alan’s own copy. I returned the book to the library and it was duly returned to him, by more secure means than those in which it arrived. I finished my research which, for what it’s worth, was later published, made possible by Alan’s selfless help. I haven’t forgotten his kindness and generosity.

Girl with a cello on the metro

In the crowded carriage I was given a space of time
To look at her for whom the doors had slid
Open and she stepped in with the cello on her back
Bright white, almost doubling her, unslung it, stood
Barely a yard from me who stood admiring her
For the allotted stops until, entering the dark
Before the last, becoming visible in the window glass
Quickly she withdrew a long and ornate silver pin
From her black hair and while the mirror lasted
Shaped up that tumble to her satisfaction
And speared it fast. I watched. The station came
She slung the cello on, the doors slid open for her
And out she stepped, into the lights, the crowd
Into the city with her hair just as she wanted it
And all her music carrying on her back.

A Trip to the Moon

My mother is moving house. She's ninety-one
and determined: words like sheltered
accommodation are coming at us from outer space.
But it's not like that, not yet. There are spare
rooms in the new place, she'll have a garden,
feed nuthatches, cook her food. Still,
down the slope will be a sanatorium,
that's the point. A clinic, an Alzheimer's wing.
She doesn't want to be a burden.
In every corner there's a vermilion string
to pull if you fall over. When I clear
cupboards I find histories in every blanket.
A scorch mark, from the winter our heating failed.
Should she sell the oversize kitchen clock
(she still gets up on steps to wind it every Sunday)
to the blind piano-tuner who took a shine to it
when he came to value a piano that's never played,
or should it stick around, in case
some grandchild might give it a home?
For the first time in her life, she'll live with things
only she has chosen. No husband or child to consider,
no furniture from aunts. She can sell,
she can give things away. Traumas of today,
contracts to exchange, dates of completion,
arguments over who will let the carpenter in
to measure up, will be forgotten
because forgetting is the issue, let's face it.
And she is, she is facing it. She'll be three miles
from family but she's going to an unknown zone.

The Taj Mahal of the North

My beauty queen of '48, I could spend hours just running my fingers through your charcoal hair and stroking its silvery strands. I love every line around your eyes because each one marks another year of a life that you've chosen to spend with me. As we take our evening constitutional — you and me and our little one — I marvel at our luck.

I steer the pram along the promenade, keeping away from the railings and the vicious lap of the waves. Despite the derelict funfair, the boarded up cinema and the needles, cans and rubber johnnies on the beach, we've never felt the need to leave. The sun is setting, the sea is rough and the distant hills are disappearing from view. At moments like this, my love, there's nowhere else we'd rather be. Your walking stick taps in time to my footsteps and there's something rather pleasing about this. I pause and you bend over the pram to rearrange our little one's blanket, without my having to ask. You show her such care — though she wears that placid expression of hers, her rubber skin not registering the biting whip of the gale.

She is a bonny wee thing, with her rosy cheeks and blue eyes and creamy skin. We've found such happiness in her, but I suppose there are those who'd say we're making do.

It took me almost the length of your pregnancy to make this doll for our unborn child. Do you remember me sneaking home early from the puppet theatre with ice-lollies and bottles of ginger beer? Do you remember me whispering "Dada's home" through your tummy? We'd been married so long by the time you fell pregnant that it felt almost too good to be true. It was a blessed time: your belly swelling and my doll taking shape. To think, I hand-picked each strand of our little one's fine blond hair from the trimmings at a local salon; I measured sand to precisely the weight of a newborn and pressed chubby dimples into her cheeks. It was hard to believe, as I painted the disembodied limbs, that the assortment of rubber and vinyl would eventually look so lifelike.

It's just as I'm thinking this that I notice her — the woman who's stepping off the bus and struggling to raise her brolly against the wind. She's put on weight in the forty-odd years since I last saw her and, like you, she now walks with a stick. Yet there's something startlingly familiar about the paleness of her face and the bright, bright blue of her eyes. Norma — that's what she's called. It unsettles me to think that her name has been there all this time, lodged inside my mind.

To my discredit, I revel for a moment in the knowledge that she's not a patch on you: my beauty queen of '48. I'd wager that Norma doesn't have a husband to help around the house, that she has no one to look after her. Now that your joints aren't what they used to be, I help you in and out of the tub. And twice a week, I wash your hair — don't I, my love — with your favourite Sunsilk shampoo.

Norma's heading towards us. I train my eyes on the dark clouds that criss-cross the amber sky, willing her to walk straight past.

"What a rotten day," she calls out. Although she's talking to you, her gaze flits to me and I worry that she remembers.

I feel suddenly ashamed of our little one. And then, of course, even more ashamed of myself. Your pride in our family's unstinting. You never flinch when kids point and laugh and call us names. "You weirdos," one of them shouted as we left for this evening's stroll — his mother stood there, smirking in the doorway, failing to chide him for his abuse.

Norma struggles with her broken umbrella: "You were in The Warblers, am I right?" She's looking closely at you but doesn't show much interest in our little one or me. "Kathy in *Singing in the Rain*?"

Norma's speaking and you're nodding and the two of you are laughing away.

"I played Lina," she's saying and it upsets me to see your face flushed with the rare prospect of friendship: someone who doesn't stare or sneer or studiously look away. I know your mind will be racing ahead of itself: you'll be imagining us all as firm friends, you'll be hearing the splutter of oil as you treat her to the world's best egg and chips.

Norma's hardly glanced at the rain-spattered hood of the pram. She probably assumes that we're babysitting our grandchild — and, of course, we do nothing to correct her. As she busies herself with her lighter, holding her cigarette to the flame, it strikes me that Norma has good reason for failing to fuss over our little one. She too, I now recall, knows her fair share of loss. Although she has the careworn look of a woman who's raised a whole brood, something tells me that she never did have a family of her own. It doesn't look as if her plans to start afresh in Liverpool can have worked out as she'd hoped.

I still remember the night I met Norma: the charcoal-grey of the sand dunes, the bright white of the moon against the rock pools, the tip of Norma's cigarette glowing against the dark. The pier looms large in these memories — it still stood tall back then, the Taj Mahal of the North. On the night I met Norma, I'd succumbed to a terrible urge to get out of the house, to stay away until you'd fallen asleep. I could no longer bear your grief or your nightly attempts to forgive. I was walking alone along the promenade to escape that moment when the weight of the mattress would shift and I'd feel the warmth of your body curling against mine: the softness of your breasts, your knees pressed into the backs of my thighs. Each night for months I'd turned away, pretending to drop straight off to sleep, hoping you'd not notice that I'd grown hard.

I remember the thick scent of the sea that night, the honky-tonk noises of the amusement arcades, and the couples sharing sundaes in the ice-cream parlour. As the night grew colder and the promenade emptied, I found myself sheltering in the warm foyer of the blue movie theatre. The box-office was closed and the film had long-since started, so I just stood there unobserved, listening to the hands ticking across the clock-face and wondering how many of the men inside had wives waiting in their beds back home.

I must have been standing there for over an hour by the time the women showed up — all bones and stilettos and mini-skirts. Their arrival came as a bit of a shock but it made sense, I suppose. Norma stood out from the others, with her blue eyes and black hair and pale, pale skin. If my memory serves me correctly, we didn't share so much as a word. She simply took my hand and I let her lead me from the cinema and back out into the night.

I can still smell the dankness of the beach hut and I can still recall that brief moment of temptation, when I could have lifted her up against the wall and manhandled her into place. But I pulled her back out of the beach hut and gestured for her to sit beside me on the shingle, feeling the smoothness of the pebbles beneath my palms and hearing the sounds of the old hotel: the waltz tunes and laughter and clinking of glasses.

"You ever thought about running away from it all?" I found myself asking, my words misting in the icy air.

"Liverpool," she said, "now that's somewhere I think I'd like."

And for a few short moments, staring into the darkness towards the Cumbrian hills, I lost myself in silent plans: I'd supply all the country's puppet theatres from my own workshop, Norma and I would dance to live bands in underground bars, with this stranger I'd wipe the slate clean.

"You fancy it then?" she piped up.

"Liverpool?"

She laughed at me and rolled her eyes towards the beach hut.

I shook my head but I let her take my hand again. We sat there for some time, holding hands and listening to the lap of the waves. I found myself telling her about the months I'd spent persuading you to rejoin the amateur operatics group, how I'd told you it would do you good to get out of the house; I could look after Elsie on my own. I told her how proud I'd felt of myself, how it had seemed like a daring thing to suggest. It must have been something about the sensation of Norma's hands around mine, because the words just kept on coming. I told her about the mashed swede you'd left for Elsie's dinner, that it was the first time I'd fed her by myself. In between spoonfuls, she'd giggled and squirmed and I was convinced she'd soon be crawling. She did ever-so-well, managing to get almost as much in her mouth as on her bib and face and hands.

Elsie and I had a great old time that evening, although she didn't show the slightest bit of interest in her dolly. I'd taken the doll from your dressing table, where you'd stowed her away, thinking that Elsie and I could play with her. But Elsie just chewed on the doll's arm and then threw her away.

It was all new to me so I took particular care when bathing Elsie, holding my hand over her eyes despite the bottle's *No Tears* claim.

I regret now having left so much of Elsie's care to you. Most evenings when I returned from the puppet theatre, you'd be bathing her. I'd hear her giggles and splashes and the lovely sound of your voice singing *Speed Bonny Boat* or the like. It's hard to imagine now that I would call upstairs to let you know I was home, and then I'd simply make a cuppa and turn on the radio. How I wish I'd joined you both in the bathroom. I could have stripped right there and then, taking off even my undies; I could have squeezed in opposite you, little Elsie between us in the tub. Now wouldn't that have been quite something to remember?

But as it was, you were out and I was alone with our daughter, and this was the first and last time I bathed her.

You'd left cold creams and muslins and you'd spent an age teaching me to change her nappy. I coddled Elsie in terry-towelling and misted her in talcum powder, just as you'd shown me. And it wasn't long before she dozed off in my arms. I felt reassured by the warm weight of her in my lap and the movements of her breath. In the middle of the night, if I concentrate hard, I can still smell the milky scent of her skin.

We looked out to sea, Norma and I, still sitting there hand in hand. That's when she told me that she knew you, that she was also in The Warblers, that she too had lost a child — a baby boy who'd been taken from her as soon as he was born. "Mum and Dad threw me out," she said. "But I'll soon have enough money to go to Liverpool and enrol in a secretarial course."

Then she held out her hand for a banknote, and she was just some prostitute again and I was just some bloke, broken and middle-aged.

Norma was standing up by then, but I pulled her back down. "Stay," I said. "Just for a while." And I told her that I'd put our daughter in the Moses basket, that I'd opened a bottle of stout and then set to work painting the face of my latest puppet. I've trawled every last detail of that night, trying to pinpoint what went wrong. The police took me to the station and questioned me for hours; they even scoured our house for clues. But the coroner's report read 'Act of God'. They say nowadays that no one's to blame for cot deaths; you said that life had dealt us a terrible hand. But I remember telling Norma that — although you tried to hide it — you'd sometimes look at me as if I'd let you down.

Time ran away with us, that night I spent with Norma, so I didn't get home till the early hours. As soon as I walked through the door, I heard your muffled sobs against the silence of the house. You were sitting at your dressing table, when I came into our room, the tears running down your face. And you were wearing the pretty, white nightie you'd bought for our wedding all those years earlier. I imagined you bathing, then dusting yourself in talcum powder and dressing in your best nightie to wait up for me. As I approached, I noticed that you were toying with the dress of Elsie's doll, the one that I had made. I knew then that you were broken, that you needed me to be strong. I placed the doll in your arms and helped you to cradle her. Once I felt sure that you held her just so, I ran your brush through your hair sweeping it away from your face. Then I dabbed your eyes with tissues and rubbed cold cream into your skin.

I helped you to stand, taking care all the while that you supported our little one's neck just as you had taught me, and then I led you both to bed. Together, we rocked our little one, and the rhythm of our sobs fell in time. Our tears were slowly replaced by the sound of our breath, and the movement of my body against yours. We did learn to comfort each other, didn't we love? But I took care that you never did fall pregnant again.

"I've just moved back," says Norma, as we head towards the bus-shelter.

Despite myself, I worry that you might undo the hood of the pram, that you might ask if Norma wants to hold our little one.

You're pointing at our place — the terrace across the road, between Alfredo's boarding house and the Polish grocery.

It takes me a moment to realise that you've invited her over for tea, that she hasn't made an excuse.

The rain continues to thrash against the bus-shelter, so we admit defeat. As you and Norma dash across the road, I linger on the promenade with the pram and wait until it is safe to cross. Nowadays, there's not one pillar poking from the sea to remind folk of the Taj Mahal of the North. No visitor here would realise that the pier used to hold sway over our skyline, that this town once brimmed with life: the ferris wheel that popped up in summer and was dismantled when winter set in; the circus troops that pitched up their tents; the women who paraded around the lido in their bathing suits. It makes my heart bleed when I think of the dance halls and bath-houses and theatres where we spent our youth, all standing derelict or converted into discotheques. We don't have so much as an annual puppet show now.

By the time I reach the front door, you've fished the keys from your bag and are showing Norma into the porch. We fall into our long-established routine, hanging up our macs to drip-dry before you head into the kitchen to make a pot of tea. But the presence of our guest changes everything. I am aware of Norma watching as I unfasten the hood of the pram, as I scoop up our little one, who's bonneted face snuggles into my shoulder in that awkward way of hers.

It occurs to me that you won't be back for a few minutes, that I'll have the chance to speak with Norma alone. I'll tell her to keep away from us; I'll tell her I wish her well.

"It's so kind of you to have me over," Norma says. "I'd have recognised your wife a mile off." Something about the breezy way she says it makes me realise that she has no recollection of me.

I'm trying to exchange pleasantries with her but I'm wondering whether it shows on my face that I feel both relieved and absurdly peeved.

"Isn't she good," says Norma.

If I can just keep our little one's back to her, Norma won't put two and two together. But she's reaching out and saying, "There's not been a peep out of her." And I'm seeing all this happen as if I'm watching from afar.

As her palms touch our little one's rubber hands, Norma starts and then draws a quick intake of breath.

"The tea'll be brewed soon," I say, as if nothing untoward has passed. "You make yourself comfortable while I give Carole a hand."

There's a flash of recognition in those big blue eyes and she's already backing out of the door. "I've just remembered that I've double booked," she's saying. "I must be getting off."

As she rushes down the front path, taking only the briefest glance back, I see once again the fear in her eyes; I feel once again the tug of her hand from mine; the way she stumbled as she made her way from the beach hut up to the promenade; the way she broke into a run when I called out to her to stay.

And it strikes me that, despite my best efforts to care for you, perhaps — in your darker moments — even you suspect the worst. And it strikes me too that I deserve it: this suspicion that's levelled at me. I did open a bottle of stout; I did become engrossed in painting the face of my latest puppet; I did fail to take care of Elsie.

"Is that the door?" you call.

"She's left," I say, turning the key in the lock. "Something cropped up."

As I head into the kitchen, you offer me my tea — a resigned expression on your face. We will take our tea at the kitchen table as we always do after our stroll, and later we'll bathe our little one. We'll coddle her in terry-towelling, then rub her with cold cream and dust her with talc, before dressing her in her new lemon-coloured all-in-one. As night draws in, we'll put her in bed with us and I'll join in your lullaby — as I do every night — although I still can't hit all of the high notes.

Becoming Santa

Gill writes 'School for Santa' on her flipchart.
This is a life lesson, not a holiday job.
She highlights the don'ts:
don't kiss the children,
don't make promises, say a pony
to a girl who lives on a council estate,
don't lose your temper. Think comfort and joy.

A roomful of Santas stroke beards and nod.
They *ho ho ho* till they breathe the role
and find a magic key to open every door.
They'll smile through requests for dolls
or lost dads,
and heed the broken record of Gill's voice:
be real, be real, be real.

The Certainty of Seagulls

I'll fix Polaris first
not Mars
that one's yours

shhh

I'm counting.

Why would I want a dozen
red roses? They can't send atom-energy
across millennia.

Second: Sirius
then three, four, five in Orion's belt.
Their names

                                        you know them.
That would be a gift.

Six is hidden.
Can you see it from
                                        the dark side of the moon?

No matter.
Cassiopeia
seven to eleven.
Like you
she prized her own words
Andromeda
(her daughter)
is uncontained

has birthed a galaxy.

I've lost count.
You'd help me
but you already know exactly
how many stars there are.

I search for my star among swarms,
offer you one.
You laugh, decline.

How can a single leaf obscure
the waxing moon?

I know you don't know.

I know
you will tell me anyway.

A wasp, drunk on rotting
passionfruit stings you.
It reminds you
of me

you can't say how.

Winter comes creeping
smoke rises. I know
with the certainty of seagulls

we will not be here to meet the spring.

Medical Records

Just a little pain, and then
the wound in my knee was drained.
"The infection's gone. You're clean,"
Mom said, wiping off her orange scissors. "When
you fall in the yard, come to me to be disinfected."

Just a little pain, and then
the world went grey around the edges. Thin
strands of gut staunched my gaping forehead.
"The infection's gone. You're clean,"
the doctor said; "I can't believe that mean
boy chucked that sharp shell at your head.
Just a little pain and then
you'll have the nicest scar anyone's ever seen."

Flaws add detail, complexity; nothing's wasted;
when the infection's gone, you'll be clean,
calm, and ready to get up again.
You'll read the story your body's recorded.
Just a little pain, and then
the infection's gone. You're clean.

Steeltown

In streets erected for Steelmen,
now corroding away amidst
brickdust and graffiti
and Shazza luvs Ali;
and derelict takeaways
that deliver to no-one.

And brokendown bicycles
carry ghosts of children.
All lost forever in these rusty
streets that were erected
for long dead Steelmen,
whose kids trudged in their footsteps
and pledged their allegiance
from cradle to grave.

And the boxes thrown up
in runaway time are now
haunted by spirits
from the furnace's ashes;
home to those whom
the steelworks abandoned.

Living out their lives on the CCTV
which hangs from the lampposts
their forefathers forged,
in the town where the world was made.

By the River

Baz and I are chopping weeds sprouting in the ash of the towpath, a community service job the magistrate gave me as first prize for nicking a car and running it into a ditch one Saturday night. It's hot work chopping dandelions, so Baz, doing his stint for shop-lifting, had gone off to search for a couple of cans while I have a bit of a breather. I'm leaning on the handle of my hoe watching a Toyota which has stopped on the bridge downriver. An old bloke climbs out and moves, a bit wonky, to the parapet. He must have seen me, but doesn't take any notice. He plonks his hands on the coping stones as though he's about to climb over. Am I about to witness a suicide? Should I shout to him? If he jumps he's dead, because I can't swim.

But the old bloke turns away, opens the boot of his car and pulls out a plastic bag, the heavy kind that might have held compost when it was new. But it was moving in a funny way, kind of jerking, and I guessed that it wouldn't be compost that was making it happen.

The old bloke thrusts his arm into the bag and pulls out a rabbit, a big white one, probably a Flemish Giant. I know that because I like rabbits, and had a Flemish Giant myself when I was a kid. He holds this one up by its ears while it frenziedly kicks its rear legs. Then he lets it go. I drop my hoe as I watch the rabbit drop from the bridge, twisting in the air before it splashes into the river. I lose sight of it when it drifts into the darkness under the bridge.

The old bloke glances towards me with no expression on his face, then turns to climb back into his car and drives away. Was he drunk, or mad? I hoped it was one or the other. I'd hate to think he'd drown a rabbit while he was sober. I've done daft things myself when I'm drunk, like driving nicked cars into ditches. But this old rabbit killer probably wasn't drunk. I think he dropped the rabbit off the bridge because he was a cruel bastard. You could tell that by the deliberate way he did it. I've had my share of fights. I've been hurt myself by characters that were pissed out of their skulls. And I've hurt a few myself when I didn't know what I was doing because I wasn't right in the head for a bit. But this old bastard probably dropped that rabbit cold sober. He was just cruel. What shook me was the simple act of letting go of the rabbit's ear like it was dead already, when I could see it wasn't, like it didn't matter about a rabbit.

I flick a dandelion clump with the blade of my hoe, watch it float away on the dirty river flowing by me as it has always flowed, carrying its suicides, its accidents, its floating rubbish and drowned rabbits. Everything has to die, that's obvious. But to be dropped off a bridge to drown. That's no way to die, even for a rabbit. Baz and I are chopping weeds because we were dick-heads, but we never hurt anybody, at least I know I hadn't.

There's nothing I can do about the rabbit. It's out of sight, probably rolling in mud on the riverbed. I chop the weeds because I have no choice. I listen to the soft sounds of the river, wait for Baz so I can tell him the tale when he comes back with the cans, both of us knowing worse things happen in the world than nicking things. And drowning a beautiful Flemish Giant rabbit is one of them.

Swifts

Shrieking hooks,
they lost their purchase on the sky
but they don't care. They tumble
into view, and out again,
unpinned, unplaceable.

The View from Crieff

All the view your eyes can eat
starts with a milky sky,
then half-solidifies
into mountains like mauve dowagers,
content to retire behind
a bank of glowering indigo matrons
who push green hills towards you,
insisting you will have some more, you *will*.

Tomskaya Pisanitsa Park, Kemerovo

for Dasha

We all matter, we are all indelible, miraculous, here.
JULIA DARLING

1.

We take a break from our discussions
About the British poetry scene.
About time too; I've bored these Russians
Quite long enough now. In between
Each post-New Gen New Generation
And last week's latest new sensation,
I have the sense they're not impressed.
Oh dear. Although I've tried my best,
When every poet is 'dark' and 'daring',
Each new collection 'vibrant', 'bold',
And last year's new is this year's old,
The sum effect is somewhat wearing.
There's rather more to art, I fear,
Than simply saying, *I was here.*

2.

We take the bus across the river.
Beneath the wide Kuznetsky Bridge
They're fishing on the ice. We shiver.
It would be warmer in a fridge.
We're driving North, past roadside diners,
The monument to Kuzbass miners,
The forest blur of greys and browns,
And summer-dacha shantytowns,
Scalectrix roads and lego churches.
The bus slows down. At last we're there.
We stop among the silent glare
And tinsel glitter of the birches
(I borrowed this line from a verse
By Mandelshtam — it could be worse).

3.

Ten minutes later, we're stood gazing
In frozen silence at these cliffs —
A frieze of hundreds of amazing
Six thousand year old petroglyphs
That stretch from Dürer-like cross hatches
To etch-a-sketchish childish scratches.
Abraded, nicked and tricked and picked,
These scrawls upon the walls depict
A pre-Deluvian procession
Of aurochs, foxes, wolves and deer,
A hunter with a pointy spear
(Or bandy-stick). Sod self-expression —
It seems to me all art starts from
These pictograms beside the Tom.

4.

The Sympathetic Magic thesis
(See Abbé Breuil, of Lascaux fame)
Proposed that it was through mimesis
That we first taught ourselves to name
And tame the growling world with patterns;
That art expands the things it flattens;
That humankind first found its tongue
When rhythmic gesture, dance and song
Marked out the grunter from the grunting;
That knocking matter into shape's
What separates us from the apes;
And that the hunted started hunting
When we began to imitate
Creation's hunger on a plate.

5.

Imagined goals are scored by winners —
Once caught by art upon these rocks
These animals were Sunday dinners,
A winter coat, a pair of socks.
No need to shiver by the river
When art's enchantments can deliver
A woolly vest to keep you warm.
A pelt fits like a well-made form,
A birthday suit (but less informal),
A fur-lined cloak in which to hide
And keep the hungry world outside,
A second skin that feels, well, normal.
In short, when we first borrowed fur,
The human soup began to stir.

6.

The world out there is strange and formless,
A wilderness of blood and force —
Art's job's to make it seem less gormless
(From *gaumr*, 'lacking sense' — Old Norse).
These primitive caricaturists
Were never art-for-art's-sake purists;
Their work was useful as an axe,
Each rock-engraving made the facts
Of Neolithic dreams still bigger.
Above the bison, bears and birds
The stick-men chasing reindeer herds,
There seems to be a flying figure
Among the stars and solar rings:
A human with a pair of wings.

7.

Cue Kubrik's famous match-cut edit
As trumpets fanfare to the dawn:
A handy tool with which to credit
The narrative of brain and brawn
(An always useful combination)
That saw us conquer all creation
And take our place among the stars.
Leonov's weightless boots were *ours*.
But you can't space-walk like a model
Or take your partner in the waltz
Unless you know which steps are false;
Before a child can learn to toddle.
As someone said, you need the knack
Of sometimes taking one step back.

8.

This Kemerovo conurbation
Was built by US Reds with dreams;
They came at Lenin's invitation
To drain the coal-rich Kuzbass seams
Which Kolchak's Whites had lately flooded,
They stayed four years, and worked and studied
Till Comrade One-Crutch learned to fly
And Big Bill Heywood's good left eye
Could see that they had half-created
A Wobbly city in the sticks.
But when, in 1926,
The colony was 'liquidated',
Historians wiped the record clean,
Almost as if they'd never been.

9.

Just like the old Siberian Yeti
Whose hairy footprints in the snow
Get journalists all hot and sweaty
At forty-five degrees below;
Though sightings are reported yearly
The cynics say that they are merely
A troupe of circus bruins who
Escaped from some old Soviet zoo,
Deciding that unspoken freedom
Sounds better than the world's applause.
The Park's bears, meanwhile, show their claws
To Sunday visitors who feed 'em
Their honeyed wages through the bars
That separates their world from ours.

10.

In Bear Rock cave a single finger
Is all that's left of some lost race
Who lacked, perhaps, the art to linger
Before they vanished without trace;
Perhaps they never learned to fashion
The world to get their morning ration;
Or else they lacked the wherewithal
To read the writing on the wall
That spelled out their abrupt extinction.
These folk were here. And now they've gone.
Like sabre-tooth and mastodon.
The hungry world makes no distinction
Between the beasts on which we prey
And those to which we ought to pray.

11.

But evidence of evolution's
A kind of messy palimpsest —
These rocks include some contributions
By later artists (*Ya bil zdes*) —
To wit, although we think we're brainier
We can't shake off the graphomania
We caught six thousand years ago
(Like writers pissing in the snow).
These bare rocks mark the clumsy stages
By which we make our slow ascent;
All art can do is represent
Our progress on their uncut pages
Before we each must disappear,
By simply saying, *we were here.*

Notes

This sequence was written while teaching briefly at the University of Kemerovo, in Siberia, in 2010 and first published in *Kuzbass XXI Vek*, March 2011. The Tomskaya Pisanitsa Park is a few miles outside Kemerovo, famous for a series of Neolithic rock-carvings on the banks of the river Tom. Alexei Leonov, the first human to walk in space, was born in Kemerovo. *Comrade One-Crutch* is the title of the children's novel about Kemerovo by the US writer Ruth Epperson Kennell. Bear Rock Cave is south of Kemerovo in the Altai Krai, the site of the recent discovery of 'Woman X' or the 'Denisova Hominin'.

See No Evil

The room was clean and simple and big for a man on his own, for someone straight out of prison, for the likes of Jimmy Ramone. Pausing inside the open door he admired the single bed with its brown blanket and green pillows, the metal desk and wicker chair, an empty vase, the sagging old armchair soaked in millions of halfway-house dreams. There was a large painting on the widest wall and he went across for a closer look, making sure he clicked the door shut first. Black-ink monkeys moved through overgrown ruins. Broken bricks poked from waves of red and purple and yellow flowers, the stems long, heads nodding. He wondered if his father was alive, if their paths would ever cross. His dad could even have painted this picture. Jimmy's lungs heaved at the idea, but he controlled his breathing, as he'd learned to do in Seven Towers, moved in close and studied the scene.

The flowers were as tall as the monkeys, all but one of these creatures walking upright, a crouched loner dragging balled fists along the ground, broad back hunched against a wobbling sun. Seven monkeys carried seven lengths of wood, and at first he thought these were staffs to help them walk, seeing as the ruins were tumbling down the side of a hill, but they held their stripped branches as if they were clubs, so he supposed he was wrong. He turned away. Inspected the room.

Thick curtains hung either side of a narrow window, offering the sort of privacy it was easy to take for granted outside of prison. He ran his right hand over the glass, pleased it wasn't chipped, cracked, broken. He opened the pane and pushed his head out into the hot evening air, realising as he did so that there were no bars, his freedom floating in a breeze of oranges and lemons. He peered into the narrow street four storeys down, digging back and seeing himself as a boy on a frosty street corner, a shivering kid checking left and right, a youngster with a drink in his hand and a song in his head. He pulled back into the moment, shifted ahead, surfing that flow of perfume. Past, present and future — it was all the same to Jimmy Ramone.

If a man wanted to survive in jail he had to diffuse time, needed to convince himself that his sentence was going to pass quickly, that life on the outside would last a lot longer than the term he was serving. But it was a non-stop battle, so if he was clever, a bit of a philosopher, he could insist that time didn't even exist, because if everything was born to grow and struggle and fade and die then why did any of what was happening to him matter? It was all an illusion. Prison became a monastery, the convict a monk. The right man could have great insights, experience bliss, his spirit breaking free and circling the planet.

If nothing lasted, though, it also followed that every single second was precious, so wasting time was the worst sort of crime. The prisoner started to panic. His heart stuttered, brain crashing as the mania of the block closed in, the violence upsetting him more than usual, the monkey monsters under his bed tracing the outline of his spine with their nails. Childhood terrors returned. A familiar voice tried to help — *go on, stab him, he deserves it, and it'll feel good, trust me, I promise you it will feel so fucking good if you kick and punch and knife one of these dirty funhouse freaks* — but Jimmy resisted the temptation, stayed near his calendar and crossed out numbers, drawing women with curved bodies and lipstick smiles. It was one way of staying in control, but what really kept him going was knowing that when he was released he would never get into trouble again. This was the truth. It was a fact.

He heard footsteps in the street and leaned out of the window again, the sound growing louder, two figures forming and slowing as they approached a neon sign. It was odd. He hadn't noticed this sign before. There was a burst of piano as a boy and girl entered the bar, and he smiled, imagined cold beer being served, could almost taste it, moved back into his room and stood straight, stretching his arms and legs and scanning the walls. He didn't know what to do with himself. It was the first time he'd been alone for two years. He went over to the desk and sat down, started tapping his fingers on the surface. His teeth chattered. Holding his hands up he found that they were trembling. He suddenly felt very cold. This scared him. Men became institutionalised, cracked up when they were released. He might have a fit, fall down and hit his head and die right here, on his own, body incinerated and the ashes scattered by a stranger. Perhaps he would end his own life.

He shook his head, angry at this weakness. He closed his eyes. Somewhere a man spoke, his voice muffled, merging with that of a woman. A radio delivered important news he couldn't understand. The smell of bread made him feel hungry, but he couldn't go out looking for food. Not on his first night of freedom. It was too dangerous. If he could get through the next twelve hours he would be safe. In the morning he would walk to the station without stopping and leave on the first train heading north. All he had to do was stay in this room. The door of the bar creaked loud and he heard a familiar song.

XXXXXXXX

Thick walls towered above Jimmy as he turned off the main road and dipped into a side street. He was feeling good, picked out every step, stopped across from the bar and took a few seconds to appreciate the sign's fluorescent wave as it washed into a palm, imagined he was in the tropics, sitting on a beach with a glass of rum in his hand. It was warm enough here, but the tension of the city was tightening, so he knew he couldn't linger, brushed fingers across his forehead and wiped water away, the neon popping and jerking him forward. He reached for the door but it swung open before he touched the handle, a boy and girl hurrying past, heads down and eyes averted. They seemed familiar and he tried to see their faces, but the features were blurred. He went inside.

Music boomed and a spinning fan cooled his skin. The bar was dimly lit and his eyes took a few seconds to adjust, a single beer tap drawing him to the counter. He had sworn he wouldn't touch alcohol tonight, not in this city, not after what happened before, but despite the promise he knew one drink wasn't going to hurt. He would make it last and enjoy the taste alone, then turn around and leave and walk straight back to his room.

The barmaid bent forward and smiled, her low-cut top showing off some fine cleavage. Jimmy pointed to the tap and watched as she poured his drink, bubbles racing up the height of an expanding glass. She fluttered lush eyelashes and licked thick red lips, soaking him in a cloud of perfume. Everything about this lady seemed exaggerated. He was pleased. She placed the glass on the counter and he handed over coins, studying her legs as she went to the till. He glanced along the length of the bar, which was narrow and led to a flickering jukebox, the overall shape of the room reminding him of the section back in prison. Fifteen or so people sat at tables, their heads lowered, while three men in black leather coats stood nearby, talking between themselves.

The barmaid held out his change and made sure their hands touched. He wondered if she knew where he had been, what he had done, if she could see his mistakes in the pallor of his skin, the dull light in his eyes, the colours of his aura, and yet he didn't feel tired or weak or broken, was enjoying the energy racing into his arm, chest, heart. He saw an electric chair, a tethered youth turning into a pig, face glistening, but Jimmy blocked the image out, refused to deal in lies, the casual dismissal of another creature's terror. He was shaking as he returned the barmaid's smile.

Jimmy reached for his glass, determined to sip and enjoy every drop. The barmaid watched closely as he brought the drink to his mouth. He finished his beer in one go and she nodded her approval. It tasted fantastic. He pointed to the tap.

Taking this second glass over to an empty table, Jimmy sat and watched the barmaid stroll down the bar to serve the three men in leather coats. He couldn't work out why they were dressed this way in such warm weather, frustrated he couldn't go over and explain the reality of what they had wrapped around their backs. He wondered if the barmaid understood the terror involved. He felt that she must. And it was fantastic leaving a world of men and being so near a woman, even brushing her hand, but he couldn't let his guard down, remembered the place he'd been drinking in before his arrest, knew the sort of violence that could occur. He would finish this one and leave, the alcohol doing its job, lifting his spirits and numbing any doubts. He was in charge, his old confidence returning. Resting his head against the wall he shut his eyes and concentrated on the jukebox, pictured the B-Block boys, all those convicts who were dreaming their lives away. He said a short prayer for the friends he had left behind.

When he opened his eyes again he found the barmaid staring at him. He realised his glass was empty. He nodded and she poured another, bringing it over on a tray with a big shot of vodka. This was on the house. She eased in close, whispering words he didn't know, a breast brushing his arm. She flicked her tongue and returned to the counter, wiggling her hips as she went, and he flashed back in time, was walking next to Ramona, his soul-mate swaying in the same way, but for different reasons. They were two runaways on an iced-up pavement, treading carefully, the gutters heavy with sludge, petrol-grey snow seeping into drains loaded with fermenting hormones. They were approaching a market and it was Jimmy who spotted the police car and guided Ramona into the crowd, over to the nearest shop window. They would look at the display with their backs to the road, wait for the police to move on, their reflections distorted in the wet glass.

A single face formed and stared back. It had huge ears, a massive snout and delicate eyelids that sagged over empty sockets. The eyes had been burned or scooped out, or maybe they had just decayed. Blood crusted what remained of the neck, rubber-skin rigid where it had been hacked at by a blade. Ramona slumped forward and Jimmy just caught her in time, before she shattered the window, holding on until she was able to drive some strength back into her legs. Ramona mumbled and Jimmy thought he was going to be sick, held the nausea down, turned his head and saw two policemen standing by their car, scanning the crowd. He returned to the pig, felt its fear, heard the screaming of its slaughter, and his disgust rose up again, nearly reached his mouth, and what made the murder and mutilation even more perverted was the pig's smile. It wasn't a modest grin or a cheeky little smirk, but a great big lucky-me-isn't-life-fantastic beam.

Jimmy waited a while before looking round again, and when he did the police were gone. He tugged Ramona away from the glass, hurrying them as best he could towards the pub at the end of the road. They passed stalls loaded with nuts and bolts and old clothes, the fruit-and-veg men with their oranges and lemons, the roast-chestnut lady poking at grey coals, a range of secondhand radios and televisions and broken neons, a bakery selling fresh bread and pies. They turned into a narrow little street and were soon pushing the pub door open, warm air cushioning their entrance. An elderly couple were leaving a table and Ramona flopped into one of the seats, the woman patting her shoulder softly, their faces lost as they went out into the cold.

Jimmy stood tall at the counter and ordered. He was under-age but nobody cared. Three leather-coated men stood on one side, four market-traders on the other. The barmaid smiled at him as she poured beer, those near him admiring her cleavage. Jimmy glanced around the pub, saw loners and couples keeping to themselves, a selection of grafters and shoppers and music-lovers talking and arguing and laughing, and then he could hear their hearts inside a jukebox that thumped out punk and rockabilly and some vintage rock n roll. Smoke filled the air, lyrics lost in the din.

He brought their drinks over to the table and joined Ramona, who grabbed his hands and rubbed hard to warm them up. This was the free world at its best — a warm pub and good beer, the chance to say what he thought, a beautiful girl who was moral and smart, the record-machine and its 45s. They guzzled stout and lager, slowly calming down, even if Jimmy couldn't stop thinking ahead. They would have to move on soon. If the police found them they would be split up and he would be sent back to the home. One more after this and then they would leave. They had to keep their heads down and stay out of trouble.

Years later and straight out of prison, Jimmy had plans. Tomorrow morning he would be sitting on a train, but tonight he could relax and listen to the songs and enjoy the barmaid's smile. He kept on drinking, toasted Ramona and that nameless pig. Prison could shock even the hardest of men, make them examine themselves and question the peck-peck-pecking order, and he thought of the animals on the work farm, the men who refused to take part in the killing. There were no release dates in the slaughterhouse. No escape and no mercy shown to the meek. He had seen the horror with his own eyes. He would never forget the cruelty of the knackers. His mood changed.

He wondered what these people in the bar would think if they knew he had just been released from Seven Towers. Some might call him an animal, but they would really mean subhuman. Others might see him as a novelty. He tried to guess which men would pick a fight, settled his eyes on the barmaid and tried to decide if she would be disgusted or excited. It would be better if she was sympathetic. He hunched over his glass. There were some truly honest people in the world, but not so many. Ramona was the best he'd ever known.

He saw them in that market pub, drinking too much and staying too long, going back out into the winter cold, careful as they headed towards the station, trying not to skid and fall. The buildings were trimmed with ice and the streetlights reflected at odd angles, and as they passed through this fluorescent corridor they neared the butcher's shop. He had looked across the road, seen the pig's head in the window, and it was glowing and cartoon-like and the two beasts behind the counter were laughing, making more noise that the whole of the pub put together. One man held a cleaver. There was a poster advertising chops. A smiling lamb frolicked in a green field.

The market was closing and rubbish was being collected. Jimmy reached into a skip and took out a lump of wood, crossed through the barely-moving traffic and reached the window, whacked the glass one, two, three, four times before it exploded. He shouted at Ramona to run as the butchers stepped forward, blades in their hands, white overalls red with blood, using some of their cheerful slaughterhouse chat — *come here you little bastard, I'm going to cut your balls off* — because that's how these people talked and thought and lived their lives, but they were fat and stunk of another creature's death and Jimmy had a head-start, one of the men slipping on the ice, the boy stopping and shouting, the second butcher near when Jimmy tumbled and fell, hauling himself back up and reaching Ramona who couldn't move as fast, and the butcher was right behind them now, Jimmy stopping to face him, running forward and cracking him on the head and watching the body collapse, hitting him three more times.

Jimmy and Ramona reached the station and trotted down the escalators. They jumped on the first train they saw and rubbed noses as the doors closed.

He couldn't help feeling pleased. He had never known how to behave himself. He was different now and one day he would find Ramona. They thought the same way, used to worry about the dairy cows, all those mothers mourning sons snatched and sent off to veal factories, their daughters raped and filled with drugs, jolly farmers castrating the boys and fingering the girls so the eyes of the innocents widened in shock and embarrassment. He hated the advertising whores and dishonest journalists who pumped out snide humour to hide the horror; the politicians and religious leaders who allowed the killing to continue and increase. Ramona cried for the scared chicks and lambs and piglets and all the innocent creatures of the world, while Jimmy raged about those responsible. The masses turned their heads and refused to see the real criminals. He hated the hypocrites who sneered and dismissed and judged. Prison had reinforced and focused his beliefs.

The jukebox was silent and he realised he was on his feet and walking over. He had been in the bar for a couple of hours and his mind was marching in a different directions. He bumped into one of the men at the bar, commented on the leather coat.

Jimmy stood in front of the machine and looked at the records — inspecting them as a man and a boy — in a foreign bar and a local pub — and the drink had hit him harder than he'd expected. He was starting to drift. Ramona and him were the only ones on this dirty planet who could hear the muttering of the meat men, the snickering of their child-molester bosses, the oohing and aahing of the fashion paedophiles in their fur and stripped skin, the great leather-buying, burger-gorging, baby-battering, tastebud-driven public. His head was spinning. He could see those meekest of souls in the slaughterhouse — lambs and piglets and calves crying for their mothers — and he felt their panic as they faced the horror, the last words these creatures heard the swearing of evil men heavy with the sex of their razors and hooks and drills and knives — angry swearing grunting rapist laughter — *dirty little bitch shitting on my boots... go on, stick that electric rod up her, that'll make her eyes water... look at him trying to hide his face, come on, cut his bollocks off* — and he could feel the fear of the section... the anger of the prison house... as if he was still locked-up... he could hear the mutter of the other men... the jabbering... the peck-peck-pecking of the pecking order... the tick-tick-ticking... and he saw the judges in their finery... the pontificators... the snobs and liars... knew he was judging them as well... but there *was* a difference... the difference between right and wrong... good and evil... there *had* to be a difference... life wouldn't make sense otherwise... there were plenty in prison who deserved to be shut away... but there were more lost boys and innocents than evil men... they had made mistakes... he had made enough in his life... but he wasn't bad... hadn't done anything wrong... not really... just a fight after too much drink... it was easily done... a way to release his fury... and he turned and saw the three leathermen standing close... sneering... glaring... snarling... cocky there in their black coats... so Jimmy moved away from the jukebox and faced them and hardened his fists.

XXXXXXXX

The room was simple and dirty and small for someone who had tasted freedom, for Jimmy Ramone pressing his head against the bars that filled one end of the barren cell. It was similar to the place they had held him in two years ago, before he was sent up the hill to Seven Towers. The smell was identical, a sour blend of sweat, piss, shit, vomit, fear. The stench of the prison house was even worse, these essentials drenched in the sheer insanity of incarceration, a rancid brand of failure that promised cancer, heart failure, clots, brain damage and every sort of infection and virus. It was also the smell of a hospital, but without the detergent and decency.

Bleached hospital corridors pulled visitors to the hopelessness of a ward lined with the elderly, a hall of memories, regrets, visions, nightmares, exhaustion. Morphine was a true friend, an angel of mercy offering sedation, silence, a drifting mental calm. Time turned full circle, moving from the wonders of potty training to the final release of incontinence. This was the place where the fears of Jimmy's prison philosophy came true. Time ran out. There was no going back, no second or third or tenth chances. Ward 6 was waiting for every man, woman, boy, girl. A single second was precious. There were never enough seconds, minutes, hours, days, weeks, months, years. Time was everything. He squeezed the bars.

What had he done?

What the fuck had he done to end up in this cell?

Thinking back a few hours...

He should have stayed in his room.

Jimmy felt the cuts on his knuckles, bruised eyes looking for a human face, but there was nobody in the corridor and he was the only one in the cell. The guards were around the corner, out of sight, drinking tea and playing cards. The ice-cream man didn't visit any more. He was dead. Stabbed to death in a prison toilet. That's what Jimmy had heard. What he had seen.

He shut his eyes.

Butted the bars.

Felt blood drop down his face.

XXXXXXXX

Excited people filled the train station, pushing past the friendly stranger leaning against a wall, doing his best to blend in. He wanted to remain anonymous, maybe release small sparks of blue-tinted kindness, the sort of colours a sensitive soul would understand. He was living the lessons of the prison yard and protecting his back, wary of knitting needles that punctured lungs, shards of glass that sliced skin and opened arteries, fingernails that ripped at a sleeping man's spine. He was ready for the back-stabbers prowling the train stations and bus depots of the world, the street-corner snipers waiting for drunks and drifters. He was a transient himself, so knew the reality. He was also a lucky man, arrested on his first night of freedom for being drunk and asleep in a doorway, the police releasing him in the morning with a cheerful warning, unaware of his past.

Jimmy saw animals crowd the platform, identified vegan sniffers and snorters, the happy faces of pigs and cows and sheep and rabbits and mice and geese and a single carrot-chomping donkey. This was a world where simple manners masked a different sort of knowledge. He was one of only a few humans who could see this bully-free alternative, but he noticed he was giggling, raised a hand to cover his mouth as a grandmother glared over, her eyes narrowing as an arm instinctively reached towards the two little girls by her side. The arm floated, holding his future in the balance, and when she lowered it and turned away and dismissed the idea of danger Jimmy felt fantastic.

His train arrived and he found a seat by the window. An elderly man sat opposite. The face was mean and pinched and cruel, but when a cloud shunted sideways and sunlight filled the carriage the expression was almost saintly. Big ears protruded from the skull. A sign of wisdom. And they seemed to be growing. The shape of the head was also changing, wrinkles vanishing as the skin became smooth and very clean. Jimmy had always liked pigs. The nose was filling out and stretching and turning into a rubber snout. It wasn't long before a beaming porker sat across from him, but Jimmy frowned, wondered if it was a trick, if he was refusing to see the evil. This was something he had learned to do as a boy, but that skill was meant to have been left in the past, and yet the past was right here in the present, and this exact moment was waiting in the future. He pulled himself together. The man's features returned. He seemed worried and Jimmy realised he had been pulling some faces of his own. The train was moving. They had already left the station behind. Jimmy nodded and smiled.

The old man meant no harm and seemed relieved, pulled a small table down and dipped into the sack sitting on his knees, taking out a bottle and two shot glasses. One hand made flamboyant gestures as the other conjured bags of raisins, pumpkin seeds, radishes, almonds. He tore each one so the contents spilled across the table. Next he produced a thick loaf of bread, finally unscrewing the top of the bottle and filling the glasses with a mystery spirit. He handed one of these to Jimmy. The man said a few words and they drank a toast. The spirit stung Jimmy's throat. It was powerful stuff. They had two more glasses and settled back in their seats.

Fields had replaced the last suburbs of the city and the train was crossing scrubland, the earth dry and dusty, a lone donkey chained to a rock in the full glare of a fast-rising sun. Jimmy could feel its heartbeat inside his own chest. There was no music. No jukebox. His mouth was suddenly dry. Eyes wet. He tried to push the donkey from his mind, concentrating on the forest ahead of the train. This was a sanctuary for runaways. His relief at finally escaping the city and heading north clashed with the anger he felt, the train picking up speed. But nothing could stop him now. He was free.

The man opposite lifted almonds and raisins to his mouth and began chewing, jaw moving slowly with a faint crunch of bone, slipped his hand back into the sack, and Jimmy wiped the tears away and blinked and focused and frowned and hoped that — *for his sake* — he didn't pull out a block of cheese or a stack of sliced ham or a lump of pork.

Jimmy closed his eyes and did his best to lose himself in the motion of the train, searching for the sort of rhythm that would calm his fear and rage and make sure he stayed safe. But he was finding it hard to concentrate, couldn't shut out the click-click-clicking of a meat-eater's teeth. He pushed his thoughts towards the beauty of that simple, private room instead, tried to examine the painting on the wall. The watercolour was wet and had run. And he could hear the tap-tap-tapping of monkey monsters under his bed. The tick-tick-ticking of the time bomb inside his head. He kept his eyes firmly shut, terrified of what he would find when he opened them again.

When She Asks for Bread, Will You Give Her a Stone?

My father wrote, "We've nothing to complain of,"
speaking of home in his infrequent letters.
"She's been treated with discipline and firm love,"
said my social worker in her annual report. Speaking of
letters, mine home were censored to obscure the rapes.
My father wrote, "You've nothing to complain of,
so why won't you behave? They said you shoved
a girl for no reason, that you steal and refuse your duties.
You've been treated with discipline and firm love,
and you're there until your character's reformed. You have
an opportunity. Most children in that place don't have parents,"
my father wrote, "you've nothing to complain of."
Meanwhile, Fallon held a knife to my throat, shoved her rough
fingers deep inside me, tongued my ear during supervised phone calls.
"She's been treated with discipline and firm love,
according to the values of this Home," a trove
of records fell to me today, at last. On the discharge papers
my father wrote, "We have nothing to complain of.
She's been treated with discipline and firm love."

Shrouds

1.

He was about six or seven, black rubbish-tip hair,
big doe-eyes, teeth driftwood-white, a painted-on
ringmaster's moustache, outstretched arm and hand held out
like a soup-kitchen ladle. I was standing beside one
of the cremation paddocks at the burning Ghats in Varanasi.
A pyre was blazing; bruise-black smoke rose up into the vacant sky
and the sun burned down over the slow, wide Ganges
and the vast, sandy tidal plain on the far side.
Garlanded chanters in a canoe rowed a dead guru out
for river-burial, the shrouded corpse lay stiffly across
the bow like the firing arm of a crossbow. The artful-dodger
street-child tugged once more at the hem of my sleeve
and I looked down into his hazel eyes to see that all my ambitions
were meaningless dreams, illusions that would vanish into smoke
at the end of my days. I felt hollow,
like a bubble, shrouded-off from anything real.

2.

As I reached into my pocket that I kept stocked
with sweets for the street-children I glanced
to the blazing pyre — a man, a fire-warden,
was picking up an arm, by the elbow,
which had fallen out and he threw it back on top
of the furnace-orange flames. When I gave
the hazel-eyed street-child the sweet,
a chocolate éclair, he clutched it in his flycatcher-hand
and then asked me for money. I looked away —
the day before I saw him hand his coins in
to a lanky teenager who had the stern eyes
of an amateur knifer. The child shrugged-off,
examining the shrouded éclair, its plastic wrapper a
black velvety blouse, which he opened, revealing
an inner wrapper, a white geisha-corset stuck sugar-tight
against the treacle skin which he peeled back
and gently released like a dove's wing onto the air
before he tossed the sallow toffee body into his gaping mouth.
I turned back to the paddock and the burning pyre,
its summit of unquestioning flame —
the detached arm had landed palm up;
the fingertips lightly cupping,
it had let go of all it had given
or been given.

Gladly in Russia

(a flabby sort of sestina)

The name of this poem comes from my misreading of the title of Sillitoe's memoir Gadfly in Russia.

1.

A train through Franco's Spain. The peace, the restlessness
of travel. (Travel to? Or from? Escaping literary fame,
perhaps? Or seeking something realer, something red
in tooth and claw?) You chat with Ruth about the Spanish Civil War,
become aware: a watchful stillness in your fellow travellers…
Police-polite, they take your passports away.

2.

(So no change there…) And all you want is — to get away.
And it's Tangier — four months of tranquil restlessness
with carousing, bed-hopping writers, early-hippy travellers…
Your first book, the film of it, have brought a tabloid fame
and so you run: from your little Midland, middle-brow town; that little war
when the *Express* branded you a card-carrying Red…

3.

(So no change there…) No point in seeing red —
you just move on. An invitation comes your way:
See Russia's reconstruction since the last Great Patriotic War…
And there's that Angry-Young-Man restlessness:
the recluse in you starts gathering maps. Not for the fame,
or the infamy: but to see for yourself the faces of fellow-travellers,

4.

the hydro-electric dams, the medals on the chests of war-heroes,
the tanks in Red Square for the May Day revels…
You meet Oksana, Marina, Valentina, Rimma Kazakova, Boris Polevoi: Reds
second, writers first; and people before all of that. Perhaps your fame
is thought useful… Perhaps a speech in praise of… And perhaps a way
can (sometimes) still be found to say — no. Call it fatal recklessness:
your anti-Soviet radio lecture, indignant against the post-war

5.

persecutions… is re-recorded, and so you are suddenly full of praise:
there is no war
against Jews and dissidents. (So no change there…)
George Andjaparidze, your escort: part-guide, part-fellow-traveller,

part soul-mate, part–NKVD… but he is a writer, and that's the restlessness,
the binding that makes your half-trust life-long…
A visit to a poet Ruth has read,
and met. You write: "We had tea and discussed poetry — what else?"
And there's that glance away,

so as not to face the microphone behind the mirror frame.

6.

The village used to have a Yiddish name. Used to. George shrugs:
we will be stopped. It has no literary use. Or fame.
Ruth's Jewish roots are there. George shrugs. Until a road-block soldier,
too young to have seen a war,
stops you, peers into the Peugeot… Asks for passports.
(So no change there…) And when you finally pull away,
spitting curses (a writer, wanting only to be well-meaning), a mapless traveller
heading back the way he came, George explains: "The boy was bored.
He liked the look of your car! He was curious, only.
He wasn't going to arrest us!"

7.

Reluctant, you relax. There is, after all, a book in this. Or three.

And — actually — sod them. Sod the lot of them.

(So no change there…)

And you go on. With your writer's life. The tireless drive:
The Radford gadfly hovers a moment, gladly moves on. To a new Jerusalem.

Empty quarter

On the eight hour lorry ride from El Fashir to Nyala, perched
on potato sacks, I am stripped of the constant bickering

of billboards and their one-upmanship of car, liquor,
sportswear, over and over. There are no other drivers

to tailgate, overtake, undertake, argue the noisy toss
with at red lights; no horns screaming at amber;

no beep of warnings to *wait, walk now, wait.*
The road unrolls its parched tongue, scoured clean

of red brick terraces, net curtains bunched into fists
for a better gawp at the neighbours. All distractions swept

off the earth's table-top: the only interruptions
a shaved hill swelling from the pebbledash desert,

a camel on the horizon, paddling sand. An ochre moon
advertises itself against indigo night. I can hear the breath of stars.

Asking for directions

Take the road past the abandoned cliff-edge
hotel. A boy will lean out of a car and shoot
at you. Don't worry. He will miss. Follow

the bullet's breath to the hospital and its folded
wards. You only think it is a dead-end. Continue
through its convoluted drainage system to a courtyard

with bricked-up doorways. Choose the only one
that's open, then along a bridle-path signed *no motor vehicles*,
past disbelieving wrecks of burnt-out trucks. Keep walking.

You'll arrive at the station breathless, too late
for your train and minus ticket, money, timetable. Stow
that ridiculously heavy suitcase in a locker and climb

the gravelled path up the hill. Yes, it gets steeper.
Your sat-nav? It won't work here. Feel your way
with the bravery you used to have when you crossed

roads without looking. Keep going. You can't miss it:
the sheer drop, the view back with its tarpaulin
of smoke, all those wooden markers.

For Want of a Nail

Their leaders bought blind, because of the cost;
the MiG 15s (ex-Afghan) wouldn't fly.
The ground troops halted, the battle was lost,
the breakaway republic doomed to die
for want of support, *for want of a nail.*

The warring factions kept up their attacks
on the besieged enclave. Their envoy's news
didn't reach them, something wrong with the fax
from the Geneva talks. Their Christmas truce
shot down, the town fell, *for want of a nail.*

The radio went off the air, the rebels
stormed the presidential palace, but the
federal forces basted them, in Goebbels'
phrase, because they needed guns not butter,
for greasing the wheels, *for want of a nail.*

The surgeon needed sleep: the drip-feed's seal
was faulty, someone left a swab inside.
The new heart failed, the rupture wouldn't heal.
They kept him on dialysis: he died
for want of a bed, *for want of a nail.*

The cargo shifted, the bow doors weren't closed.
The lorry hit a car and shed its load.
She'd be here if the council hadn't closed
the school, she had to cross the busy road,
victim of the cuts, *for want of a nail.*

The walkway fell fifty feet from the deck.
Rescuers were late, the ambulance stalled.
The owner said there'd been a safety check
last year, it wasn't the company's fault
that corners where cut, *for want of a nail.*

warning not heeded, *for want of a nail,*
nor safeguards observed, *for want of a nail,*
usual precautions, *for want of a nail,*
normal procedures, *for want of a nail,*
no proper funding, *for want of a nail.*

The phone line broke, the deadline expired,
they stormed the plane, the hostages were shot.
The talks broke down, the army marksman fired.
They couldn't reach the trapped people, and not
for want of trying, *for want of a nail,*

disaster waited, *for want of a nail,*
the president killed, *for want of a nail,*
his aides couldn't help, *for want of a nail,*
the government fell, *for want of a nail,*
a spokesman claimed, *for want of a nail.*

My Mate Sid, and other Middle East memories

Remember Derby in 1978? I do — it was *my* town. Yes, I know in 1977 it became a City but I always referred to it as a 'town', and still do. It was the Derby of my childhood in the '50s and '60s, of trolley buses and Midland Drapery, of a Market Place that really was one, the shops and stalls on Cockpit Hill, of an actual ice factory on the Ice Factory Island. The Derby of glory years at the Baseball Ground, of Clough and Taylor, and Dave Mackay; of championships and memorable European nights; of Real Ale, pints of Bass in the Exeter Arms, and evenings in the Blessington Carriage.

And of course it was the Derby of my parents Ellen and Walt, brother John and twin sisters Maureen and Christine, and their families. I was 24, still living at home, fairly shy, not adventurous, and working for the Railways at the Technical Centre on London Road. So why get a job in the Middle East with the Arabian American Oil Company (Aramco)? After all I wasn't exactly typical ex-pat material. Well, the money helped (especially as it was tax-free), but mainly because I wanted a complete change. There was no significant other in my life. Friday and Saturday nights usually saw me propping up the bar in Clouds or Baileys, trying to pluck up the courage to start a conversation with Miss Right. To be honest even Miss Wrong would have been better than nothing!

My best mate applied for a job abroad, so I thought, *Why not?* After interviews, medicals, visas and goodbyes, I left Derby Station in the early hours of a cold, damp night in September 1978. I was on the 'milk train' to London St Pancras. Arriving before the Underground opened, I picked up my two suitcases, and the handle came off one. Great start: 120 miles down, only 3,000 or so to go, and I could only carry one suitcase at a time. Don't ask me how I managed to get everything to Heathrow, but there were lots of banged ankles and shins on the Tube train that morning ...

Talking to the man next to me on the plane I smugly told him where I'd be working. He took me in at a glance: pale face, cream suit (I thought it looked tropical), shirt and tie, and told me with a wry smile that most people on-board were there for the same reason I was, and were traveling back to Saudi Arabia, from 'leave'.

As the plane descended, darkness fell, hiding the view of the desert, and just the bright flames of the gas flares on the oil wells were visible. Suddenly I realised, I was there, in the Middle East! Disembarking, a blast of 80 degree heat hit me (this at 8pm!) and suddenly my jacket, shirt and tie didn't seem like such a good idea after all. The main airport building was chaos: heat, crowds, a multitude of different languages, all heard at nothing less than shouting level. There were westerners, Arabs in western suits, Arab men in local garb, Arab women covered head to toe in black, and the Police, who looked about 15 and carried machine guns!

Customs chose my suitcases to open. Out fell an assortment of clothes, books, pots, pans, plates, bowls and cutlery (which it turned out I didn't actually need!) Their faces were a picture as they watched me try to fit the whole lot back in. This done, a tug-of-war ensued between me and a local taxi driver, who wanted to whisk me away to my destination. The only thing was, I didn't know where I was going, and had no local money to pay him. Fortunately my 'meeter' turned up, and soon I was sitting in air-conditioned luxury in an American car the size of our back garden. The bright lights diminished as I was driven from Dhahran, and out into the desert.

Soon we arrived at North Camp Contractors' facility, my home for the next 12 months. Fencing, barbed wire, gates, guards, and row upon row of portable accommodation units, 32 rooms per building with communal toilets and showers, and a welcome pack of bedding, towels and soap. I felt like an extra in *The Great Escape*. Still, at least I had my own room, which even had a spare bed and wardrobe. So I relaxed, lay back, and thought wistfully of the family I missed already, and the great adventure I had only just embarked on.

This reverie was disturbed by the arrival of a small, middle-aged man wearing only a suntan and a pair of off-white underpants. "I'm your roommate for the next year, and that's my bed. Now shift!"

Apart from this territorial misunderstanding, we got on well (although I was a bit worried when he told me he'd had his penis broken playing football, but I suppose we all need a claim to fame, and at least he never offered to show me!) His job often took him away from North Camp, and his contract gave him three weeks' UK leave for every six weeks worked, so I often had the room to myself.

Through him I soon met kindred spirits, single Brits away from home for the first time, in similar jobs and grades, and I soon became part of what we called the North Camp Escape Committee, unofficially headed by the older and wiser Cliff Notley. Cliff was ex-Rolls-Royce, and a former PA to the great Brian Clough, and had even typed out his resignation letter! One lad from Liverpool had us in tears with a never-ending stream of jokes. Turned out his Dad went round all the clubs and wrote the jokes down so he could memorise them!

I soon got to grips with learning the ropes; getting to know colleagues, and coping with the heat (not the language, as everyone spoke English). It was a proper United Nations workplace: Brits, Americans, Arabs, Egyptians, Lebanese, Indians, the list went on. Then there were the cultural differences. Many Saudi Arabs wore the traditional long white thobe (shirt), and white or checked guttrah (headdress), and their wives wore head-to-toe black coverings. Arab women weren't allowed to drive cars (even Western women could only drive in private compounds), and walked a few paces behind the men. At certain times they even begged on street corners while the men sat drinking coffee and smoking hookah pipes. A world away from what I'd known before.

Brits were third, or fourth-class citizens in terms of pay and status. The dust-bowl that was North Camp had facilities, like recreation halls with televisions, pool and table tennis; cinemas and swimming pools, football pitches (even a sex doll for hire which explained the outbreak of a sexually transmitted disease in an all-male camp!) However all were basic compared to Main Camp in Dhahran, a little piece of America in the desert with better facilities, sprawling homes, colourful gardens and lawns. Back home in Derby I could get a bus into town, have a few beers, go bowling in Duckworth Square or catch a film at the Odeon or ABC. Now I was being told that, on Main Camp, my ID pass didn't allow me into the cinema or bowling alley, that I couldn't go for a swim a game of squash unless as a guest. I couldn't even shop at the commissary (supermarket). Don't get me wrong, other nationalities fared a lot worse but it still rankled with us.

Then there was the censorship, which meant that any TV program or film showing physical contact between men and women was censored, badly. One moment J.R. Ewing would be moving in smoothly on his latest conquest and then — bang — they would be 10 feet apart adjusting their clothes! Newspapers and magazines were a scream, thick marker pens used to delete inappropriate words, and pictures of exposed female flesh; sometimes pages were ripped out completely. We wondered who had the better job, the censors who got to read all the words and examine the pictures, or whoever was making a fortune selling black marker pens to the Authorities.

Evening trips to the nearby towns were a welcome break from life on camp. Cheap gold and even cheaper pirate music cassettes were very popular. We'd pore over items, weigh up choices, queue and reach the till, only to be ushered out as the shops closed for prayer. Half an hour later, with the Mutawa (religious police) patrolling to make sure no-one broke the rules, the doors would reopen and we'd again form a queue.

Fred (a lovely but dour Yorkshire lad) could see the cloud in every silver lining and wouldn't spend 20p if he could get away with 10p. One night, arriving home late, looked even less cheerful than usual, and it turned out he had been turfed off the last bus to make room for some Saudi Arabs and Americans with more senior passes. It was a reminder of our lowly position, but it cheered us up imagining the look on Fred's face when he realised he would have to pay for a taxi. We could almost hear the hinge on the padlock of his wallet squealing in protest.

A lot seemed unfair: the rules we found ourselves under, the Saudi Arabian attitude to women, the way we ex-pats were treated, and the restriction on access to facilities. However, fighting it achieved nothing. Those that did, lasted only a short time (one Brit only making three days!). It was a matter of accepting that we were visitors to another country, that we didn't have the right to challenge a centuries-old culture, and that we were being paid relatively well to do a job in their country under their rules. In other words, 'get on or get out'.

The job I'd signed up for involved worldwide purchasing of plant, equipment and supplies for major projects such as gas plants, seawater desalination and port construction. But (outside of work and especially after the first year when I moved to Dhahran Main Camp following promotion) I still had plenty of time on my hands.

Spare time was spent reading, playing pool or table-tennis, sunbathing, picnics, watching TV or listening to those cheap music cassettes (which by the way were rubbish). Occasional house-sitting was a welcome change of scenery, as well as educational. I quickly (and messily) learned that cat poo floats in a toilet, but a whole tray of cat litter doesn't. And, being surprised by a homeowner returning early from vacation, that not all French women were glamorous. This one was less Brigitte Bardot, more Hilda Ogden. No wonder she needed to keep a sex toy that was a cross between a Scud missile and a road drill on her bedside table!

I was missing my family and friends, and I missed watching the Rams. Sport helped fill that time and eased the homesickness. In Derby, I played football only occasionally on a Sunday. I always tell people I played most, and the best, of my football abroad, like Gary Lineker did years later at Barcelona. Except of course he was a tad better than me …

We restarted the Aramco Dhahran Football Club, organised matches and training, and sorted out kit and refreshments. Mostly, games were played on hard, dusty, packed sand pitches, or sometimes on Astroturf which left nasty friction burns if you weren't careful with sliding tackles. Our team was a collection of Brits, Americans and even a Lebanese international, and we were fairly successful over the next two years. Our best win was 12-0 against a team from British Aerospace. Thirty years later at Bombardier, I met a procurement manager who had been in the opposing team. He still bore the emotional scars!

We played our Cup Final in sweltering heat at a 20,000-capacity stadium where there were more players than spectators. I even arranged a game against a Bahraini oil company team, only for the Iran/Iraq War to get in the way. Scud missiles flying overhead persuaded us to call the match off.

We lost a 'friendly' against a team from the crew of HMS Active, but had a great time introducing them afterwards to the delights of the local illicitly produced booze, and tried to look innocent when a lavish formal buffet reception degenerated into chaos, as sailors 'bombed' fully clothed into the swimming pool as the effects of the alcohol took hold.

I still had time on my hands, so I coached a team of 7 and 8 year old American and Arab children: the Dhahran Hawks. Surely my qualifications were impeccable: I'd seen two league title wins, and was at Wembley when the Rams lifted the Charity Shield. Surely the magic from Clough and Taylor, and Dave Mackay had rubbed off on me?

Nope.

The Hawks didn't win a game.

Or draw.

Or even score a goal.

Amazingly, I was invited back to coach them the following season. I rose to the challenge, and we won the League in style — CHAMPIONS! Proudly, I walked at the head of the Hawks as they received their medals and trophies.

I wish it was solely down to my coaching skills, but the key was a new player: a young, blond American who joined because his friend was in the team. Bigger, taller and stronger than most his age, he was a born goal-scorer who blasted it into the net in from all angles, and inspired his team-mates to do the same. His reputation was such that, pre-season, an opposing coach rang me to say that if we didn't take it easy on them, he'd call the game off!

A benefit of coaching the Hawks was getting to know some of the families, who kindly took me into their lives and homes, giving me a taste of the family life I was missing. I joined them for barbeques, picnics, birthday parties and Christmas celebrations, a world of difference from my first Christmas Day at camp in 1978. We felt down, thousands of miles away from home and family, so we decided to dress up in our best suits, shirts and ties for our Christmas dinner and posed for photos. The Americans in

T-shirts and shorts thought we were a bunch of crazy Brits but it did the job and cheered us up.

Any celebration calls for a drink and in Derby, I only had to walk into any pub or off-license. Beer must have been about 40p a pint in those days and a bottle of spirits a few quid at most. Saudi Arabia, however, was a 'dry' country.

Except it wasn't really. And probably isn't even now.

Remember Geordie home brew beer kits? We'd buy one while on leave, remove the label, then back in Saudi brew beer in the wardrobe. Very nice it was, too. The Americans even sold beer kits in the commissary on Main Camp, in the baking products aisle under the brand name 'Vitabake'.

There was a thriving black market for alcohol, imported by the container-load and sold at vastly-inflated prices. One night a mate got his hands on a bottle of Bells for £28, a fortune in those days, so of course I volunteered to help him drink it.

The most popular drink was called 'sadiqi', Arabic for 'friend', which we called 'Sid'. Colourless, tasteless and odourless, it mixed with anything, and was mostly produced in home-made stills. After one exploded (taking out the side of someone's garage) Aramco quietly issued improved equipment for safety reasons. Uncut Sid was about 140 per cent proof (equivalent to around 70 per cent alcohol by volume), and was normally 'cut' to half that strength. I made the mistake of drinking uncut Sid at a party at my boss's home, where I got outrageously drunk and felt ill for two days afterwards!

It was Sid that no doubt accounted for the portly American who one night wandered disorientated into Frank's room a few doors down from mine, and wrapped only in a towel, opened the wardrobe door and tried to take a shower. Frank was a bit put out, but we told him to be grateful he hadn't mistaken it for the toilet.

The official line was that alcohol was banned, but as long as you kept it quiet, drank in private, and never sold it to locals, it was fine. Once, after a few Sids, I smuggled a bottle into an official company 'do', it was only afterwards I realized what the consequences could have been if I had been caught. The American father of one of my Hawks players was caught selling alcohol to Saudi Arabs and was given the choice of bundling his family on a plane back to the States that night, or be arrested the following morning and face imprisonment or strokes with a cane. They left that evening. His son was no loss as a player (he ran like Bambi on ice and had the ball control of a brick wall) but that wasn't the point; the lad got caught up in his father breaking the rules and the whole family suffered the consequences.

When my first contract came to an end, I looked forward to my first holiday in 12 months. Some people headed for more exotic climes, but not for me the tourist spots (and fleshpots) of Bangkok. Greece, Spain and the like held no attraction for me. I'd spent much of my spare time swimming in the Gulf; I'd sunbathed on Birds Eye and Ras Tanura beaches, in temperatures in the 80s and even above 100 degrees. No, I was heading back home for five weeks in Derby.

On the overnight flight to Heathrow I couldn't sleep or drink, I was so excited. The passenger next to me had other plans and got quietly and totally drunk, which was fine until he spilt red wine down my cream coloured suit and fell asleep with his head on my shoulder. I moved him upright, a wise move as it turned out. He woke, and promptly threw up in his own lap. Served him right!

I took the train from London to Derby, a station that was cold, uncomfortable and unappealing, but I didn't care: it was so good to be back. I hired a car, a dark blue Ford Capri which I thought might make me look like Bodie or Doyle from *The Professionals*. I probably looked more like Cowley. At home we hugged, Mam, Dad and me, and we were all a bit misty-eyed. Nothing seemed to have changed, but of course I had. I was not the same person who had nervously left town a year ago. I was already looking forward to another contract with Aramco, much to the puzzlement of my parents who thought one year would be enough. Promotion and more than 50% pay rise helped me decide. The next five weeks were spent visiting family, relaxing and renewing acquaintance with old friends, including Messrs Marstons and Bass. I even became a property-owner, following some wise advice from Cliff Notley: "Get yourself a house — bricks and mortar for the future."

Returning to Saudi Arabia, I resolved to take short breaks in the UK, paying for my own flights rather than working a full year again. On one trip, in June 1980, I met Linda, a friend of the people who I'd bought my house from. Our evening out went well and we resolved to keep in touch by letter and perhaps meet up again on my next trip home. How prophetic that arrangement would be.

Fast forward to Christmas 1980. I looked forward to a pleasant, relaxing holiday season with my family, having spent the previous two Christmases abroad. I met up again with Linda for a lunchtime drink a couple of days after I got back. Within a week, I had fallen head over heels in love with her. Within two, I'd asked her to marry me; amazingly, she said yes. By the end of the third and final week of my holiday, we had bought engagement rings and set a date for the wedding.

I left for Saudi once more, resolving to work through until the next September when I would leave Aramco for good, and return for the wedding and our married life together. It only took a few days to realise I'd been mistaken in thinking I could settle back into life and work in Saudi as if nothing had changed. I went out to the Middle East for the experience, both personal and career-wise. The money was good, but it had never been the main factor. Now I had something, no, somebody, much more valuable. I missed her, and no amount of money could make that worthwhile. After a couple of weeks, I wrote telling Linda how I felt, and she replied that she felt the same but hadn't wanted to tell me; it had to be my decision.

Dhahran or Derby, loneliness or Linda?

No contest!

I handed in my resignation, worked my notice, and left Saudi Arabia behind for good in March 1981. In October, we were married in Mackworth and honeymooned in Los Angeles, Hawaii and San Francisco. Our son, Andrew, was born a year later and our daughter Catherine in 1985. We've continued to live in Derby, while my subsequent career has taken me to the less exotic climes of Birmingham, Chesterfield, Coventry and Nottingham.

It was difficult packing in my job and moving thousands of miles away from everyone I knew. But my time in Saudi Arabia gave me confidence and valuable work experience, great memories, and introduced me to people I'm proud to call my friends and stay in touch with even 30 years on. It led to me meeting Linda, and to marriage and family.

Yes, the hardest decision; but also the best decision I ever made.

In the Department of Poetry

Our paths may cross again, they may not. But I wish you success for the future. I don't think you are a person who is easily defeated through life as you are by nature a peacock which shows at times its beautiful feathers.
MARGARETHA DEN BROEDEN

In the Department of Poetry something is stirring:
it is a rare bird shitting on a heap of certificates.
He bears the beautiful plumage of a rebel,
flying through the rigid corridors,
the stifling pall of academic twaddle.
He pecks at the Masters' eggheads,
scratches pretty patterns along the cold walls of poetic power.
He cares not a jot for their fancy Awards,
their sycophantic perambulations,
degrees of literary incest.
These trophies for nepotism
pass this peculiar bird by
as he soars
high
above the paper quadrangle,
circling over the dying Heads of Culture,
singing sweet revolutionary songs,

showing off

his brilliant wings

that fly him
into the ecstasy
of a poem.

How Many Genii Does it Take to Change a Light Source?

We are standing on the shoulders of giants

Who are themselves
Standing on the shoulders of giants

Back through the generations of giants
Like a huge acrobatic pyramid

Eventually

The whole of humanity
Will reach up to the stars

Take the sun out of its socket
And insert a new one

Wild Bill's Celestial Jazz

for Wild Bill Davison 1906–1989

...no harder-driving, or more masculine, cornet in the entire business.
EDDIE CONDON

Born in Defiance (that's geographical as well as literal)
wailing b flat into a life of lust and vice

that your appetites craved until the grave —
a bolshie enough bastard to take such a calling further.

And should such a place exist and you had entered there
via some loophole or celestial, administrative balls-up

(or maybe God called you to teach Joshua a thing or two)
then I'd fear for His angels: any with cocks

would be seduced into joining you on a frenzied bacchanal;
any in a frock had best watch her tits and crotch.

No doubt angels are inclined to forgive. And so they should;
their brass would only sound sweeter fuelled by such ferocity.

And all the Blessèd tapping their feet as your thunder
blew over your home. *Wild Bill*, they'd say. *Defiant in death.*

The Goods

Well, since we're talking bass players and the like, let me tell you about Gamp and Harris. Not their real names, by the way, but what they were called on the circuit. You're from out of town, so I guess you won't know about them. No, I thought not. Which means that you won't have heard them in action. A pity, that, a great pity, you being a bass man yourself. Yeh, you'll get to spell ours, no problem. Buy him a pint and he'll probably let you have the whole of the middle set. I take it you wouldn't object? Still, no need to be this early to take a claim. I mean, I prefer getting one or two down before the music starts, sort of anaesthetises the pain, but it's not like old times, if you know what I mean. Back in the day even local groups could fill a place. And if it was a London band, it was be there for opening time or don't bother. But not now. I mean look around. Half an hour to curtain up and the place is still empty. No, I'm always first in. The rest of the outfit will be along soon as they've ironed their trusses.

Yes, right. I'm on trombone. As you so rightly observe, the case is a give away. Used to play a bit with Gamp and Harris, *if* we could get them. Looked forward to those occasions, everyone did, they gave any band they played with a lift. I'm not saying they were world bearers. Not Walter Page and Philly-Jo. Not even nationally known, though more than a few of us reckon they should have been. They could have shown the way to some of the Mr Bigs from down London.

Like? Well, for instance like … No, better not. No names, no pack drill. Let's just say that either of them was an asset to any band you'd care to hear, and not just on a wet Monday night in Arnold. But put them together, as they always liked to be, and then you'd got something special. One plus one makes four.

Yes, *of course* they should have been better known. But they didn't like to travel, simple as that. Well, to be straight, Harry wouldn't have minded, but Dave said no. And his thumbs-down put the kibosh on gigs far from home.

Anyway, to fill you in. Harry Silver played bass, Dave Gams was a drummer, and like most semi-pros they hung on to the day job. Harry cut hair in the Gents Saloon run by an old mate from army days. *CLEAN CUT* it was called. Original or what? But as Harry said, it took care of the bills.

Dave was his own boss. A bits and pieces man. Ran errands for anyone who'd pay him to ferry goods from pillar to post. In heavy demand, too, and he kept his van spotless, engine always in good nick, gears smooth as a Buck Clayton lick, up early and out; but by the end of each and every day he'd had enough of driving. That's why they only ever did gigs in and around the city. The van wasn't going anywhere that Dave didn't want to go, and he didn't want to go more than ten miles from home, fifteen at most and then only for what my old ma would have called a king's ransom. So after a while band leaders out of Nottingham stopped bothering. Goodnight Vienna, I mean. There's always someone else to hire.

You'd see Dave's van about town any day of the week. *GAMS HOME DELIVERIES*. Dave got the lettering done professionally. Black and white. Very tasty, he reckoned. *GAMS HOME DELIVERIES*. That's how they got to be called Harris and Gamp. Mr Gamp, someone started calling Dave. Very droll. Get it? Gamp — home deliveries? OK. And then, because he and Harry were mates who always used Dave's van to get to gigs, Harry became Mr. Harris.

If they minded they never said so. They may not even have got the joke, not until it was explained to them, and anyway they like jokes. Well, some of them. Yes, it's true, drummers do get picked on. *Who do drummers like to hang out with? Musicians* — that kind of thing. Bass players have it earlier, though apparently not in the world of "classical" music — what we used to call Longhair, where the musicians all went to college and learned to hold their sheet music the right way up. You've probably heard the one about the convert where the orchestra takes an interval break and the leader of the second violins discovers the bass player huddled in a corner. What's up? "The oboist untuned one of my strings," the bass player tells him. "Well, re-tune it." "But he won't tell me which one it is." Yes, a banjo joke in the jazz world, I know, I know. Old as pre-electric records.

Old jokes didn't worry Gamp and Harris. The older, the better. Harry told jokes while he cut hair. Any road, he told the one. You must have heard it, though no doubt the name of the place would have been changed. Anyway, in Harry's version some bloke goes into the barber's in Sandiacre. "I want my hair but like Frank Sinatra," he tells the barber. "Can you manage that?" "Certainly, sir," the barber says. "Take a seat. We'll soon have you looking the very image of Ol' Blue Eyes." So the bloke sits down, sheet's tucked round him, out comes the scissors, snip, snip, snip, snip. Ten minutes go by and then the barber says, "Right, job done, and to your satisfaction I trust," handing the client a mirror. Client takes one look and yells "That's not how Frank Sinatra has his hair cut." "It is when he comes here," the barber says.

Harry must have told that plenty of times between nine to five while he was making with the short back and sides. And Dave, he was quick with the chat. Always had a line to offer the ladies. Bringing in a chair or table he's carted over from an antique shop. "Any other way I can service you, I mean be of service. If you think of something, give me a bell and I'm all yours."

Whether he got anything out of it I doubt, but I never heard that anyone took offence. Anyway, unlike Harry, Dave wasn't married. Harry's wife, Enid, now she was a lovely lady. Used to sing a bit with various groups, especially if Harry and Dave were on stand, but then she retired from what she called the high life of Mansfield Working Men's Club and took part-time work as a barwoman. Always well turned out, and she'd still sometimes be with them on a gig, sing a couple, *Summertime*, *Ghost of a Chance*, say, but eventually she packed it in. Reckoned her voice couldn't stand the pace. Stayed loyal to the bar work, though.

Like I say, Dave wasn't married. Didn't even have a steady woman, just the one-nighters or, as someone said, the one-afternooners. If that. 'Course, you heard rumours. But as I say I doubt Dave was the gigolo some claimed. Not that the image did him any harm and off stand he was the one who always got the ladies' attention. Bit of a natty dresser, smiled a lot, never without a word, whereas Harry tended to keep the lip buttoned.

But on stand it was all change. Depending on the music, Harry could do you Papa Slow Drag, a more-than-passable imitation of Blanton, and, when the mood took him, shut your eyes and you'd swear you were listening to Slam Stewart. You don't often hear bass players being applauded, do you? Well, you'd know. But they'd put their hands together for Harry, *and* without being asked.

Now here's a funny thing. Take a deep breath. Dave was the reverse. Mr Invisible. What, I hear you ask, a drummer dodging the limelight? Difficult to credit, I'll grant you, but it's true. Never went further than an eight-bar break. Apart from that he handled the traps so you didn't know he was there until he stopped playing. *Then* you noticed. He was ace on brushes. Lovely light touch. Harris and Gamp. I tell you, together they were the best round here by a long chalk, they really were. Anyone starting a band wanted those two.

Mind, Harry had a bit of back problem. Someone wondered whether that came from leaning over to whisper in a customer's ear. You know, "something for the weekend," or "a little bird told me about a cert for the 2.15 at Haydock Park." But Harry said, no. It was an occupational hazard of bass players. Being on your legs for hours at a time, leaning at an odd angle to get at the strings.

Yes, thanks. Just a half.

Well, all musos have their problems. With guitarists it's arthritic fingers, which can also get to keyboard players. Brass, the lip goes. Reeds are OK but there are other deficiencies. You know the old joke about the salesman in the bar who could talk to anyone on their own level? Taps one bloke on the shoulder. Can I ask your IQ? 200. No sweat. Ten minutes on astrophysics, giving as good as he gets. Tries the next bloke. 150. So they talk geo-politics. Then he asks a third. "My IQ is 35," he's told. "That so?" the salesman says. "So what reeds do you use?"

It depends on who's telling the joke, of course. But you wouldn't do a take-down joke about bass-players or drummers, not to Harris and Gamp, you wouldn't. Well out of order. Not that they came on as prima donnas. Not a bit of it. Solid citizens, the pair of them. Always on time, dressed to rules, whether it was black-and-white job or scuff order, and *never* drink taken. I mean, some musos are on the wild side. And not just because of the booze or nose powder. It seems to go with the territory. Knives, for instance. Mingus, Dizzy Gillespie in his younger days. He carried a knife, did you know that?

No, can't say I've come across anyone wielding steel in these parts, but guns, yes. When the lads came back after 1945 there were plenty of service revolvers came with them. And of course Bechet was a hero. *Les Oignons, The Fish Seller, Petite Fleur*. You wouldn't get through an evening without playing at least one of them. He'd been deported from England in the early

20s, as I expect you know, then Germany. They put him on trial in 1929, Frankfurt, I think it was, for perforating a pianist's kneecap. His defence — defence mark you — was that he'd been aiming at the banjoist. Ah, banjoist jokes. What's the difference between a chiropodist and a banjoist? A chiropodist bucks up the feet.

Sure, there are still a few wild men in England, not as many as in Scotland, it's true. Find yourself on the receiving end of a Glasgow kiss and it can take weeks before your lip heals. You don't get that here, not in good old Nottingham, though I've seen a couple with guns in their waistbands, fantasists dreaming that Bulwell is Basin Street. One was up from Kent. Claimed Chatham Dockyard was like the waterfront down in Delta City. Dream on! Dapper Dan he was called, loosed off his shooter one night outside his local right after a gig, and all the shop alarms on the Queen's Road started up like it was early closing in Hell. By the time the old Bill came looking we had him wedged under a bar table but next day Dapper Dan was strongly advised to return to from whence he came. He's back here now, I'm told, but minus the shooter.

Harris and Gamp were on that particular gig, guesting, helping to put bums on seats. In fact it was Dave's kit, heaped round the table, that kept Dapper Dan from the prying eyes of the boys in blue.

Harris and Gamp. They'd play with any band, never bother too much about the money, they loved playing.

Well, there was an exception, one outfit they avoided if they could — we all did. You won't have heard of Ron Wardell, will you? Trumpet man. No, well, good, keep it that way. The emphasis is on second syllable. War*dell*. Known locally as Ron Wardell and His Music from Hell. It was, too. R.W. could only play in two keys: B flat and F. "Play" is a bit of an over-statement, by the way, like calling the Gobi Desert a deepwater lake.

No, it's my shout. Landlord? Same again, please.

Where was I? Oh, yes. R.W. But if he was *that* bad, you're no doubt wondering, how come he got any work? Undercutting others, that's how. He was a crafty sod, I'll say that for him. Soon as he heard of a new place opening up he'd be round to see the manager. "Have you hired a band yet? Really? How much you paying them? That's too much. They're robbing you blind. Tell you what, I'll put in a group for £50 less." That's how R.W. got the jobs. It usually meant that opening night coincided with closing night. Sometimes it didn't even take *that* long. One of the lads reckons that the record for R.W. being invited to sling his hook was half-an-hour, by which time most of the punter had left, those who hadn't been forewarned, that is. The latter were the lucky ones, took an evening off, put their feet up and spent a few hours in front of the telly. Some used to wonder how the old bugger was able to get away with it for so long. I put it down to the greed and stupidity of managers, plus a muso or two in need of money who could actually play, as a result of which R.W.'s band would occasionally sound only a bit south of bloody awful.

Anyway, to get to the point. One night R.W. was booked to open at a pub some way out of town. For once he'd managed to put together a decent line-up, himself excepted, but there was a little problem. The drummer and bass player were coming down from Sunderland. R.W. hadn't asked Harris and Gamp, he knew they'd say no, but then everyone else local turned him down. Drummers discovered a subsequent engagement or were off for a month to bury an old grannie in Utrecht, bass players he tried were sorry but, would you credit it, the instrument was in for long-term repair, and no, it was impossible to borrow one.

Luckily for R.W., his reputation hadn't yet spread to Sunderland. Maybe it was stopped at the Humber, put into quarantine, I don't know. Anyway, the Agency he went through had had word there were musos up there gagging for work, so they got on the blower and managed to reel in two-thirds of a rhythm section from what was known to be a decent group.

But then, half an hour before starters' orders, the pub fields a phone call. There's been a crash on the M1, traffic backed up, nothing moving and won't be for several hours. You can kiss goodbye to the men from Sunderland making the gig.

So what does R.W. do? Of course! Puts out a May Day call to Harris and Gamp. He tries Dave's place first. After all, Dave's the wheels. No answer. OK, Harry's up next. Enid answers. She's in a hurry, she tells him, works on a Tuesday night, or had he forgotten. But anyway she can't be doing with his pestering her. "They're on your gig or had you forgotten that, too? They left there an hour ago which means they'll be with you in the next few minutes." And with that she slams the phone down.

Well, R.W., who everyone reckons is a few bricks short of a load, though not when it comes to muscling in on someone else's gig, at first thinks thank god for that. We'll be OK. Job saved.

But then it comes to him. An hour earlier Harris and Gamp couldn't have known they'd be wanted for the gig. As far as they and anyone else knew, it was Sunderland to the rescue. So what's going on?

The question must have been agitating both halves of his one working brain cell an hour later when there was still no sign of Harris and Gamp, and the management, having listened to the band, such as it was — and there's not much you can do with three front-line and a guitarist, especially if the trumpet lead sounds like a bullfrog with the runs — had given R.W. his marching orders. R.W. always maintained that if he'd had a full rhythm section that night he'd have got a regular booking. And Russ Conway is Teddy Wilson.

Of course, the story of what happened or rather *didn't* happen that night got around. It was bound to. But here's the funny thing. Neither of Harris or Gamp said anything, wouldn't so much as mention it. Not a peep, nothing. Schtumm. Silent as the grave they were.

A bit weird, that. At first some of us tried asking, but we soon gave up. They'd shrug and turn away, or just stare at you. I mean, there's only so many times you can stand to get what Benny Goodman's sidemen used to call "the ray," you know, the look he sent someone who hit a bum note or missed an intro. Not well-loved, Goodman. You hear the one about two musos who bumped into one another on Broadway, and one asks the other "You want the good news or the bad?" "The good." "Benny Goodman's dead." "So what's the bad news?" "He died peacefully."

But we all liked Harris and Gamp. They were good mates with most of us. That was what made it odd. Why the looks? The heavy silences? There were those that reckoned Enid was covering up for Harry. He was there all the time and she knew he wouldn't want to spend an evening in R.W.'s company. But that doesn't explain why Dave didn't answer *his* phone. Well, he could have been out, though if so it wasn't on any other gig, because that night, as it happened, there weren't any other gigs, not in our area, and like I say, Dave never travelled. If the job wasn't on his doorstep, so to speak, he wasn't prepared to take it.

Makes you wonder, doesn't it? Someone dropped a rumour that the two were involved in some dodgy deal. Liberating metal for scrap, say, or disposing of smokes or booze they'd come by from a parked-up trailer. There was a lot of that going on at the time. But it didn't seem likely. Harry in particular was Mr Reliable, and not only at four-to-the-bar. He was an honest man, I'm sure of that. It's possible that Dave didn't always ask many questions about the goods he was carrying, but I'm positive Harry kept his own nose clean and I don't see Dave risking anything, not with Harry alongside.

Do I have an explanation? No, I don't, that's for sure. There *was* a whisper that maybe Harry and Dave were a bit, you know, that way inclined, and that they'd crept off to some hotel or were parked up in a lay-by for a spot of how's your father. Not that it makes any odds. I mean, what counts is the music, and, like I say, those two were ace.

Yes, the past tense. You noticed. The fact is that Dave died a few years ago, got his van smashed into by some dozy truck driver who'd been on the road for too many hours and gone to sleep at the wheel. After that, Harry never played again. End of Harris and Gamp.

Did we try to get him back on stand? You bet we did. You can't afford to be doing without a bass player like Harry. He was quality. I know for a fact several outfits offered him top dollar, but no dice, he wouldn't be tempted. Said his back was too bad. The last I heard, he and Enid had left town. Someone said that their marriage had gone downhill, she'd been seen with one of the bar staff at the place she worked evenings, but I wouldn't know. I only know that he was a damn good bass player. As Dave was a damn good drummer. Right out of the ordinary, those two, top drawer.

The goods? Yes, I like it. They were the goods, alright. I'll drink to that.

Solti in Nottingham

It was 1982 and I couldn't believe my luck! Sir Georg Solti, the world's most famous conductor (after Herbert von Karajan), was coming with the London Philharmonic Orchestra to open Nottingham's Royal Concert Hall.

Glittering like a Cubist Christmas tree along South Sherwood Street, the twelve million pound venue was the jewel in the crown of Nottingham's revamped cultural centre. Grafted onto the recently refurbished Theatre Royal and freighted with international aspirations, this prestigious European-style concert hall clearly had to produce an artistic roster of commensurate quality, with Solti blazing the trail.

As music director of the Chicago Symphony Orchestra and a regular guest maestro at the Vienna Philharmonic, it seemed inconceivable that such a remote figure should ever appear in the East Midlands of England. But Solti's recent appointment as chief conductor of the London Philharmonic — an orchestra used to touring provincial UK locales and a regular visitor to Nottingham — meant sooner or later he would appear in the city. Flyers and posters advertising the event were widely distributed well in advance while Pearson's record department had Solti posters and album covers displayed throughout the store.

I wasted no time in securing a ticket and managed to get an excellent seat high up in the one of the side balconies with a clear view of both the platform and the striking, hexagonal construction of the hall's interior, inspired no doubt by the vineyard configuration of Berlin's Philharmonie (perhaps Karajan would be next, I wondered).

But for now, Solti was topping the bill and Beethoven's mighty *Eroica* symphony the main part of the concert. Striding briskly onto the podium, Solti got straight down to business. Following a curt bow to the audience he spun round and with a spiky, combative jab of his baton, brought Beethoven's vision of symphonic grandeur vividly to life. At nearly 70, Solti remained an electrifying presence and conducted the 50 minute masterpiece with a spry alertness and natural command that belied his years. The LPO played with a brilliance and polish normally associated with a big American orchestra, meriting a standing, cheering ovation from a clearly appreciative

Nottingham audience. The Royal Centre had arrived!

After the concert I was allowed to see Solti in his dressing room to get an autograph. Up close, he bore a striking resemblance to Ray Harryhausen's Triceratops from *One Million Years BC* but remained as spiky and determined as he had been on the podium.

I thanked him for the concert and asked him if he was going to record the *Eroica*.

"YES!!! I HAVE ALREADY DONE IT MIT MY ORKESTER IN CHICAGO! ADD IT TO YOUR COLLEKSHUN!" came the deafening reply.

I then ventured that I was trying my hand at conducting myself and — if he didn't mind my asking — was there any special advice he could give for a beginner such as I. He promptly picked up his baton, drew the 4/4 sign forcibly in the air and announced: "VUN, TWO, STHREE and a FOUR. THE REST IS UP TO YOOOOU!!!"

I let a silence pass and then said the only thing I could: "Can I have your autograph, please?" Whereupon he brandished a huge marker pen and practically drilled a hole through the frontispiece of my programme book. Like the title page of Beethoven's *Eroica*, the hole can still be seen today ...

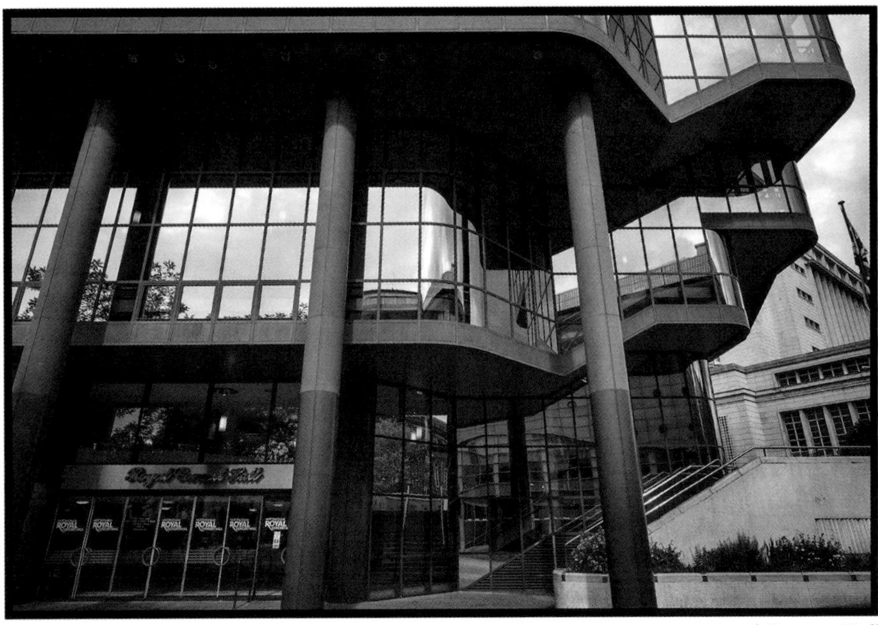

Royal Concert Hall

Sketching in Beeston

I recognised her at once,
she was even smiling as she sat down,
ordered coffee and a Danish pastry,
looked around,
for a moment holding my gaze.

The waitress brought her drink,
her glazed swirl of pastry.
I watched her eat in silence
and waited several minutes
before I began to sketch again,

her oval face,
dark, shoulder-length hair
with the centre parting,
her hands resting in her lap.

I propped a menu card in front of me,
to hide what I was doing,
had almost finished
when suddenly she stood up,
came across to my table.
She sat down,
still with that enigmatic smile.

"I hope it's a good likeness," she said.
"It's probably been done better," I replied.

A Writer Visits

i.m. Alan Sillitoe

He was one of the easiest.
No demands.
Easy to find
with the aid of
a studio photo
that didn't take off 20 years
and easily visible, mainly
because of his *hat.*

He always spoke well.
There were no *requests* —
for a separate room,
a particular wine, a hairdryer,
Rennies, silence.
Just a bar with a pint
if convenient, and questions,
from *him* about *us.*

There was, however, *the pipe.*
No concessions.
At the sound-check
a fixed steely eye
beneath the alarmingly
prominent 'no smoking' signs.
A simple equation —
this would be about *him.*

He missed herding the sheep.
Couldn't come.
Being a freeman and having the right
to lead all those sheep (well that one)
right over Trent Bridge. No mind.
Strikes me he was already
a pretty free man and not much
of a one for   *sheep.*

Lost Again: a Letter to Mr Sillitoe

Dear Alan,

I'm in good company between these pages. But do I have a right to be here?

I'm not in any way suggesting it's presumptuous of me to button-hole you; to give you, whether you want it or not, when you can't shut me up, when you can't answer back, a piece of my, for what it's worth, mind.

That's not my nature.

I'd like to think I might be related (however distantly) to them Nottingham lambs, "the city's traditional roughs" you called them, revolting anti-authoritarian plebs who slugged it out in the Old Market Square for whichever side would fill them with sufficient gin and who burnt down the Castle when the toff who lorded it over them voted against Reform.

I might be related: mentally, I mean, not physically; aspirationally perhaps, not actually; mouthily certainly, not muscley obviously.

Yet I will admit to being somewhat over-awed, in these pages, assembled in your honour. Because you mean so much to us. You know you do. How can I forget when I was a young lad reading one of your tales (naturally I can't remember which one) when your first-person cyclist looks over the Trent valley spread out before him from the summit of ... Carlton Hill! You weren't just telling a story set in our home town. You were giving international endorsement to my own suburb! Between covers! Of a book! From a library!

You must know what that did for us. Because something similar happened to you when you were a young lad coming up against Lawrence writing about Ilkeston. You'd been there before us, paving the way.

Not much to succour us in them days. Not even a regional TV franchise. The Queen of the Midlands was but a remote eastern antennal adjunctive outpost of Associated Television. We had to suffer the ignominy of Midlands Parade! No-budget adverts for corner shops; carpet warehouses; late-night chemists in West Bromwich, Sutton Coldfield and Walsall. Places remote from us as West Germany, South Korea and Warsaw.

No wonder we were so fixated on our local legend who put us on the map. When, in the wonderful Errol Flynn movie, revolting anti-authoritarian peasants whisper: "Meet Robin at the Major Oak in Sherwood. Pass it on!", I considered that ordinance as the very burden of my responsibility. Now and forever. And later, much later, when the penny finally dropped that the series which had been my founding fiction as a child, was pseudonymously penned by blacklisted reds, I finally got the picture. No wonder Robin Hood was my first political role model. Now and forever.

But into that miasma of marginal geographical neglect, there was a writer from our city; a writer who'd created a character to give a face to what you call "the brash self-confidence" of Nottingham, our "idiosyncratic and independent" spirit.

Alan, your work validated us. Your success granted us existence.

It's not like that round here now, of course. These days if you play tin-can-lurgy in the streets of Forest Fields or Carrington chances are you'll bruise the shins of some passing short-listed, prize-winning author. NG is getting like LA where every waiter has a screenplay that will never get out of development.

I remember seeing you wearing a black trench-coat. You looked really sinister. How I always wanted you to look. The next week I went out and bought a mac just like yours. But I stopped short at the facial hair.

That was the night in the Council House when you were given the keys to our kingdom, conferring upon you the ancient right to drive sheep across Trent Bridge. Must have been wonderful for a prophet to be honoured on his own patch at last, eh?

So do I have a right to be here?

Whenever I open one of your books I'm faced with an intimidating bibliographical catalogue of works that I've haven't read — not read yet. But there is one volume that's always on my bedside table and into which I continually dip, probably a work you might have thought ephemeral, occasional. It's a travel book. I'd like to get round to catching up on your Russian trips one of these good old days. But this is closer to home. This is a book I like for the photographs taken by your son David (perfectly capturing the heavy skies and monochrome of those surroundings we affect and strain and pretend to love so much) as well as for your deceptive prose: an apparent simplicity masking a complexity of thought, an ambiguity of feeling about who you are and where you come from. You're talking to me directly in *Alan Sillitoe's Nottinghamshire*.

What an achievement to be so topographically associated. Like Dickens's London, Hardy's Wessex, Lawrence's Erewash ... Catherine Cookson country.

Now do I have a right to be here?

We have so little in common. You were west and we were east. Me dad were Plessey and me mam were Players (remember what they used to say: "All the world's an ashtray and men and women merely players.") Your lot were Raleigh and Sturmey Archer. Our side moved out from Sneinton and St Ann's to Bakersfield and Carlton. Your side would've moved out from Radford to Bilborough and Strelley. Your angry young man's Arthur Seaton. My peaceful old man's Arthur Eaton. A universe of characterological difference in that one missing consonant. The west side called each other "yoth" and "blue" and "serry". In the east it was "duck" and "chicken" and sometimes even, I regret to admit, "sausage".

Well, everyone says "duck".

I spent years at university explaining to lovely chums educated at the likes of Cheltenham Ladies College that this is an ungendered non-sexist term applied indiscriminately to one and all, young and old, male and female. And besides, I can't help it. It's the defining addication of where I come from. But that, of course, was before I learned that our favourite appellation was derived, not from the farmyard, but from the Old Norse *dokke* which means, I'm sorry to say, doll. Perhaps it *is* misogynist after all, me duck.

So little in common. I've never known what it's like to do a moonlight flit: "Always" as you put it "one turn of the handcart wheels ahead of the rent man's flat feet." I never lived through a world war; never saw service against insurgents in Malaya, never entered the inside of a TB ward. But we both name characters after Notts villages: you have a fictional town and me a fictional university of Ashfield: too resonant a monochromatic place name not to purloin.

But perhaps the greatest difference between us is that I came back to live here and, for my terrible transgressions, whatever they might be, I stayed. Twenty five years on Dog End Alley within the sound of Little John's bells. You wrote: "I haven't lived in Nottingham since I was eighteen, and only left it to find to find out what was beyond, not because I disliked it." How could I ever blame you for going? I keep trying to leave for that great beyond; I keep getting dragged back somehow.

Living in Nottingham is like living in a castle — you're constantly in a state of siege. The first time you get broken into the insurance people insist you install a burglar alarm; next internal door locks; then bars on all the downstairs windows; after that electronic gates whose pin number you struggle to summon into consciousness when you weave your way home off the tram with one or two too many inside. All this or they won't pay up the next time (because there's always going to be a next time). Your pockets jangle with a fat bunch of keys. You've become your own jailer.

We've had the lot in the last quarter of a century. That Peeping Tom who stalked our daughter. Nearly caught in the act once. I chased him down the street waving a stick but he had a bike and eluded me. The copper who turned up — eventually — asked, "What would you have done if you'd caught him?"

I didn't have a clue.

"I'll give you a tip. If it does happen again and you do catch the bastard, make sure you drag him back across your property line before you have a go, sir."

That pretty little arsonist, always wide-eyed at the front of the crowd when the fire brigade's siren screamed down Forest Road to douse her conflagrations in yet another abandoned garage.

Then, after reading Rupert stories to my grandson, I'd be out checking for empty syringes and filled toggies (found one yesterday as it happens, for the first time in some while, somebody's trip down memory lane, certainly not mine) before I'd feel safe to let him and his chums out to play in the yard. Where we live might locally be known as 'The Green' but, believe me, it's nowt like Nutwood. Did Mister Bear in his plus-fours have to avoid the solicitations of whores as he walked back from delivering his young cub to nursery? I can't remember reading 'Rupert and the Call Girls'.

The last break-in but one was really quite memorable. Coming back from town in the early afternoon, I saw a police car parked outside and found my wife at home, unexpectedly called away from her work as a community midwife in the Meadows. This time the cack-handed burglar had smashed through the double-glazing, instantly setting off the insurance-demanded alarm. One of my lovely neighbours had called it in (strong bonds are forged in adversity by those of us who persist in occupying Dog End Alley for more than a season). So the gonif had only had time to nick the video and DVD before legging it. I came in to hear my dear wife shout with some urgency, amazement even in her usually unflappable Australian voice: "Come and look at this!" What fresh horror could this unwelcome guest have violated upon our happy home? The telly he'd not had time to steal was on and together we watched a replay of the second hi-jacked plane smashing into the World Trade Centre, putting our trivial loss into some kind of global perspective.

Folk who think they know the likes of us have the nerve to say: You're a writer; it's all material; experiences to be carved out of this bitter inner-city ground, as your grandfather once mined coal from Gedling pit. But these are not my kind of tales!

When I was living in Gotham City (Washington Irving, who visited our county, came up with that name for New York from stories he'd heard of a Nottinghamshire village because he considered his fellow Manhattanites to be, like the Wise Men of Gotham, a parcel of fools), I'd be walking along 14th Street, the wind-chill factor off the Hudson River freezing snot to my cheeks, colder than Nanook of the North's mother-in-law, when suddenly in my frozen imagination I'd find myself walking across Slab Square, echoes of the string trio drifting from Yates's, scraping an out-of-tune semblance of Kettelby's *In a Persian Market*. Back again. Home sick.

These days, I'll be on those yellow sands of Mooloolaba, screwing my weak northern eyes up against the chiselling sunlight of the southern hemisphere, watching container ships out beyond the crashing surf of the Pacific, exporting mineral wealth to the new world power in China (dug from the Australian earth today as my ancestors mined the black wealth that once lay beneath our feet), hotter than a dead dingo's donger, drier than a pommy's shower curtain, when suddenly my sweating imagination is drawn back to Alfreton Road, incapable of escape, lost again in Nottingham.

Was that how it was for you in Majorca, Alan? Channeling factories and twitchells from the world of your childhood where you could, as you so memorably put it, "outdream everybody". Streets all lost now, together with what you also called their "irreplaceable spirit".

In your words: "I may be harping too much on the past but in my view the greatest mistake a writer can make is to look more to the future than to the past. A writer who poses as a prophet ends by confusing his soul, and confounding the souls of those who are tempted to listen. Art is confirmation, not affirmation."

I'm definitely with you on the prophets. Spare us, please, from bare-faced messiahs who have the gall to use their stage to preach what they don't know, what we don't need to know. But I'm not so convinced by your "confirmation" angle.

I guess I've got used to gaining comfort from a lack of security; footfalls disappearing, as on those elusive paths you attempted to negotiate on your walk along the banks of the Trent in *your* Nottinghamshire. I'm anxious lest it might feel even more destabilising were I to find my feet treading upon solid ground.

Again you say: "I feel that the more memories you have the deeper you can dive down into yourself. The danger is that you'll get stuck in the mud or weeds, unable to come up, strike air, and go on living to create more memories."

And I say: every crossword solver knows 'lost again' is an anagram of 'nostalgia': a word that means 'home sickness'. As for myself, I'm nostalgic always and already sick for a city always disappearing from view before my eye can get it into focus. Sick for a home already slipping away before my fingers can grasp hold. A home you left to become yourself; a city you wrote into becoming.

I'll finish with a story that I *do* want to tell. Set not here, but down in your deracinated metropolis. I was at the Odeon Leicester Square for a film premiere (all right, it weren't me being papped on the red carpet). The after-gala do was in the sublime surrounds of the Battersea Power Station. A muddle in the middle of nowhere, way after midnight, dress code black tie, vodka (which you love) flowing freely. So I had to get a taxi back to my cheap B&B.

I took to the driver from the moment I got into his cab. I won't say his name because I don't know whether he'd want me to rattle away his family skeletons — though he knew I'm a writer so let the teller beware. I was his last fare and after he'd dropped me off in WC1 he was going back to Cheam, a comedy address known to the likes of us as the quondam residence of Anthony Aloysius St. John Hancock. As we drove along the embankment he asked me what film I'd seen that night: it was a new version of *Great Expectations*. (A book, I think, that was one of your favourites, Alan?)

He said: "Charles Dickens. I love that film — the old black and white one. David Lean. What's your favourite scene? There's one that means so much to me. The young lad..."

"Pip..."

"Yeah. He's come into money, hasn't he? Living the idle life in London. Then he gets a visit from the poor chap who'd brought him up in the country..."

"Joe Gargery, the blacksmith..."

"Yeah, yeah. And he's ashamed and embarrassed to see this man who loves him so much and who cared for him so well but Pip's become a snob treats him really badly ... later he realises what he's done and he feels terrible."

"It's one of the best moments in the book."

"I've never read the book. Perhaps I should. Because that scene means so much to me."

I wanted to know why.

By now we'd reached my temporary gaff in Bloomsbury. The driver turned off the meter and the two of us carried on jabbering together for the next three-quarters of an hour, exchanging secrets only strangers who know they're never going to see each other again can confide to one another.

He told me: "My old man was an alcoholic and me mother threw him out. One day I was coming out of school and I saw him ... across the street ... waiting for me in a long muddy coat, worn-out shoes, leaning on the railings, can in hand, swaying ... swaying. You know what I did? I put me head down and walked off the other way. Never forgot it. Never forgiven myself..."

A long pause. Then he said: "But it all comes around, don't it?"

"What do you mean, my friend?"

"I'm in this cab all hours, seven days a week so my son could get a place at the grammar school. He's a clever lad and had to pass the exam but we still have to pay. His friends have dads who are doctors, lawyers, stockbrokers ... That's how it is in Surrey. I asked him why he never brought any of them home. You know what he said? 'I can't bring them here. Why don't you get a bigger house?' Why don't I get a bigger house!"

This bastard country. Will some things never change?

We still have work to do. We must not get lost again. If I don't have a right to be here, then I don't know where I ought to be.

Dosvedanya, duck.

Yours sincerely,

Michael Eaton

No Further South is North

Daniel Defoe's modern reputation for creative journalism leaves the veracity of his three-volume travel guide *A Tour Thro' the Whole Island of Great Britain* (1724–27) open to debate. Exactly when he made his various 'circuits' of the nation is unknown. But whenever it was that he crossed the River Trent in Nottingham and headed north east towards Derbyshire and the Peak District, he was all too aware that he was entering a different kind of Britain. "Having Thus Passed the Rubicon" was how he put it, grandly comparing the Trent to the Italian river crossed by Caesar's army. In doing so, he defined a feeling and even a conviction that the Trent marks an important geographical and cultural border — the one between southern England and the rest of Britain, better known as the North. Since Nottingham is the largest urban settlement on the river this also suggests that Nottingham itself marks the true beginning of the North Country with all its truculent attitudes and speech patterns.

In modern times the idea that the Trent marks a border in the nation was stated at length by ardent Trentophile Peter Lord in *Portrait of the River Trent* (1968). Addressing the issue head on in a chapter titled 'The Great Divide', Lord said that the river was a line of cultural and geographic "demarcation and division" which even reaches down into the very rocks beneath one's feet. If you dig deep enough you will find coal on one side of the river and gypsum on the other. Getting into his stride, he goes on:

"On one side the Trent laps a land of Hereford cattle, Stilton cheese, Loughborough bells, Melton Mowbray pies and Quorn hunting pink; on the other it involves mills which have been spared the whole history of the factory age, tall chimneys, bellicose pot ovens, great cooling towers, slag heaps and spoil tips, children called 'bairns' and tea that is 'mashed', not made."

Although Wikipedia lists a handful of earlier historic and literary references to the Trent-as-border idea, there is in fact a fact a strong suggestion that the Trent was regarded as the great divide at the dawn of written history — in the Roman period and perhaps in the Iron Age which preceded the Roman invasion of Britain in AD43. According to the Roman historian

Tacitus, at the start of the winter of AD47 rebellious Britons took advantage of a change-of-command in the Roman army and fought to regain conquered territory. The incoming Roman governor, Ostorius Scapula, reacted quickly, defeated the rebels and then sought to calm the situation by disarming suspects south of a fortified line between the Severn and the Trent. Or the Severn and somewhere-or-other. The Latin sentence in question names the Severn (Sabrina) but the river Antona is unknown:

cunctaque castris Antonam et Sabrinam fluvios cohibere parat

In 1883 scholar Dr Henry Bradley stated that the Latin, as passed down from antiquity, was garbled and proposed that a single letter should be changed so that the first part of the sentence read *cunctaque cis Trisantonam.* Since *Trisantona* was believed to be the Roman name for the Trent it could now be said that the Roman army's early frontier ran diagonally across the country with the Trent at its northern terminus. Although there have been those who thought the Antona was perhaps the Avon (and, alarmingly, the modern Everyman's collected Tacitus edition names "the Avon and Severn") the proof of the frontier line appears still to exist in the 220-mile length of the Fosse Way which zooms from Axemouth in Devon to Lincoln and passes through Nottinghamshire as the A46. Indeed, near East Stoke, the Roman road came so close to the Trent that a bridge was built at a place called *Ad Pontem.* This early road, which bulldozed through tribal boundaries to connect legionary fortresses at each end, effectively marked a division across the new Roman province: conquered lands to the south and east; as-yet-unconquered tribal kingdoms to the north and west of the Trent.

While the Roman frontier across Britain would ultimately come to rest at Hadrian's Wall, the Severn-Trent frontier would continue to have relevance for settlements and military dispositions since, as successive Roman governors appreciated, it was north of this line that Britain's true hill and mountain country began. It was no accident that most Roman villas were crowded into the south and south east while very few were built in the Pennines where the soil and the people were less kind to Romans.

Defoe knew his Roman history and described in detail his travels along the Fosse Way and thus his likening of the Trent to the Rubicon had an added resonance which may have been intended. Twenty years after his travels were published, Bonnie Prince Charlie's army of Highlanders halted at the Trent, at Swarkestone Bridge in Derbyshire, and decided to return to Derby and ultimately to defeat at Culloden in Scotland. Thus, in 1745, the Trent marked the deepest penetration into England of the country's last invading army; a 'Rubicon' in a broader sense that in this case was not crossed, much to the appreciation of the Hanoverian regime and panicking Londoners.

Intriguingly, even before the Romans arrived in Britain the Trent seems to have marked a boundary between tribal identities and lifestyles. North of the river, starting in the Peak District, were the lands of the pugnacious hill-dwellers and Pennine clans — Brigante, as the Romans called them. South and east of the river, in east Nottinghamshire, Lincolnshire and Leicestershire, were the Corieltauvi who have been too casually written off as peace-loving farmers. Although this is unlikely given the bellicose tribal rivalry of Iron Age society, and because it fits too easily into the soft southerner/hard northerner stereotype, there were certainly differences between the two peoples. The Corieltauvi had gold and silver coins on which they named their rulers with Latin letters; the Brigantes had no coins at all. The Corieltauvi surrendered to the Romans; the Brigantes were invaded but never truly pacified.

This issue was also touched on by Peter Lord: "It is tempting to believe that the differences between people and cultures north and south of the river today are an echo of the division between Romanised Coritani [the earlier word for Corieltauvi] and independent Brigante." Yes, it is tempting. So is there any evidence that the Trent was regarded as a cultural border further back in prehistory? In his 2004 book *Trent Valley Landscapes: the Archaeology of 500,000 Years*, David Knight says that the river has always been a "natural physiographic divide between the uplands of the north and west and the lowlands of the south and east … its location at the interface between the high and lowland zone of Britain makes it unique among major English rivers." Trouble is, signs of any human existence along the river for most of the 100,000 year span since the Trent Valley took on its current form are rare.

Yet, as archaeologists learned in 2010, there was definitely a day at the end of the last Ice Age, around 13,000 years ago, when a group of late

Paleolithic hunter-gatherers made camp near the river and one individual sat down and expertly chipped away at lumps of flint to make small hunting tools. They could tell he or she had been sitting down because the bits of waste flint made a sitting-down shape between his (or her) legs where they had fallen to the ground. This remarkable sign of ancient individual human activity did not offer any evidence about the Trent as a social border in such distant times, but it's worth noting that the flint-knapping took place in an area now known as Farndon Fields, just south of Newark and to the immediate east of the Fosse Way, which was being dualled by the Highways Agency when the rare flint discovery was made. The Roman road followed the river, just as the hunter-gatherer group had done many centuries before, perhaps as they trailed herds of migrating reindeer. Since the flint was not local it may have been obtained or traded in from sources that were many miles away.

University of Nottingham art historian Nicholas Alfrey wasn't convinced that the river was considered to be a divide when he and colleague Stephen Daniels curated their *Trentside* exhibition at Djanogly Art Gallery in 2001. Alfrey certainly could not find paintings or photographs which illustrated the point. But, with 35 years living in Nottingham under his belt, Alfrey feels that it is north of the river that Britain's true North begins. "The north of England does have a different character but what gives it that character is the Pennines," he says. "In Derby you could be in a Midlands city but the moment you move just a few miles north Derby you're in the North. You feel it in your blood. And it's a tremendous feeling. The landscape changes. So when people say the Trent is the great divide I don't think they mean it literally and that on one bank is this and on one bank is that. Peter Lord does have these images — if you dig a hole on one side you get gypsum and black coal in the other, but that is just not true! And later on with the miners' strike the conflict was so different in Nottinghamshire than it was in Yorkshire that there was a feeling of the North and the Not-North, but that had nothing to do with the Trent."

Does the Trent-as-border idea have any relevance today when cultural differences are blurred by the internet and mass mobility? After all, a river is just a river and there are bridges across it. Peter Lord's description of the North also sounds dated now. Yet survey after survey tells us that a North-

South economic divide still exists in Britain. And within Nottingham itself the Trent is sometimes regarded as a border and even a barrier between communities on opposite banks.

Three examples. In his sometimes acidic 1977 booklet *Nottingham: a Guide*, John Sheffield says with disarming frankness that part of the appeal of West Bridgford was that the Trent acted as "a moat" which separated if from the "grimy industrialism" of the city, particularly The Meadows on the north bank. In 2007 a proposal to build a cycle bridge across the Trent between Beeston Rylands and Clifton was withdrawn because, according to a BBC report, some Beeston people feared it would lead to an increase in crime. In early 2015 another cycle bridge was proposed between Colwick and the more affluent Lady Bay. I interviewed people living on both sides of the river and while the idea was broadly supported by everybody, only in Lady Bay were fears expressed of thieves coming over from the north bank.

It is tempting, as Peter Lord would put it, to try to make all this fit into the ancient North-South divide template. But cities are more complicated than that and anyway Clifton is on the south bank of the Trent. Nevertheless, Nottingham is still a place of sharp divisions between areas of wealth and poverty, opportunities and their absence. Wherever one chooses to pinpoint the North-South divide, the river Trent — which rises in the Midlands then turns its back on the South to head for the Humber estuary — arguably still provides its Rubicon.

Contributors' Notes

Viv Apple left school at 14 to work in her father's garage and workshop (cf '*Feeler Gauge*'). She later became a primary school teacher, and has written poetry and prose from an early age. Her pamphlet, *Thinking it Over,* was published in 2009 and she has been widely published in magazines. Viv is currently Chair of Nottingham Poetry Society and Vice-President of Nottingham Writers' Club, where Alan Sillitoe was a member in the 1950s.

Dr Keith Armstrong was born in Newcastle upon Tyne and now resides in Whitley Bay. He is coordinator of the Northern Voices Community Projects creative writing and community publishing enterprise. He was awarded a doctorate in 2007 for his work on Newcastle writer Jack Common at the University of Durham where he received a BA Honours Degree in Sociology in 1995 and Masters Degree in 1998 for his studies on culture in the North East of England. His poetry has been extensively published in magazines such as New Statesman and Poetry Review as well as in the collections *Splinters* (2011) and *The Month of the Asparagus* (2011) and broadcast on radio and TV. He has performed his poetry throughout Britain and abroad. In his youth, he travelled to Paris and he has been making international cultural pilgrimages ever since.

Neil Astley is editor of Bloodaxe Books, which he founded in 1978. His books include novels, poetry collections and anthologies, most notably the Bloodaxe *Staying Alive* trilogy: *Staying Alive* (2002), *Being Alive* (2004) and *Being Human* (2011). He has published two novels, *The End of My Tether* (2002) which was shortlisted for the Whitbread First Novel Award, and *The Sheep Who Changed the World* (2005).

Alan Baker grew up in Newcastle-upon-Tyne, and has lived in Nottingham since 1985, where he is editor of poetry publisher Leafe Press. His latest poetry collections are *all this air and matter* (Oystercatcher) and *Whether* (KFS).

Ross Bradshaw runs Five Leaves Bookshop and its associated publishing firm, Five Leaves Publications, who recently reissued Alan Sillitoe's novel *The Open Door* under its Bromley House Editions imprint. Ross has lived in Nottingham since 1979 where he is involved in the local literature and political scene. His articles and reviews, and very occasional poems, have appeared in assorted labour movement, peace, Jewish and literary journals.

Brick is a cartoonist and comics creator. Short-listed for the MIND Book of the Year Award (2011), his last book is nominated for two Eisner Awards (2015). As John Stuart Clark, he is the author of two travel books and numerous adventure travel articles, short stories and comix crits.

Ian Brookes teaches at the Department of Culture, Film and Media at the University of Nottingham. His work on Alan Sillitoe includes '"All the Rest Is Propaganda": Reading the Paratexts of *Saturday Night and Sunday Morning*' in Adaptation: The Journal of Literature and Onscreen Studies 2:1 (2009), 17–33. He has also published work on American cinema in the Journal of Popular Film and Television and contributed several entries to *The Grove Dictionary of American Music* (OUP, 2013). He is currently working on a collected edition of essays on the American film director Howard Hawks and a study of film noir.

Derrick Buttress was born in Nottingham in 1932. He left school at 14, working in various factories until he took a degree at York University at the age of forty. His poems have been published widely in magazines. Several of his radio plays were broadcast by BBC Radio 4 and two television plays by BBC 2. Four poetry collections were published by Shoestring, including the latest, *Welcome to the Bike Factory*, 2014. A memoir, *Broxtowe Boy*, was published in 2004, also by Shoestring. Its sequel, *Music While You Work*, was published in 2007. A collection of short stories, *Sing to Me*, was published by Shoestring in 2012.

David Constantine is a Fellow of Queen's College, Oxford. His prolific writing career includes short fiction, a novel, translations, and ten collections of poetry. He is co-editor of the Oxford Poets imprint of Carcanet Press, and has been a chief judge for the T.S. Eliot Prize.

David Cooke was born in the UK but his family comes from the West of Ireland. He won a Gregory Award in 1977. His retrospective collection, *In the Distance*, was published in 2011 by Night Publishing. A new collection, *Work Horses,* was published by Ward Wood in 2012. His poems, translations and reviews have appeared widely in the UK, Ireland and beyond in journals such as Agenda, Ambit, The Bow Wow Shop, The Cortland Review, The Interpreter's House, The Irish Press, The London Magazine, Magma, The Morning Star, New Walk, The North, Poetry Ireland Review, Poetry Salzburg Review, The Reader, The SHOp and Stand. He has two collections forthcoming: *A Murmuration* (Two Rivers Press, 2015) and *After Hours* (Cultured Llama Press 2017).

Andy Croft has written and edited over 80 books, including poetry, biography, teenage non-fiction and children's fiction. Among his books of poetry are *Nowhere Special*, *Just as Blue*, *Great North*, *Comrade Laughter*, *Ghost Writer*, *Sticky*, *Three Men on the Metro* (with W.N. Herbert and Paul Summers) and *1948* (with Martin Rowson).Writing residencies include HMPs Holme House, Frankland, Moorland and Lindholme. He writes a regular poetry column for The Morning Star, curates the T-junction international poetry festival on Teesside and runs Smokestack Books. He lives in North Yorkshire.

Jeremy Duffield was Chair of Nottingham Poetry Society 1988–2014; and Treasurer NPS 1984–present. He has had two poetry collections published and has won several poetry competitions including Swanage Open, Lancaster Litfest Competition and Poetry Society Nonsense Poem Competition. He also won the Waterstones/Derby Telegraph Short Story Competition two years in succession; and has had his poem *The Hartington Hawker* set to music and recorded by 'Mills & Chimneys' folk band. Jeremy's plays have been performed at The Pomegranate Theatre in Chesterfield, and by local amateur dramatic groups as well as readings at Arts in the Bar events.

David Duncombe lives in Matlock. He was an English teacher, worked in Nigeria, and served in the Army and the RAF. He was headteacher of a

Derbyshire school. Besides drama and stories for radio and two novels for children, his poems have been widely published, including five collections. He was awarded a Hawthornden Fellowship and has won first prizes in several competitions.

Michael Eaton was born in Sherwood and studied Social Anthropology at King's College, Cambridge before becoming a dramatist working in film, television, radio and theatre. *Fellow Traveller*, about an exiled blacklisted Hollywood screenwriter writing a children's version of Robin Hood, won Best Screenplay at the British Film Awards in 1989. *Charlie Peace — His Amazing Life and Astounding Legend*, about the notorious 19th century portico thief and murderer, premiered at Nottingham Playhouse in 2013. His film *The Masks of Mer* concerned the making of the first ethnographic cinematographs by Alfred Haddon in the Torres Strait and was followed by a Radio Three drama *Head Hunters* in 2014. In 1999 he was awarded the MBE for Services to Film and was visiting Professor in the School of Creative Writing at Nottingham Trent University and has recently written a community drama for the 170th anniversary of the Nottingham School of Art.

Brett Evans lives, writes and drinks in his native north Wales. His poems have featured in UK and online journals such as Bare Fiction, Butcher's Dog, The Frogmore Papers, Ink Sweat & Tears, The Interpreter's House, Other Poetry, and Poetry Wales. He is a co-founder and co-editor of the prose and poetry journal Prole. Brett's debut poetry pamphlet, *The Devil's Tattoo*, was published by Indigo Dreams Publishing in 2015.

Ruth Fainlight was born in New York City, but has lived in England since the age of fifteen. She studied at Art College, lived for some years in France and Spain, and in 1958 married the writer Alan Sillitoe, who died in 2010. Ruth Fainlight has published thirteen collections of poems in England and the USA, as well as two volumes of short stories, and translations from Spanish and Portuguese. Her translation of Sophocles' *Theban Plays*, done in collaboration with Robert Littman, was published in 2009 by Johns Hopkins University Press, USA. Books of her own poems have appeared in

French, Italian, Portuguese, Romanian and Spanish translation. She received the Hawthornden and Cholmondeley Awards in 1994. Her 1997 collection, *Sugar-Paper Blue*, was shortlisted for the 1998 Whitbread Award. Her *New & Collected Poems* appeared in 2010. In 1985 & 1990 Ruth Fainlight was Poet in Residence at Vanderbilt University, Nashville, Tennessee, USA. She has served on the Council of The Poetry Society, is a member of the Society of Authors, and was appointed a Fellow of the Royal Society of Literature in 2007.

Carl Fellstrom is a freelance crime journalist who has contributed to *The Sunday Times, The Independent, The Guardian* and *Sunday Telegraph*. He has worked on Channel 4's *Dispatches* series and a number of BBC documentaries. He is also the author of *Hoods*, an expose of organised crime in the UK.

Martin Figura was born in Liverpool in 1956. He was recently described in a hospital referral letter (bad back) as "a pleasant 58 year old gentleman". His collection and show *Whistle* (Arrowhead Press) was shortlisted for the Ted Hughes Award and won the 2013 Saboteur Award for Best Spoken Word Show. He won the Poetry Society's 2010 Hamish Canham Prize. He's published two pamphlets with Nasty Little Press: *Arthur* and *Boring the Arse Off Young People.* He's now working on his new show and collection: *Dr Zeeman's Catastrophe Machine.* He lives in Norwich with his wife Helen Ivory. He works part-time at Norwich Writers' Centre and runs the monthly literature event Café Writers. www.martinfigura.co.uk.

Melvyn (Mel) Fisher was born in 1954 and lives in Littleover. Literally Derby born and bred — Boots in the Intu Centre stands where his parents' house in Bloom Street once was — his career in purchasing has encompassed diverse industries including transport, oil, nuclear, vehicle leasing, mobile phones, utilities and train building. He is currently in a senior Procurement role with a major global cash security company at their UK Head Office in Nottingham. Married with two children, his interests are Derby County (he is a longstanding and long-suffering season ticket holder), white knuckle rides (the higher and faster the better) and rediscovering his childhood love of superhero comics as they are turned into films. Mel has only three regrets: not being any good at golf, selling his comic collection to buy THAT cream coloured suit, and not getting to meet Brian Clough. He is often mistaken for Mel Gibson — not.

Neil Fulwood has published three film studies books: *The Films of Sam Peckinpah, 100 Violent Films that Changed Cinema* and *100 Sex Scenes that Changed Cinema*, though he denies authorship of that last one if his mother's present. Neil's poetry has appeared in journals and magazines including The Morning Star, Butcher's Dog, The Black Light Engine Room, The Lampeter Review, Prole and Ink Sweat & Tears. He's married, holds down a day job and divides his spare time between the pub and the cinema.

Harry Gallagher lives and writes on his beloved North East coast. Much of his material stems from his proud upbringing in The People's Republic Of Teesside, where he was fortunate to work alongside the last generation of men to fight iron and steel in their masses. He performs regularly across the North and his poetry has been published by Black Light Engine Room, Alliterati, Material and others. He was a major contributor to *Thrills 'n' Chills* (Wild Wolf, 2015) and has two pamphlets available, *How It Is: Snapshots From A Northern Town* (Heddon Quarry Small Press, 2015) and *Dark Matter III* (Black Light Engine Room Press, 2014). He also gigs as a singer/songwriter and is an award-winning playwright.

Rosie Garland was born in London to a runaway teenager, and has always been a cuckoo in the nest. Novelist, poet, singer in post-punk band The March Violets, she also appears in cabaret as twisted alter-ego Rosie Lugosi the Vampire Queen. Her poetry has been widely published, including Mslexia, Rialto, The North and The East Coast Literary Review. She's performed internationally, from the Cheltenham Festival of Literature to the Bowery Poetry Club, New York. Her latest solo collection is *Everything Must Go* (Holland Park Press 2012). Her debut novel *The Palace of Curiosities* (HarperCollins 2013) was The Co-operative Bank Book of the Year 2013 and second novel, *Vixen*, was a Green Carnation Prize nominee. Rosie is passionate about libraries and independent bookshops. Her latest project is a sequence of poems drawing on her experience of working for two years in Darfur, Sudan. http://www.rosiegarland.com

Cathy Grindrod is the author of five poetry collections, the most recent being *The Sky, Head On* (Shoestring Press). She was Derbyshire Poet Laureate from 2005-2007. She has also written three prize-winning plays, and the libretto for the oratorio, *More Glass Than Wall*, shortlisted for a BBC Radio 3 Composer of the Year Award. She works as a writing facilitator and mentor, specialising in writing for wellbeing.

Pippa Hennessy used to be a software developer but she's better now. She's Development Director at Nottingham Writers' Studio, Project Director of Nottingham's bid to become a UNESCO City of Literature, and works at Five Leaves Publications. In her vanishing spare time, she writes poetry, fiction and creative non-fiction, and has also published short graphic fiction.

Kevin Higgins's poetry features in the generation defining anthology *Identity Parade — New British and Irish Poets* (Ed Roddy Lumsden, Bloodaxe, 2010) and in the recent anthology *The Hundred Years' War: modern war poems* (Edited by Neil Astley, Bloodaxe April 2014). *The Ghost In The Lobby* (Salmon, Spring 2014) is Kevin's fourth collection of poems. Kevin's blog is http://mentioningthewar.blogspot.com

Nick Humphreys was born in Nottingham, England in 1968, working predominantly in the medium of (illustrative) painting under the 'actual size' moniker, has also worked extensively in music, a multi-instrumentalist primarily focused on percussion. Nick gained a BA(Hons) degree in fine art at Nottingham Trent University in 2007. He is now the co-founder of INSTAR, a sci-art organisation which brings together contemporary art with the natural sciences to curate, produce, exhibit and inspire new creativity drawn from the wonders of the natural world.

Robert Kenchington was born in 1966 and began his career as a reporter for the Nottingham Evening Post. He went to be a feature writer for East Midlands Allied Press and freelance critic for The BBC Music Magazine and

Gramophone. He later wrote and edited in-house publications for Pearl Assurance, Aberdeen University and The Rank Organization. As a published author, Kenchington has produced a short story compilation, *The Chamber of Screams,* and the official biography of film and television actor Shane Briant, for whom he has written and acted with in a variety of YouTube videos, including sequels to Briant's cult Hammer film roles from the 1970s. Robert Kenchington currently resides in Rutland.

John King is the author of a number of novels, among them *The Football Factory* and *Human Punk*, while *See No Evil* links to another of his titles, *The Prison House*. He is also a publisher and editor, running London Books with fellow writer Martin Knight. John began reading Alan's work as a teenager in the late 1970s, *Raw Material* one of his favourites in a stream of paperbacks bought in the Uxbridge branch of WH Smith. He was thrilled to meet his hero in 1999. Over the following years John and Martin became firm friends with Alan and the three formed The Flag Club, a society of authors based at The Lamb & Flag pub in Covent Garden, Central London.

Martin Knight is a British author born in 1957. His novels include *Common People* and *Battersea Girl.* Martin has also collaborated with footballers George Best, Peter Osgood, Dave Mackay and Charlie Cooke on autobiographies. His book *Gypsy Joe*, about a Romany boxer who became a professional golfer was selected as The Observer Sports Book of the Year. Martin and fellow author John King are the owners of London Books, who specialise in republishing iconic working-class classic novels and in Alan Sillitoe's 80th year re-released his 1970 title *A Start in Life*. Martin has also launched, ran and sold several businesses in the media monitoring sector.

Joanne Limburg's collections include *Femenismo* and *Paraphernalia* (both Bloodaxe) and *The Oxygen Man* (Five Leaves Press). She has also published *Bookside Down* (Salt), a collection for children and *The Woman Who Thought Too Much* (Atlantic Books), a memoir. Her first novel, *A Want of Kindness*, was published by Atlantic Books in July 2015.

John Lucas, who is Professor Emeritus of the Universities of Loughborough and Nottingham Trent, is a writer, publisher (of Shoestring Press), and semiprofessional jazz musician. Among his recent books are *Things to Say: Poems, Next Year Will be Better: A Memoir of England in the 1950s,* and, with Allan Chatburn, *A Brief History of Whistling*, all from Five Leaves Publications. His next novel, *Waterdrops*, and critical study, *Poetry in English in World-War Two*, are from Greenwich Exchange, who will also publish his new collection of poems, *Portable Property*, and his critical monograph on George Crabbe.

Paul McMahon is currently nominated for the Forward Prize. His poetry has been published in The Threepenny Review, *The Salt Anthology of New Writing, The Montreal International Poetry Prize Global Anthology,* Poetry Salzburg Review, Ambit and Orbis. Prizes include: the Keats Shelley Poetry Prize (2015), Ballymaloe International Poetry Prize (2012), Nottingham Poetry Open Competition (2012), Westport Arts Festival Poetry Competition (2012) and the Golden Pen Poetry Prize (2011). Additionally, he has been placed second for the Basil Bunting Poetry Award (2012), the International Salt Prize for Poetry (2013) and the West Coast Eisteddfod Poetry Competition (2012). Paul was awarded a Literature Bursary for poetry from the Arts Council of Ireland in 2013, selected for the Poetry Ireland Introductions Series in 2014, and has been selected for the Prebooked Readings at the Cork Spring Poetry Festival (2015).

Roy Marshall lives in Leicestershire where he works in adult education and writes poems and short stories. His pamphlet of poems *Gopagilla* was published in 2012 and a full collection of poems, *The Sun Bathers*, is available from Nottingham's Shoestring Press.

Graham Mort is Professor of Creative Writing and Transcultural Literature at Lancaster University. He was awarded a National Teaching Fellowship in 2015, has worked extensively in Africa and is currently helping to develop research projects in Kurdistan. *Visibility: New & Selected Poems*, appeared from Seren in 2007, when he was also winner of the Bridport Competition short story prize. His book of short fiction, *Touch*, was published by Seren in 2010 and won the Edge Hill Prize. A collection of poems, *Cusp*, was published by Seren in 2011.

Henry Normal was born in Sneinton in Nottingham; his dad and his elder bother worked at Raleigh. He has published six books of poetry, including *Nude Modelling for the Afterlife* (Bloodaxe). Henry supported Steve Coogan on Steve's first tour, performed for three full runs at the Edinburgh Festival and is featured reading a poem in the Julian Temple film *Glastonbury*. For the past 16 years he has run Baby Cow Productions with Steve Coogan, making over two hundred award winning TV shows including *Gavin and Stacey, The Mighty Boosh, Moone Boy* and *Uncle*. He has produced several films including the Oscar nominated *Philomena* and The Alan Partridge film *Alpha Papa*. He is most proud to be a producer of his wife Angela Pell's film *Snowcake* starring Alan Rickman and Sigourney Weaver.

Bernard O'Donoghue was born in County Cork in 1945. Since 1965 he has lived in Oxford where he taught Medieval English Literature at Wadham College. He has published six volumes of poetry of which the most recent was *Farmers Cross* (Faber 2011).

Kate O'Shea lives in Dublin. Her chapbook *Crackpoet* is available on Amazon. She was short listed for the Cork Literary Review Poetry Manuscript Competition and the Patrick Kavanagh Award twice. She is widely published in journals abroad. Her latest publications were in The Seranac Review, Orbis, Cyphers, Outburst, and Prole. Most recently she has been nominated for a Pushcart prize in America. New work by Kate is appearing this year in three anthologies.

Sue Pace has over 120 short stories, personal essays, poems and non-fiction articles published in regional and international formats. This includes not only literary journals in the USA, but also journals in Australia, the UK and Canada. Her poems may be found in several *Open to Interpretation* coffee table books. Her plays have been produced in Seattle, Portland and at the West Coast Ensemble in Hollywood, CA. She was a "Distinguished Writer in Residence" at Seattle University and recently received an Honourable Mention in Nimrod's Katherine Anne Porter competition. Her work may be found in Calyx, Prole, Epiphany and Nimrod.

Ruth Padel has published nine poetry collections, most recently *Learning to Make an Oud in Nazareth*, short-listed for the T.S. Eliot Prize. Her prose includes a novel featuring wildlife in India and a book on tiger conservation. She is Poetry Fellow at King's College London, Fellow of the Royal Society of Literature and a Trustee of the Zoological Society of London. Awards include First Prize in the National Poetry Competition and a British Council *Darwin Now* award. www.ruthpadel.com

Harry Paterson is the author of two books for Five Leaves Publications: *Look Back in Anger: The Miners' Strike in Nottinghamshire 30 Years On* and *Making Plans for Nigel: a Beginner's Guide to Farage and UKIP.* Originally from Alloa in Scotland, he now lives in Nottingham with his wife Sue, a freelance photographer. He has three children, one granddaughter, too many cats and not enough books. He plays guitar badly, stud poker erratically, chess with a growing consistency and eight and nine ball pool with a degree of proficiency. He also loves Indian food, anything from the Laphroaig distillery, Alloa Athletic, and books. Passionately. Oh, and the symphonies of Gustav Mahler. Equally passionately. Go figure. www.harrypaterson.com

Mark Patterson is a professional journalist who has written for regional daily newspapers, national broadsheets and a diverse range of magazines including The Northumbrian, Creative Teaching and Learning and Organic Gardening. He is also the author of *Roman Nottinghamshire* (Five Leaves Publications, nominated for Book of the Year by Current Archaeology magazine) and the forthcoming *Roman Derbyshire*, by the same publisher. An essay, 'A Short Walk Up Dere Street', was published in the anthology *Maps*, also published by Five Leaves. Based in Nottingham, Mark is art editor at the monthly magazine LeftLion and writes an urban cycling column there called Spokenword. His current/future book projects focus on tracing the oldest walking tracks and a social history of walking in subject areas such as work, emergencies and military route marches. Mark's interests include archaeology, ancient history, art, cycling, long distance walking, landscape and that only brings us up to L.

Mark Piggott was born in Manchester in 1967, brought up in West Yorkshire and has lived in London since 1985. He's the author of two published novels, *Fire Horses* (2008) and *Out of Office* (2010) both published by Legend Press, with three other novels at various stages. Mark's had around 20 short stories published in anthologies and magazines including Aesthetica, 3:AM and Pulp Books. As well as writing fiction he's a journalist and has had dozens of major features published in the nationals. As is often the case with these types, Mark has been forcibly removed from a wide variety of jobs including warehouseman, caretaker and lecturer. Although he rarely has anything interesting to say, you might find Mark on Twitter or if you're really bored visit his website at markpiggott.com. Mark's hobbies include drinking.

Bethany W. Pope is an LBA winning author, and a finalist for the Faulkner-Wisdom Awards, the Cinnamon Press Novel competition, and the Ink, Sweat and Tears poetry commission, placed third in the Bare Fiction Poetry Competition, second in this year's Bristol Poetry Prize, she was long-listed for the Bare Fiction short-story contest, short-listed for The Arianne's Thread Poetry Contest and she was recently highly commended in this year's Poetry London Competition. Bethany was recently nominated for the 2014 Pushcart Prize. She received her PhD from Aberystwyth University's Creative Writing program, and her MA from the University of Wales Trinity St David. She has published several collections of poetry: *A Radiance* (Cultured Llama, 2012) *Crown of Thorns,* (Oneiros Books, 2013), and *The Gospel of Flies* (Writing Knights Press, 2014), and *Undisturbed Circles* (Lapwing, 2014). Her first novel, *Masque,* will be published by Seren in 2016.

Tony Roe has worked for the BBC for over thirty years, first in radio before moving to TV at the end of the eighties. He spent more time in court than most criminals during a decade and a thousand stories in TV News. He has been making TV documentaries since 1990. The subjects have been varied from prisoners during the first Gulf War to child killers; rock musicians with Rick Wakeman to a World War One film with Kate Adie. He has been Series Editor of the current affairs programme *Inside Out*, in the East Midlands, since 2002 which has so far involved researching filming and producing over a hundred eight minute films. Tony is a Trustee of the Child Migrants Trust and in any spare time likes being at home but also runs, cycles, walks, travels and watches his favourite football team.

Penelope Shuttle lives in Cornwall. Her most recent publication is *In the Snowy Air,* an Iota/shots pamphlet, Templar Publications, June 2014. *Heath*, a book-length poem sequence in collaboration with John Greening, is in preparation. She is currently working on a new collection, provisionally titled *Will you walk a little faster.*

David Sillitoe works as a staff photographer for a UK broadsheet newspaper. His other time is spent with motorcycles, cookery, photography, and his family.

Emma Claire Sweeney hails from Birkenhead. She read English at Cambridge, graduated with distinction from UEA's Creative Writing MA, and was awarded an OU faculty scholarship for her PhD. She teaches at City University and New York University. Her fiction has won Arts Council, Royal Literary Fund, and Escalator Awards, and has been shortlisted for several others, including the Asham, Wasafiri, and Fish. Emma Claire's appointment as Writer-in-Residence at Sunnyside Rural Trust culminated in the publication of *The Memoir Garden* — a collection of poetry from the words and experiences of adults with learning disabilities. In collaboration with Emily Midorikawa, she runs SomethingRhymed.com — a website about female literary friendship. She has written for *The Guardian*, *The Independent on Sunday*, and *The Times*. Her debut novel *The Waifs and Strays of Sea View Lodge* will be published by Legend Press in 2016. www.somethingrhymed.com
www.emmaclairesweeney.com
@emmacsweeney

D.J. Taylor is a novelist and critic whose books include *Orwell: The Life*, winner of the 2003 Whitbread Prize for Biography, and, most recently, a collection of short stories, *Wrote for Luck.*

Maria Taylor is a poet and reviewer born in Worksop, Nottinghamshire. Her poems have appeared in several publications including The Rialto, The North, Magma, Ambit and many others. Her debut collection, *Melanchrini*, was published by Nine Arches Press and shortlisted for the Michael Murphy

Memorial Prize. She teaches at De Montfort University and lives in Leicestershire. She blogs at: http://miskinataylor.blogspot.co.uk/

Jason Williamson lives in Nottingham. He is 44 years old, married with a daughter, and singer for Sleaford Mods. An ex worker in the unskilled field of factory labour, warehouse labour, shop retail labour, the labour of unemployment, alienation and occasional despair. A life-long practicing musician which led to the opportunity of finally become a fully-fledged professional musician. An occasional writer for various websites and papers.

Bryce Wilson is a freelance writer living in Austin, Texas. He writes for the magazines Art Decades and Paracinema, and has served as the film columnist for *The San Luis Obispo New Times* for the last decade. He is also the author of *Son of Danse Macabre*, a personal history of the last thirty years of horror media.

Mike Wilson is a writer, musician, performer, teacher and manager of teachers who lives in Nottingham. He has written over eighty 'easy-reader' books for teenaged reluctant readers for Hodder-Murray. He wrote and performed in *Teeth Like Razors*, a theatre piece depicting the interacting lives and works of Bertolt Brecht, Kurt Weill and Hanns Eisler, which toured the country to great acclaim in 1999–2000. A first collection of poetry, *Desperanto*, was published by Smokestack in 2009, and a long poem, a half-parody-half-homage contemporary satire in the style of Lord Byron, appeared in Five Leaves' widely acclaimed *A Modern Don Juan — Cantos for These Times by Divers Hands* in 2014. Mike's poem in this anthology was written for a commemorative event in tribute to Alan Sillitoe which was held at Nottingham's Council House.

Ruth Fainlight & Alan Sillitoe

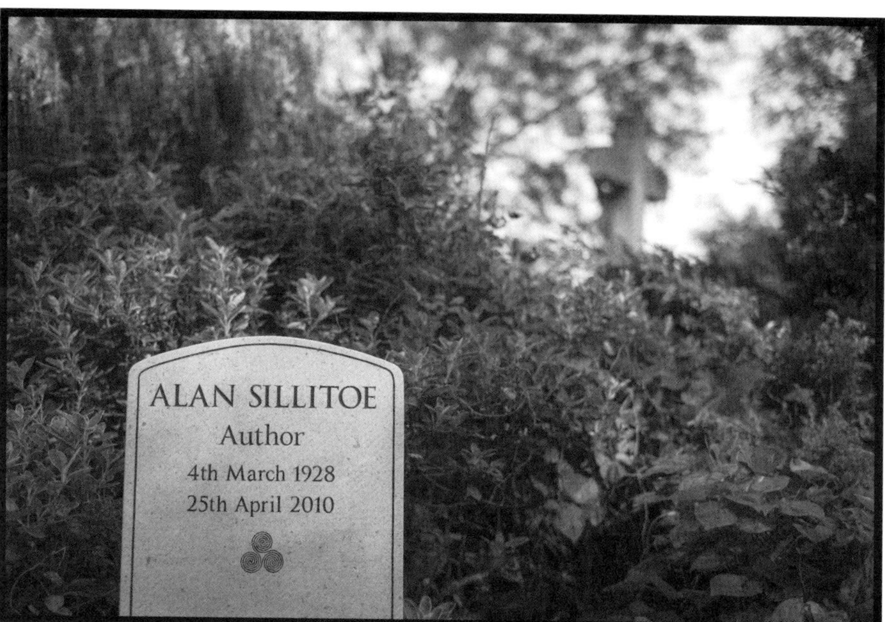

ALAN SILLITOE
Author
4th March 1928
25th April 2010

Highgate Cemetery, London

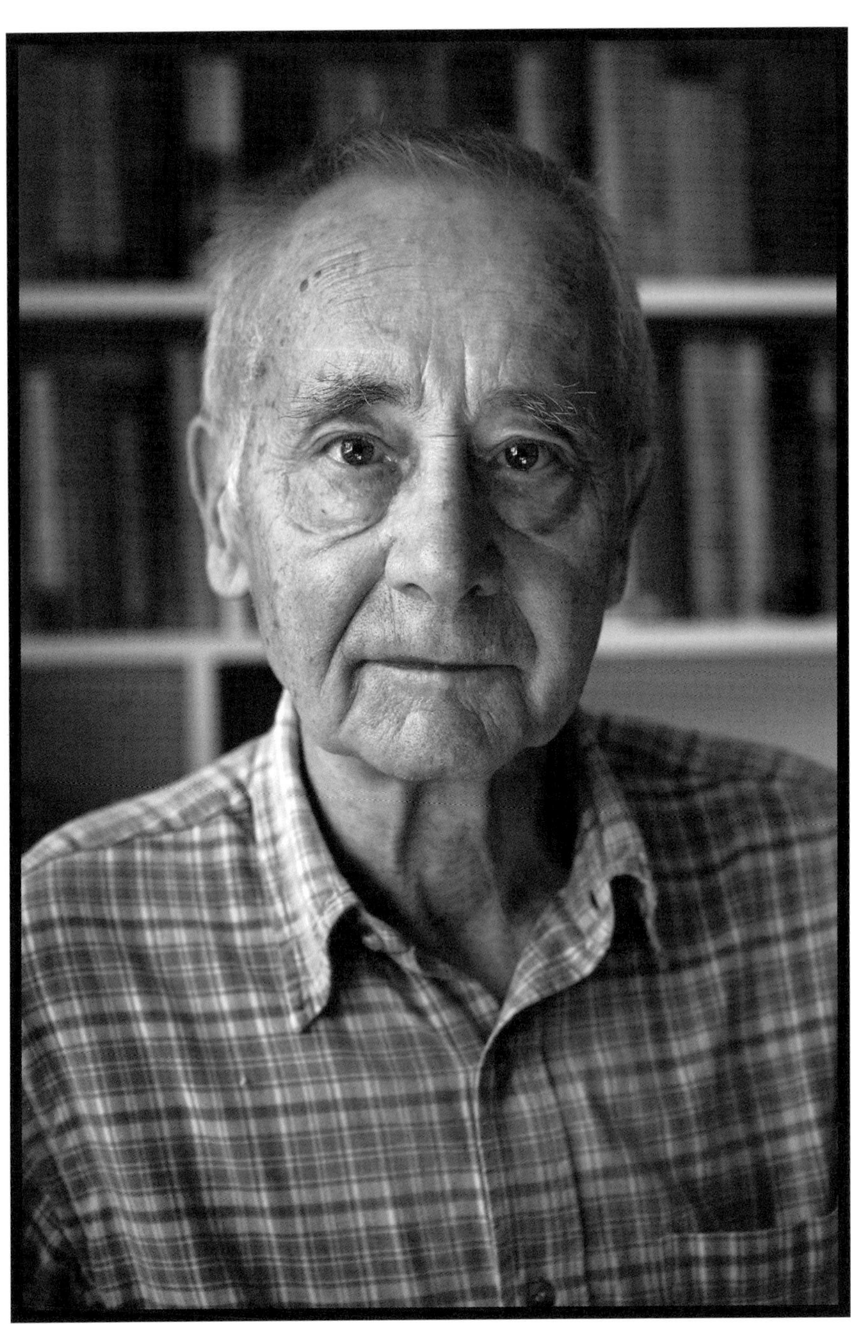

LuciferPress is an independent Nottingham-based Imprint, formed in 2015 by Neil Fulwood and David Sillitoe.

It is developing an eclectic list that includes poetry, prose, photography and journalism.

The name was inspired by Alan Sillitoe's poetry collection - *Snow on the North Side of Lucifer.*

As a not-for-profit enterprise it avoids the commercial imperative, and is committed to publishing vivid, relevant, and vital work.

www.luciferpress.co.uk

Notes

The Friars' Trail

The religious houses, churches and hospitals of medieval Berwick-upon-Tweed

John Convey

February 2021

Published by John Convey First published February 2021

ISBN 978-0-9954621-2-0

Email: john@conveys.org

Graphic design by Dan Convey: i.danconvey@gmail.com

Any profits from the sale of this book will be donated to charity

Printed by Martins The Printers, Berwick-upon-Tweed

Acknowledgements

I would like to thank the following for their help: Linda Bankier for proof-reading and making helpful suggestions for improving the book; Linda and her staff at the Berwick Record Office for advice and providing sources; the staff at Berwick Library, Berwick Museum and Art Gallery, Northumberland Archives at Woodhorn, National Library of Scotland and National Records of Scotland in Edinburgh, the British Library and the National Archives in London. As ever, thanks to my wife Eileen for helping, and to my son Dan for designing the book.

The following were kind enough to allow me to reproduce images etc from their holdings: British Library, National Library of Scotland, Berwick Record Office, Northumberland Estates, Historic Environment Scotland, Scottish Borders Council (Coldstream Museum), Council for British Archaeology & Leicestershire County Council, OpenStreetMap and Alan Williams Archaeology.

The photographs without acknowledgement are the author's own. Thanks to the proprietors of the Castle Hotel for allowing me to take photographs from their building.

Every effort has been made to ensure that all copyright holders have been contacted and agree to images being reproduced; I apologise if I have made any errors on this count, and will endeavour to correct these in the future.

Cover: impression of the Cistercian Nunnery in Bondington, courtesy of Alan Williams.

To my wife,
our children and their spouses,
our grandchildren,
and our wider family and friends

Disclaimer

The information herein is given in good faith and is believed to be accurate. No responsibility is accepted by the author for any omissions or errors, nor for any loss or injury howsoever caused. The author would welcome any corrections which could be incorporated in this work in the future. Contact: john@conveys.org

CONTENTS

Chapter

	Introduction	7
	Trail Map and Key	8
1	The Trail	10
2	The Trinitarian Order and St Edward's Hospital	17
3	The Order of the Friars of the Sack	27
4	The Dominican Order	32
5	Maison Dieu Hospital	41
6	Bondington: Church of St Mary the Virgin and Church of St Lawrence	46
7	Bondington: Cistercian Nunnery of St Leonard	50
8	The Franciscan Order	56
9	Hospital of St Mary Magdalene	64
10	Church of Holy Trinity with St Mary	68
11	Church of St Nicholas	71
12	The Carmelite Order	73
13	Hospital of St Bartholomew, Spittal	82
14	Other possible establishments with unknown locations	
	Augustinian Order of Friars	84
	Leper House	90
	Hospital of St Leonard	90
	Unknown Building, Walkergate	91
	Postscript	92
	Appendix	94
	References and Bibliography	96
	Index	114

INTRODUCTION

Some names currently in use in Berwick-upon-Tweed, Tweedmouth and Spittal - such as Magdalene Fields, Holy Trinity, St Mary's, Marygate, and the name Spittal itself - all hark back to medieval times, an era when the church was prominent in the lives of the people and where priests, monks and friars, churches and hospitals, priories, abbeys and friaries were a common sight in every area of the country. Thus the Hospital of St Mary Magdalene - which was located near the current golf course where it meets Northumberland Avenue - is remembered by Magdalene Fields; and Holy Trinity, the current Parish Church now incorporating the former St Mary's Church, was a medieval foundation dating from around 1120. There was an even earlier foundation of St Mary's Church in Bondington - along present day Castle Terrace; this name of St Mary's has had at least four manifestations over the centuries and the name is still used, now with Holy Trinity. The name Spittal is derived from 'hospital', as there existed a leper hospital named after St Bartholomew, reputedly in the area of Spittal Farm; the parish church of adjacent Tweedmouth is also named after St Bartholomew. There is a detailed plan of the sites of religious buildings in the town on Page 23 of the "*Northumberland Extensive Urban Survey*", 2009.[(C27)]

The idea of linking the sites of the medieval religious establishments by a 'trail' and giving detailed information about each one requires a great amount of imagination as there is next to nothing to 'see' of these foundations! Hopefully, by consulting the detailed description, maps, photographs and details of any archaeological investigations that have taken place it might be possible to visualise how the town would have looked with its churches, priory, friaries and hospitals in place.

Walking the 'Trail' around Berwick (approx 6km/just under 4 miles) takes roughly two hours, depending on the speed of walking, the route followed, and how much time is spent trying to 'visualise' each site. In addition, the 'branch' to Spittal from the Bridge takes about 30 minutes one way (approx 1.75km/1 mile).

The initial and key source used in this study is Cowan & Easson's *Medieval Religious Houses in Scotland*;[(A7)] although relying heavily on this and many other sources, this work is the author's own. Any mistakes or omissions will be corrected in future. New information may arise - especially if brought to the surface by archaeologists; or in the words of John Scott, whose book *Berwick-upon-Tweed: History of the Town and Guild* contains much information about religious houses etc,..."*it is possible that much that is now obscure may be yet made plain*"![(C30)]

TRAIL MAP AND KEY

1. The Trinitarian Order
2. St Edward's Hospital
3. Friars of the Sack
4. The Dominican Order (after relocation)
5. Maison Dieu Hospital
6. Church of St Mary the Virgin (21 Castle Terrace(?)), Bondington
7. Church of St Lawrence (St Laurence) (48 Castle Terrace(?)), Bondington
8. Cistercian Nunnery of St Leonard, Bondington
9. The Dominican Order (prior to the relocation near bridge)
10. The Franciscan Order
11. St Mary Magdalene's Hospital
12. Church of Holy Trinity with St Mary
13. Church of St Nicholas
14. The Carmelite Order
15. St Bartholomew's Leper Hospital, Spittal

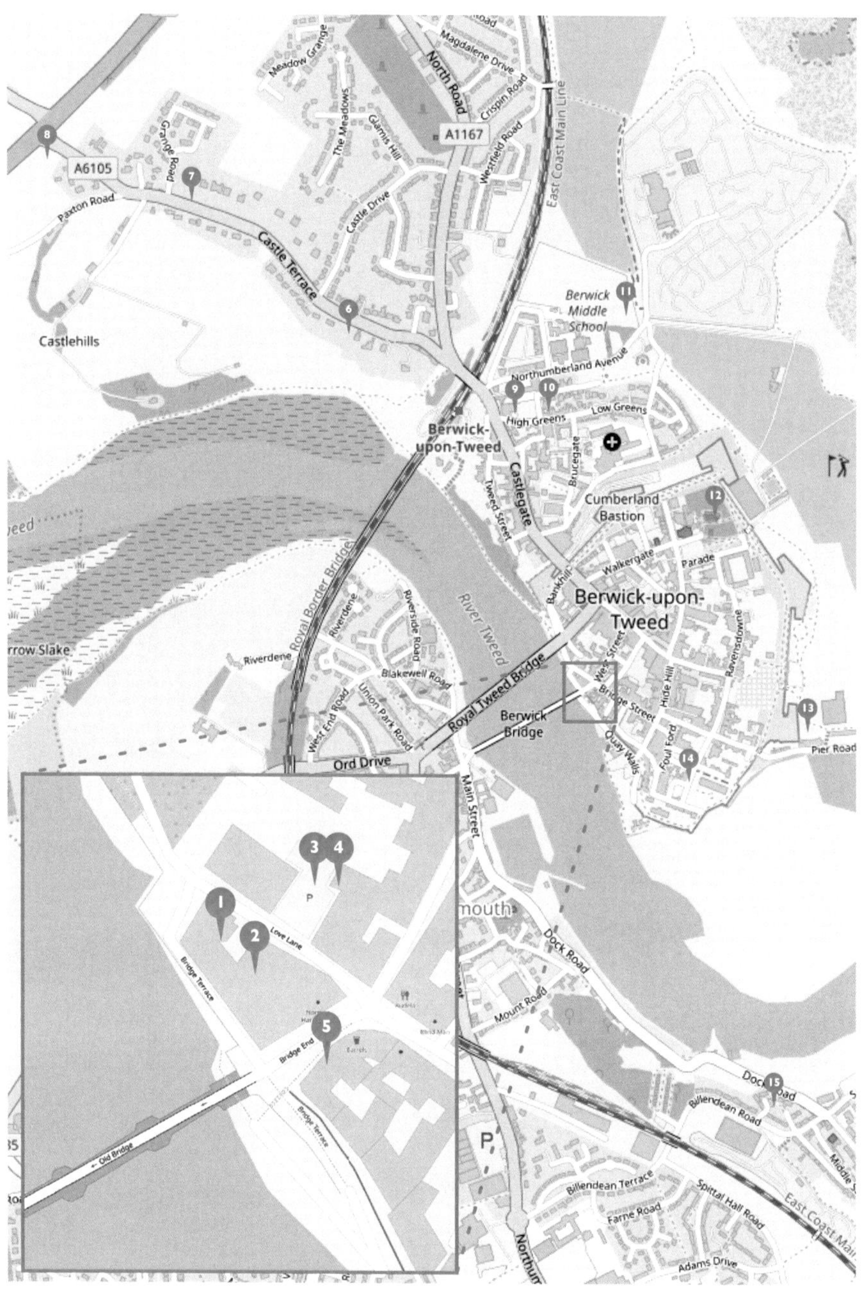

Meadow Grange
Magdalene Drive
North Road
Crispin Road
The Meadows
Glamis Hill
A1167
Westfield Road
East Coast Main Line
Grange Road
A6105
Paxton Road
Castle Drive
Castle Terrace
Castlehills
Berwick Middle School
Northumberland Avenue
High Greens
Low Greens
Berwick-upon-Tweed
Castlegate
Tweed Street
Brucegate
Cumberland Bastion
Royal Border Bridge
River Tweed
Riverdene
Riverside Road
Bankhill
Walkergate
Parade
Berwick-upon-Tweed
Ravensdowne
West Street
Bridge Street
Hide Hill
Blakewell Road
Royal Tweed Bridge
Berwick Bridge
Union Park Road
West End Road
Quay Walls
Foul Ford
Pier Road
Ord Drive
Main Street
Love Lane
Bridge Terrace
Bridge End
Old Bridge
Dock Road
Mount Road
Dock Road
Billendean Road
Billendean Terrace
Spittal Hall Road
Farne Road
Adams Drive

CHAPTER 1

The Trail

The Trail begins where the old timber bridge over the Tweed would have connected Bridge Street with Tweedmouth; this was a very busy part of Berwick at that time, the bridge - while the town was in Scottish hands - being the route south to England. Bridge Street (earlier name *Briggate,* the 'street leading to/from the bridge') was a main shopping street along with the High Street (*Marygate*); also nearby was the Quay, important for the fishing industry. There have been at least four timber bridges documented, with the latest one being shown, a little upstream of the present Jacobean stone bridge, on the *True Description of Her Majesties town of Barwick* map of about 1580.[See Chapter 5][E1]

For the location of the foundations numbered 1 - 15 in this Chapter, please refer to the map and key on previous pages.

There were five foundations clustered around the north end of the bridge, the **Trinitarians** and **St Edward's Hospital**; the **Friars of the Sack**, whose site was taken over later by the **Dominicans**; and the **Maison Dieu Hospital.**

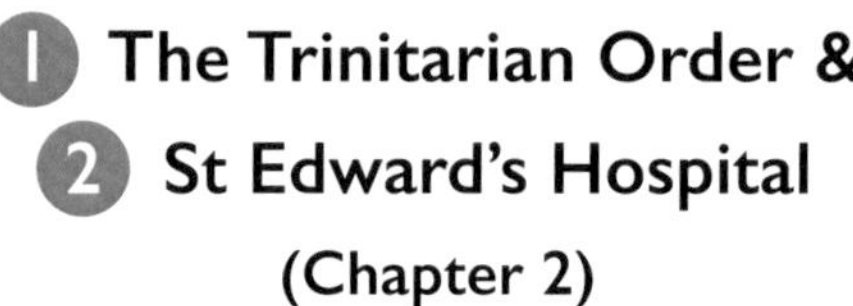

1 The Trinitarian Order & 2 St Edward's Hospital

(Chapter 2)

Founded in the thirteenth century and located at the north end of the timber bridge existing at the time, probably on the south side of what is now Love Lane. The Trinitarian house, *Bridge House,* was annexed to Peebles around 1474, by which time it had become uninhabitable. St Edward's Hospital for the sick and poor was founded before 1234.

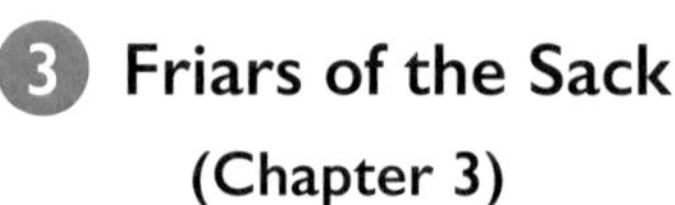

3 Friars of the Sack

(Chapter 3)

A short-lived friary, founded in 1267 and dissolved between 1274 and 1285. The site is most likely where later the Chapel of Ravensdale was situated on the north side of present day Love Lane; today the site is partly covered by Tintagel House and adjacent land. When the Friars of the Sack vacated the site it was taken over by the Dominicans.

4, 9 The Dominican Order

(Chapter 4)

The house of the Dominicans was established in Berwick-upon-Tweed before 1240. Initially it was situated close to the castle, but around 1289 the friars moved to the site previously occupied by the Friars of the Sack [see above] in what is now Love Lane. This house was probably one of four houses in Berwick that survived until the Dissolution in 1539.

5 Maison Dieu Hospital

(Chapter 5)

This hospital was founded before 1281, and possibly survived as a hospital until the Dissolution in the 1530s. It was adjacent to, and east of, the Trinitarians in *Bridge House*, near what is now the east side of Bridge End where the former bank building and the *Barrels Ale House* pub are located.

The 'Trail' leaves the Love Lane area to eventually reach Castle Terrace, where the medieval village of Bondington was located. Walk up Bank Hill, under the road bridge and reach Marygate by Scots Gate; a later medieval church dedicated to **St Mary** existed on or near the site of Scots Gate. At the time the Elizabethan ramparts were being built the church was removed to make way for the ramparts: "The *Church of St Mary's....placed almost on the site of the present walls on the east side of the street at the present Scotchgate*".[C30] In 1648 it was stated that the church had been removed when the walls were built; remains of a churchyard were found when building a water cistern a little further north than the gateway.[D7c][D9] A covered reservoir, probably the water cistern referred to above, exists at NT 9965 5314, otherwise there is no further information.[D18] Walk up Castlegate where, on the right opposite Railway Street, is the nineteenth-century **Church of St Mary**, built in 1857-8; the foundation stone was laid on 20 Oct 1857 and the church consecrated the following year. This church closed in 1989 and the congregation joined that of **Holy Trinity**; around

1994 the building was converted into residential accommodation.

Continue up Castlegate, walk over the railway bridge and take the left fork onto Castle Terrace. In medieval times the area of Castle Terrace and continuing to Duns Road formed the village of **Bondington**. It is fortunate that recent archaeological investigations have added much to the knowledge of Bondington and its religious establishments.[(K5)(K10)(K11)] The three religious sites there that have been excavated in recent times are the Church of St Mary, the Church of St Lawrence, and the Cistercian Nunnery.

If you are approaching from Berwick town, the first of these sites, **21 Castle Terrace**, is on the left just before Castle Drive and, not surprisingly, just after No 19, 'Highcliffe'! There is a board giving information about the site. **No 48 Castle Terrace** is further up the road on the right-hand side, just before Grange Road. The site of **St Leonard's Nunnery** is further up the road, which changes its name to Duns Road after the junction with Paxton Road; pass all the houses on Duns Road and the site is the field on the left before the A1 bypass. All three sites are on private property and inaccessible to the public, but can be viewed from the road.

[N.B. There is an alternative route for the Berwick section from Love Lane to the junction of Castle Terrace and Duns Road, virtually traffic-free but longer. Take the path, *New Road,* along the river to the end of the tarmac path; turn right up 'Askew's Walk' to the old Paxton Road. Turn right and walk along, admiring the views of the town and sea until you arrive at the junction of Castle Terrace and Duns Road. Turn left to find the site of the Cistercian Nunnery].

6 Church of St Mary the Virgin & 7 Church of St Lawrence (or St Laurence) Bondington (Chapter 6)

Both these sites are on private land. Number **21 Castle Terrace** has been 'tentatively identified' as the site of St Mary the Virgin Church, although it's not certain. An information board at the site gives a brief history and illustrations as to how the church would have looked. It is thought the church existed from the early twelfth century until about the middle of the thirteenth century.

Number **48 Castle Terrace (Cheviot House)** has been 'tentatively identified' as the Church of St Lawrence, although this is not certain. This too dates from the early twelfth century; there is no mention of it in documents after the end of that century. Future archaeological reports may give us more detailed information.

8 Cistercian Nunnery of St Leonard

(Chapter 7)

This Nunnery was founded before 1153 and as a result of recent archaeological investigations the exact site is now known. It possibly lasted until the Dissolution in 1539. An illustration of how the buildings would have looked can be found in the detailed archaeological reports and on the front cover of this book.

After viewing the three sites of old Bondington, retrace your steps towards the town as far as the railway station bridge. Cross the main road and walk down High Greens. The site on the east side of the main road, including the garage, was the location for the **Dominican Friary** (9) (Chapter 4) before the community moved to the site in Love Lane. It is thought that adjacent to but to the east of the original Dominican Friary, the Franciscan Friary was located; both were within and backing onto the Edwardian walls. From High Greens turn left up Bell Tower Place. The present day Holy Trinity School and the houses on the north side of Bell Tower Park were built along the line of the Edwardian walls, so the two friaries would have occupied the area around which you are now standing.

10 The Franciscan Order

(Chapter 8)

This Friary was established around 1231. As mentioned above, the general area of the location is known - along the walls east of the Dominican Friary - but not the exact location. The house was suppressed around 1538/1539.

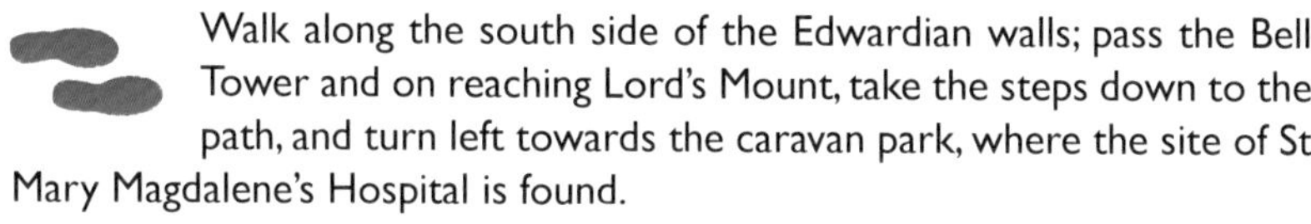

Walk along the south side of the Edwardian walls; pass the Bell Tower and on reaching Lord's Mount, take the steps down to the path, and turn left towards the caravan park, where the site of St Mary Magdalene's Hospital is found.

11 St Mary Magdalene's Hospital

(Chapter 9)

The location of this hospital is on the corner where Northumberland Avenue and the road to the golf course meet, above the first green. It is thought the hospital dates from around the end of the thirteenth century. It may have ceased to function as a hospital by about 1431/1432, when it was called a 'free chapel'. From around this time it was linked with the hospital at Segden which was sited just under two miles to the north.

Retrace your steps along the path by the side of the golf course and carry on all the way to the Cow Port. Go through the Cow Port and take the gate immediately on the right [or carry straight on and find the gates leading into the Church and its graveyard]; this path brings you onto the ramparts from where you get a view of the Church of Holy Trinity & St Mary.

12 Church of Holy Trinity with St Mary

(Chapter 10)

The present church dates from 1650-1652, but there was an earlier Church of Holy Trinity which is 'generally believed' to have been located south of the present Church, probably in the present graveyard. The former church may have existed from early in the twelfth century and there is an illustration of it on the *True Description*... map of around 1580

Retrace your steps to Cow Port, walk through the Gate and take the path on the right which wends its way along by the side of the ramparts. Pass the children's play park and eventually arrive at the houses of Devon Terrace, and the steps leading down to Pier Road. This area would have been the location for the Church of St Nicholas.

13 Church of St Nicholas
(Chapter 11)

This Church is thought to date from the thirteenth century, and was located near or above the site of the malthouse in Pier Road, with the churchyard extending back toward the walls as far as the cricket ground. A corner tower of the Edwardian walls nearby was named St Nicholas' Tower. It is not certain when it ceased to exist.

Walk down the steps to Pier Road, turn right and walk through Ness Gate, along Ness Street and turn left into Palace Street East. Walk down as far as the entrance to Governors Gardens. In this vicinity was located the Carmelite Friary.

14 The Carmelite Order
(Chapter 12)

This Friary was founded in Berwick in 1270 and survived until the Dissolution in 1539. Its location 'traditionally' is on The Ness close to, or part of, the Governor's House and Gardens. If its buildings were still standing then, it is possible that it is illustrated on the *True Description*… map of around 1580.[E1]

From the Palace Green area make your way to the town wall. Walk along the wall to the old Berwick Bridge, cross over the bridge and turn left along Main Street, then left along Dock Road as far as the **Church of St Bartholomew**. After visiting the Church, walk through the graveyard to Church Road and left along Well Square. Take the path in the far right hand corner of the Square and along Well Road, to Mount Road. Turn left until you see steps on the right leading to a lane; this will take you up to a disused railway line and part of the '*Lowry Trail*'. Walk to the end of this path and then down to Dock Road; almost immediately walk up again along Riverview Park to reach Billendean Road. Turn right and right again into Hallowstell View - this is the reputed site of St Bartholomew's Leper Hospital.

15 St Bartholomew's Leper Hospital
(Chapter 13)

This hospital for lepers and sick poor was established before 1234 and is thought to have survived until the Dissolution around 1535. The reputed site of the hospital is on Hallowstell View, on the former Spittal Hall's land.

Here the trail ends! There is a bus stop opposite the end of Hallowstell View where you can take the **B1** bus back to Berwick.

There are other establishments in the town that are recorded but their locations (at the moment!) are unknown:

Augustinian Friars
(Chapter 14)

Leper House
(Chapter 14)

Hospital of St Leonard
(Chapter 14)

Unknown building on Walkergate
(Chapter 14)

CHAPTER 2

The Trinitarian Order and St Edward's Hospital

Origins and Early History of the Trinitarian Order

The Trinitarians were known by various names including the Red Friars, the Trinitarian Order of Friars for the Redemption of Christian Captives, and Mathurins. They were not a mendicant order (i.e. they did not beg for alms) unlike other orders of friars, and were allowed finance through endowments; their income was split in three equal ways: maintaining the brethren, supporting the poor and poor pilgrims or travellers, and for the redemption (ransom) of captives in the hands of non-Christians resulting from the Crusades and pirating.[(A7)(F9)] They followed the Rule of St Augustine, and wore a white habit with a red and blue Greek cross on the heart - the colours being symbolic of the Holy Trinity; illustrations of the habit can be found on the current Trinitarian website.[(F9)] Redemption and mercy were, and are, at the very centre of the Trinitarian Order. Each house included a minister, with three clerks or priest-brethren, and three lay-brothers - the house in Newcastle, founded in 1360 by William de Acton, comprised a warden, three chaplains of the order, three poor and infirm persons, and three clerks '*to teach school, and instruct in the chapel of the house*'.[(A7)(F2)] This number was sometimes increased and the complement was revised in 1267 to a minister and five brethren.[(A7)]

The Order was founded by St. John de Matha and St. Felix of Valois at the end of the twelfth century, with the Order and its Rule being approved by Pope Innocent III in 1198.[(F9)] Their houses in Northern Europe were centres of recruitment and collection of funds - though some were hospitals.[(A18)]

The first generation of Trinitarians had some fifty foundations throughout France, Italy, Spain, Portugal, Luxembourg, Scotland, England and Ireland. The Order continued to grow and by the end of the middle ages there were twelve provinces of Trinitarians with approximately 150 houses in Europe. The late sixteenth century was a time of reform both in the Church and the Order. Today's Trinitarians are the direct descendants of this reform movement.[(F9)]

The Trinitarians in Berwick-upon-Tweed: foundation, location and early history

Joseph Bain, in an article in the *Proceedings of the Society of Antiquaries of Scotland* of 1887, gives the number of Trinitarian houses in Scotland as 'ten or eleven', including Berwick-upon-Tweed and nearby houses in East Lothian and the Borders; the first house in England was founded around 1200 in Hounslow.[(F1)(A18)] Four only of the heads of these Scottish Trinitarian houses appear on the *Ragman Rolls* as doing homage to Edward I at Berwick on 28th Aug 1296; these included Friar Adam, minister of the Order of the Trinity at Berwick….and Friar Thomas, master of the House of the Holy Rood of Peebles…: "*Berewyk, miniftre del ordre de la Trinite de, Frere Adam*".[(B44)] This appears to be the first documented reference to the house in Berwick-upon-Tweed. There is extant in the National Archives in London a seal of the Trinitarian house from around 1300 when Adam was Minister. The main part of the seal (see illustration) is about 38mm long; the diameter of the smaller, round, ones about 25mm[(B39d)] A description is given in the *Calendar of Documents Relating to Scotland:"The Father with nimbus, enthroned, with uplifted hands, a rod or spear encircled by a wreath on dexter, a cross on sinister side; beneath, a monk praying: 'S' 'MINISTRI ORDAINS SCE TRINITATIS DE BERWIK'"*.[(B8s)]

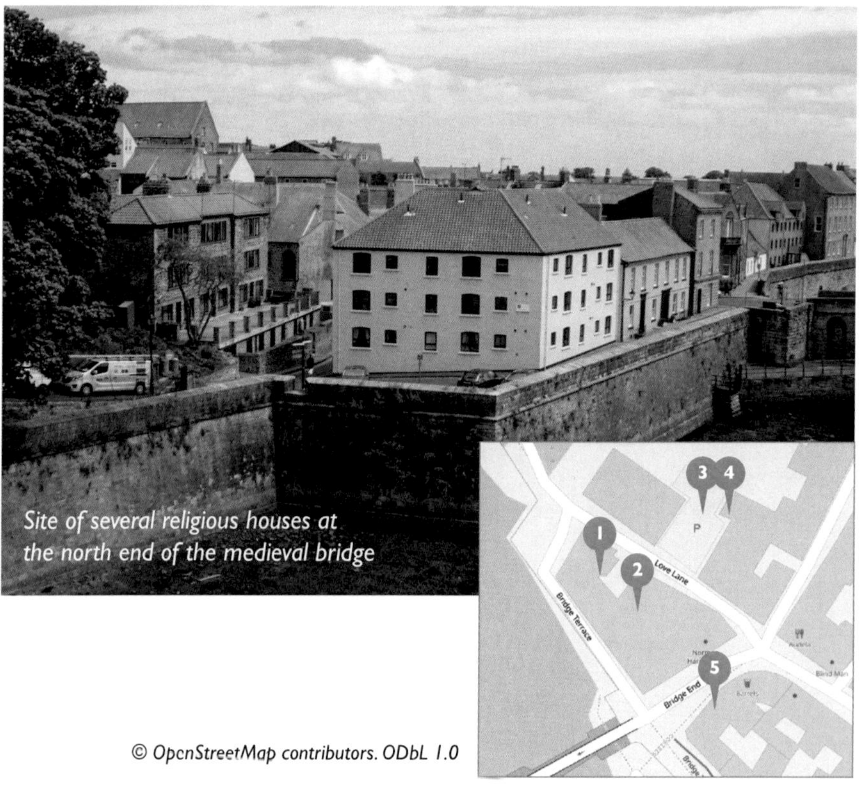

Site of several religious houses at the north end of the medieval bridge

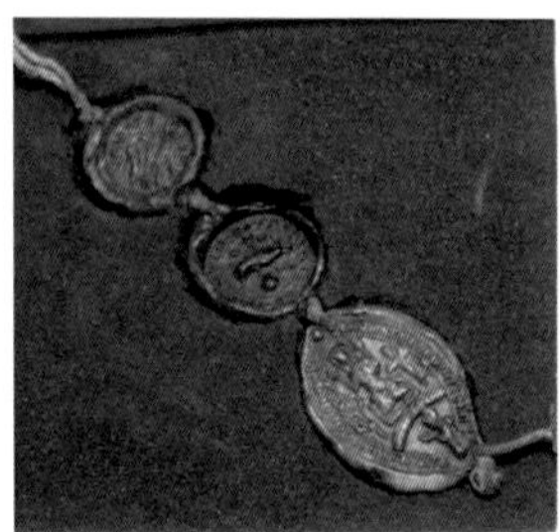

Seal of the Trinitarian Friary, Berwick
Courtesy of The National Archives Ref SC 13/D46B.
Licence: OGL http://www.nationalarchives.gov.uk/doc/open-government-licence/version/3/

Cowan and Easson write that "The Trinitarians settled in Berwick before 1240-8 when their foundation here was given custody of the new house at Dunbar by Christina de Brus":

> *"To all who see or hear this writ Christina de Brus, Countess of Dunbar, Greeting in the Lord : Wit ye that I, with the assent and will of Sir Patrick, Earl of Dunbar, ...and also of the venerable father in Christ David, by the grace of God Bishop of S. Andrews, have given, granted, and by this my present charter confirmed to God and the Friars of the Order of the Holy Trinity and the Captives my house which I founded in Dunbar with all its belongings and chattels .....To be held by the said Friars in pure and perpetual alms as freely, quietly, fully, and honourably as any other alms in the kingdom of Scotland is held and possessed, so that the Minister of the House of Berwich, for the time being, will have perpetual care and charge of the said house, who shall also find a friar to be Chaplain in the said house and continually celebrate divine service piously and devoutly for the quick and the dead :......In testimony whereof I have appended my seal"*: Witnesses, etc.(A7)(B13)

"They may have established themselves in the hospital of St Edward or Bridge House on their arrival, though it is only from 1306 that there is evidence of their possessing Bridge House",(A7) Adam still being the Minister at the time: "*Adam ministrum domus pontis Berewici...*". Adam is mentioned in relation to a meeting of Dominicans in Newcastle in 1306.(B29)

Scott refers to the foundation of the Trinitarian convent in Berwick by William the Lion, who died in 1214; he gives as the source Chalmers' *Caledonia* Volume ii: *"A Convent of Red or Trinity Friars was founded in Berwick by William the Lion. In 1267 those friars entered an agreement with the Prior of Coldingham about building an oratory within the parish of the Holy Trinity in South Berwick".*(B15)(C30) This date of 1214 is repeated in *Historic England Research Records;*(D18) however this claim is not confirmed by Cowan and Easson.(A7) There was a close association between the Trinitarians and St Edward's hospital, 'the hospital of the Bridge of Berwick', which was founded in 1234; "*soon after its foundation it came into the possession of the Trinitarians*".(A7)

Hospitals in medieval times

The term 'hospital' as used in medieval times generally had a different meaning from that which we understand as a hospital today; hospitals (also often called hostels or hospices), were charitable places where 'hospitality' was dispensed, and only a few were exclusively for the sick, such as leper hospitals. The hospitals existed for people in need - the poor, sick, travellers and pilgrims, seafarers, the aged and infirm. They ranged in size from one room to very large establishments, with the majority being small-scale;(A26) they were ecclesiastical institutions, so would include staff who were clergy, brothers and sisters and who would be engaged in the liturgical life of the house as well as looking after the paupers, the sick and poor travellers, and in the ports such as Berwick-upon-Tweed, the seafarers.(B38) There were three broad categories of hospital: leper houses, non-leper houses, and almshouses.(A31)(B38) It is estimated that there were about 170 hospitals in medieval Scotland.(A34)

Hall lists the main dedications of hospitals in Scotland as: the Virgin Mary (15), Saints Leonard (12) and John (10), and with St Mary Magdalene (6) also well represented; he gives a final list of 178 medieval hospitals in Scotland, with a strong concentration in East Lothian.(A34) "This figure represents almshouses, bedehouses [almshouses for bedesmen or women, i.e. *persons who are paid to pray for the soul of another*], poorhouses, leper hospitals, hospices for travellers and pilgrims, hospitals for the care of the sick, and a sizeable group whose function is no longer identifiable.(D17) The three most common types of hospital in medieval Scotland appear to have been poorhouses (39), almshouses (26) and leper hospitals (23)".(A34)

Leper houses, by the nature of the illness involved, were generally located away from centres of population. They were "*combinations of prison [isolation hospital], the monastery, and the almshouse*".(A19) As with other hospitals, they were monastic or semi-monastic in their constitution. "*In Scotland, all men were forbidden to harbour lepers, and lepers were forbidden to enter a town except on Sundays, Wednesdays and Fridays from 10am until 2pm, and not then if there was a market on those days*".(A19) Most leper houses were founded in the second half of the twelfth century; and by the second half of the fourteenth century the disease seems to have died out in England.

In 1283, the Guildry of Berwick-upon-Tweed ordered that "*No leper shall come within the gates of the borough and if one gets in by chance, the sergeant shall put him out at once. If one wilfully forces his way in, his clothes shall be taken off him and burnt and he shall be turned out naked. For we have already taken care that a proper place for lepers shall be kept up outside the town and that alms shall be there given to them*".(C22) It is clear from this that at least one leper hospital existed outside the walls of the town by this date [but location is unknown], and those with leprosy were being cared for. [See Chapter 14]

As we will see below, there were several hospitals in and around Berwick-upon-Tweed; unfortunately there are no visible remains of these hospitals. There are reconstructed ruins [see photos] of the hospital of St Leonard just north of Alnwick, beside the road which was part of the medieval version of the Great North Road.(C33) In Lancashire there is a gem near Ribchester where the chapel of the medieval hospital [St Saviour's Chapel, Stydd], located in the middle of a field, is still used for services

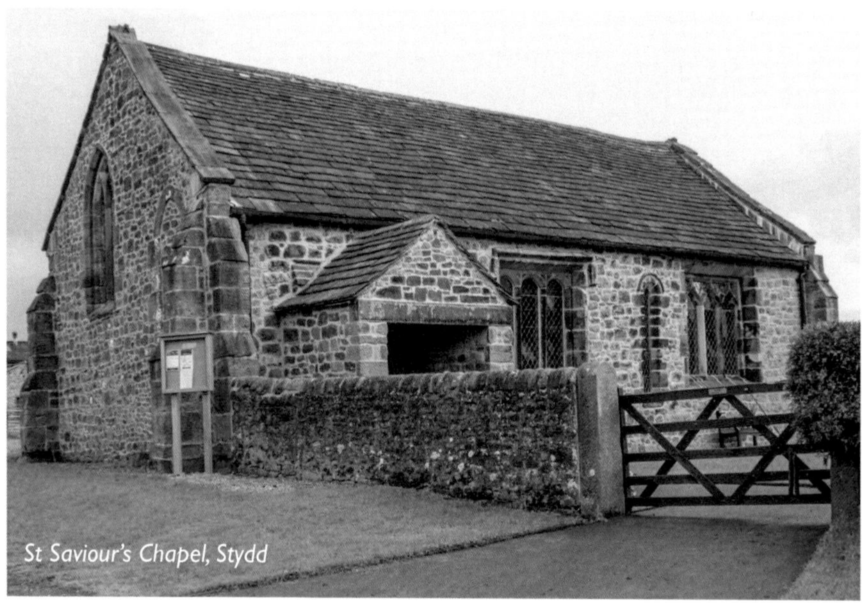
St Saviour's Chapel, Stydd

St Leonard's Hospital Alnwick (and right).
(Courtesy of Northumberland Estates)

over 800 years after its foundation. [See photo]. Of the hospitals in Berwick-upon-Tweed itself, St Edward's Hospital is associated with the Trinitarians.

The Hospital of St Edward

Charters make reference to a grant made before 1234, of the church of Kettins (Ketenes) to this hospital for the maintenance of the sick and poor. This church - close to Couper Angus and south west of Forfar - still exists and continues to be used for services.[F5]

"William, Minister of the Kirk of St Andrew (Bishop of St Andrews), have freed the Kirk

of Ketenes, granted by us to God and the Hospital at the Bridge of Berewic (hospitali de ponte de Berewic) for the perpetual sustenance of the infirm dwelling there...."; "*....granted the whole Kirk of Ketenes and by this our charter confirmed to God and Saint Mary and the Hospital of S. Edward of South Berwiche for the sustenance of the paupers in the said hospital.*"[(B13b)] 'South Berwick' was often used in medieval documents to distinguish Berwick-upon-Tweed from North Berwick.

Henry III granted protection without term for the master and brethren of the house of St Edward on the bridge of Berwick on 1 Aug 1246.[(B11b)] [See No 2 on the location plan and photo of the hospital site as it looks today]. According to Cowan and Easson, "*soon after its foundation it came into the possession of the Trinitarians*". Later references show that the designation "Maison Dieu" was applied to the Trinitarians' hospital; this appears confusing as there was a separate foundation named Maison Dieu close by [see Chapter 5], but the Maison Dieu and St Edward's Hospital may have been separate foundations originally, the one under secular supervision, the other placed under regulars.[(A7)] On 20 February 1338-9 Edward III ordered an inquest into the lands and tenements of the *Domus Pontis*' (Bridge House); the King ordered that all lands and tenements be restored to the keeper of the house.

There are no visible remains of the Trinitarian House 'Domus Pontis', but the location was near the old bridge (i.e. the timber bridge that preceded the stone Jacobean bridge which still exists), on the south side of Love Lane. The coloured plan or bird's eye view of Berwick-upon-Tweed, entitled, "*The true description of Her Majesties town of Barwick*" from about 1580, is unfortunately of no help as to the buildings that might have existed on the north side of the bridge at that time.[(E1)] Could archaeology come to the rescue?

Archaeological Investigations around Love Lane

A number of archaeological investigations have taken place over the years in the Love Lane area; it is uncertain whether any of these throw light upon the Trinitarian House, however. None of these excavations seem to have taken place on the south side of Love Lane where it is likely *Bridge House* was located, i.e. close to the bridge from England. In medieval times Bridge Street would have continued along what is now Love Lane to the north end of the bridge as it then existed - about 40 yards upstream from the present Jacobean stone bridge; the present Bridge End would not have existed. In 1997 Northern Archaeological Associates conducted an investigation on the north side of Love Lane on the site of the medieval Chapel of Ravendale (sometimes called Ravensdale, Ravensdonne or Ravensdell), and uncovered a wall and graves dating from the thirteenth to seventeenth centuries; the Chapel is more likely to have belonged to the Dominicans rather than the Trinitarians, as the Dominicans [see Chapter 4] took over the site from the Friars of the Sack [see Chapter 3] in the later thirteenth century.[(C25)]

Tyne and Wear Museums conducted excavations in 1998, and they also uncovered further burials - the confirmation of the presence of a medieval graveyard over a considerable portion of the yard led to the abandonment of the proposed construction works; both archaeological reports suggested that the site was that of a religious house.(F3) In April 2003 Alan Williams Archaeology conducted a watching brief during the cutting of foundation pits for the reconstruction of Tintagel House balcony; no archaeological deposits belonging to either the chapel or the associated graveyard belonging to the medieval religious establishment which occupied the site were disturbed during the cutting of the foundation pits within the area of the balcony.(C32) The Tyne and Wear Museums Archaeology Department carried out a watching brief, reported in 2004, on groundworks for a gas main at the south-west corner of Tintagel House.(G7) Most of these excavations are listed on the Archaeology Data Services website.(C2)

Berwick-upon-Tweed Trinitarians: later history

In 1328, on August 31, "*the King in fulfilment of the treaty with Robert King of Scotland, that religious houses in either kingdom should have restoration of their possessions in the other, commands the escheator citra Trent to deliver those of the Master and brethren of the Domus Dei of Berwick-upon-Tweed...similar, mutatis mutandis, for the Minister and brethren of the Holy Trinity of Berwick bridge, to said bishop...*"(B8d)

In the period 1355-1357, "*Master John of Allerton was the chief carpenter, and John of Morpeth, described as 'carpenter of the Baron of Greystock' (then keeper of the town), made a long brattice* [a temporary breastwork, parapet, or gallery of wood erected on the battlement of a fortress, for use during a siege(D17)] *round the Maison Dieu by task for £10, and another between the Maison Dieu and the Bridge-house for £5".*(B39c)(B23) This may be evidence to confirm the Trinitarians and St Edwards hospital, Bridge House, on the south side of Love Lane, connecting with *Maison Dieu* further along Bridge Street towards the east. Further documentary evidence for the Trinitarians comes in the Papal Registers of 1386: "*...to give to David de Strevelyne, canon of Glasgow, ... the church of Ketines, in the diocese of St. Andrews, said to be appropriated to the Trinitarian minister and friars of the Bridge of Berwick in the same diocese...*"(B9a)(F6)

In the following year, 1387, the ninth of the pontificate of Clement VII, a meeting in Arbroath in the diocese of St Andrews, summoned a "*Friar Andrew of the Order of the Holy Trinity for Redemption of Captives, and a discreet man Sir David de Stryflyn.... to hear final sentence, ordinance and decreet upon the Parish Kirk of Ketness in the said diocese of St Andrews, which each of the foresaid parties claimed to pertain to him by sale ... we ...declare, that the said Kirk of Ketnes, with its rights and all pertinents has pertained, pertains and ought to pertain to the Order of Holy Trinity for Redemption of Captives - which is ruled and governed by the Master of the Bridge of Berewick and the Friars of that Order -... To the said Order, and the Friars thereof, and Friar Andrew Master of the Bridge of Berwick, holding of and adhering to our lord the King, shall be returned and restored, as so far as we are able we return and restore....*"(B13a)

In the Papal Registers for 1446, there is mention of a John Kendal(d) being received as a friar in Berwick:

> "*To the abbots of Holywood (de Sacro nemore) and Corsregole in the diocese of Glasgow and the provost of Lerida (Ilerden.). Mandate to cause John Kendald, rector of the chapel of St. Mary Grace's (de Gracia) in the diocese of Glasgow, M.A., to be received as a friar of the Trinitarian house of Berwick (de Beruico) in the diocese of St. Andrews, and to receive his profession. He is in due course to resign the said chapel, value not exceeding 3l. sterling*".(B9c)

And in the following year, 1447, John Guthere, a Trinitarian friar, is made to resign from position of administrator "*of the house of Berwick (Bereuici) in the diocese of St. Andrews*".(B9d) In 1456, there was a papal mandate relating to three brethren of the Trinitarian Order:

Cross Kirk, Peebles (plus right and overleaf)
(Courtesy of Historic Environment Scotland)

> "*...The pope has been informed by Robert Clogstown...that David Crach, minister of the Trinitarian house of the place of Berwick and rector of the rectory of the parish church of Reenos (? rectius Ketnes) in the said diocese, canonically annexed to the said house, in order the more quickly to obtain the said house and rectory, promised by oath to give and assign, and did assign, to Peter Stirlyng, a Trinitarian friar, a moiety every year of the fruits etc. of the said house and rectory, and also two chaldrons ... of victuals to the vicar of the said rectory, and also made divers unlawful contracts.... that David is a public perjurer and simoniac, ...*" The outcome seems to have been that the Pope removed possession from the three guilty people and transferred the possessions to the said Robert Clogstown, a Cistercian monk of Cupar.(B9e)

The buildings of the Trinitarian house in Berwick by this time are "*greatly ruined*"; and on 3 Feb 1473/4 the house, which is described as long wasted '*so that no brother of our order is able to dwell there*', was annexed to the Trinitarian house of Holy Cross,

Peebles by the Head Minister of the Order in Paris.(B9m)(F8) This was confirmed by Papal Mandate on 2 March 1475:

> "*To the abbot of Scone in the diocese of St. Andrews. Mandate, as below. "The recent petition of John Blenk, preceptor called minister of the Trinitarian house of Holy Cross, Pleblysz [sic], in the diocese of Glasgow, contained that Robert, preceptor-major called the minister of the said order, seeing that the house of Berwik, of the said order, in the diocese of St. Andrews, had long ago been devastated by a raid of the English, and was so much in ruin that no brother of the order could live therein, united the said house and the parish church of Ketnes' in the said diocese of St. Andrews, which is annexed thereto, to the said house of Holy Cross, and appointed the said John as preceptor called minister of the said houses as one house, granting that he and his successors might receive as many to make their profession of the said order as could be maintained with the goods of Holy Cross, and give them the regular habit. The pope therefore, at the said petition, orders the above abbot, if he find the facts to be as stated, to approve and confirm the said union and grant etc. by papal authority*".(B9g)

This union of the houses of Berwick and Peebles was subsequently confirmed by James III.(A7)(B49c) There is no evidence for any revival of Trinitarian activities in Berwick after this date. Some of the Ministers from Adam onwards are listed in '*The Heads of Religious Houses in Scotland from Twelfth to Sixteenth Centuries*'.(A35) A short history of the Trinitarians from the Dissolution until the present can be found on the Trinitarians website.(F9)

Other Trinitarian Friaries in the vicinity(A7)(B15)

The Trinitarian house most closely associated with the Berwick house is that of Peebles, as the Berwick house was annexed to Peebles in the 1470s after the Berwick house had fallen into disuse/disrepair [see above]. There are still remains of the Trinitarian church and outline of the convent in Peebles - the *Cross Kirk*. The church has existed since 1261, founded after the discovery of a 'magnificent and venerable cross' and a man's skeleton; it became a place of pilgrimage as it was believed that the bones were of a bishop martyred by the Romans. It was served for most of its existence by Trinitarians friars, but there was no convent of friars built until 1474, which was about the same time that the house in Berwick was united with that of Peebles. The fact that the church was already in existence probably accounts for the fact that the cloister and claustral buildings were built to the north of the church,

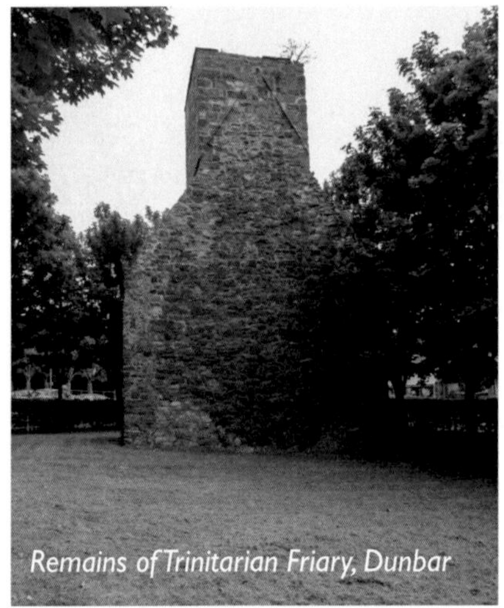
Remains of Trinitarian Friary, Dunbar

whereas they would normally, but not always (e.g. Cartmel Priory), be built to the south of the church.[(D11)(F4)] The church was abandoned and unroofed in 1784, and by 1811 much of the south wall had fallen. It is, however, the best preserved urban friary in Scotland.[(D8a)]

Nearby, in England, there was a Trinitarian House in Newcastle, which was also associated with a hospital; the house was founded in 1360 and survived until the Dissolution in 1539. St Michael's, also known as Holy Trinity or Acton's Hospital, was founded by William de Acton, a burgess, and it was for a warden, 3 chaplains of the order, 3 poor and infirm persons, and 3 clerks '*to teach school, and instruct in the chapel of the house*'. It was on the site of Wall-Knoll, from which the Carmelites had moved in 1307.[(C18)(A17)] There were several houses in the Borders and East Lothian, including Dirleton, Houston (which also included a hospital), (possibly) Ancrum, and Dunbar[(F7)], where there is the remains of the tower of the church (see photo) later converted into a dovecot.[(A7)]

Work of the Trinitarian Order

As we saw above, the aim of the Trinitarians was three-fold: to maintain the brethren, support the poor and poor pilgrims or travellers, and to facilitate the redemption (ransom) of captives in the hands of non-Christians resulting from the Crusades and pirating.[(A7)(F9)] Their income therefore was divided three ways, and all three had to be managed. In several places as well as Berwick they managed hospitals, such as in Newcastle and Houston. Along with the Order's mission of ransoming Christian captives, each Trinitarian Community served the people of its area by performing works of mercy.[(F9)]

CHAPTER 3

The Order of the Friars of the Sack

Origins and Early History of the Order of the Friars of the Sack

The Order of the Friars of the Sack, known also as the Friars of the Penitence of Jesus Christ or Sack Friars, was one of the short-lived Orders of the thirteenth century. They were a mendicant order, and their name, according to Matthew Paris, derived from the humble sack-like cloth of their habit. They followed the Rule of St Augustine.[A1] The Order first appeared in Provence in 1240s in urban areas, providing pastoral care, and begging for their sustenance. Their life was based on poverty and the spiritual benefit from penance. In 1251, by which time they had founded thirteen houses, they sought papal approval and in 1255 they were authorized to preach (with the permission of diocesan bishop). By the 1270s the Order had spread across much of Europe - Provence, France, Spain, England, Germany, Italy and a single friary at Acre in Holy Land. By 1274 there were at least 122 friaries, probably more than either the Carmelites or Austin (Augustinian) Friars. In England there were at least 18 houses, the first being founded in London in 1257; a house was established nearby in Newcastle in 1266, and the one Scottish house in Berwick the following year.[A1]

The Order was organised into 'Provinces'. At the head of the Order was a Rector General and General Chapter or Assembly. Each Province had a Prior answerable to the General Assembly, and in turn each house in the Province had a Conventual Prior answerable to the Provincial Prior. The number of friars within a house was usually twelve, but was often more. Their constitutions set down that their houses were to be 'small and humble'.[A1]

The Sack Friars obtained income from begging, with no income from fields, vineyards, or rents. Each house had its own 'terminus' - specific area for begging. They were allowed gardens and workshops as well as a church and convent. 'Unnecessary painted images' were prohibited; but each house had its own seal. The Constitution required that high altars be dedicated to Jesus and his mother Mary, but this was not always followed. The Order had specific devotion to Mary, Augustine, St Michael and Mary Magdalene.(A1)

A key date in the history of this Order is 1274, when the Council of Lyons decreed the suppression of any orders founded after 1215; they weren't allowed to make further recruitment. The Friars of the Sack was the largest Order suppressed, as they were numerically probably third behind the Franciscans and Dominicans. According to Chettle, the Friars of the Sack were not very popular with the writers of the time.(H1) After their suppression, many of the houses were taken over by other Orders - in Berwick-upon-Tweed the house was taken over by the Dominicans (see below). "*The Friars of the Sack were an expression of the spirituality of penance and renunciation potently combined with evangelism so characteristic of vast numbers of men and women in the thirteenth century Latin Church. They did not survive long enough for this to change*".(A1)

Friars of the Sack in Berwick-upon-Tweed: foundation, location and history

The Friary in Berwick was short-lived, being founded in 1267 and dissolved between 1274 and 1285.(A7) A charter of Roger, prior of Coldingham, dated 18 May 1267, declares that his monastery has conceded to the Friars of Penitence of Jesus Christ that they may erect buildings and an oratory within Coldingham's appropriated parish of Holy Trinity of South Berwick. The friars pledged themselves to do nothing to the prejudice of Coldingham Priory.(A7)(B45b)As mentioned above, in 1274 the Council of Lyons decreed the suppression of any orders founded after 1215, which included the Friars of the Sack; thus on 17 June 1285, the Bishop of St Andrews was instructed to sell the friary at Berwick to the Dominicans and use the proceeds for the benefit of the Holy Land.(B9k) This mandate is repeated the following month in Theiner:

> "*Mandate to the bishop of St. Andrews to sell to the prior and convent of Friars Preachers, Berwick, as their own place is too far from the town for the people to come to confession and sermons, and for the friars to visit the sick, the place in the said town late held, but now left by the Friars of Penitence…The price is to be handed over to the Holy Land subsidy, or for the poor or other pious uses by the ordinary of the places, in accordance with constitutions of the council of Lyons.*"(B9h)(A7)(B9k)

There must have been disagreement over the value of the site, as four years later the Friary had still not been sold:

> "*Mandate to the bishop of St. Andrews and Geoffrey de Veçano, clerk of the papal camera, if they ascertain that the place which the Friars of Penitence had been estimated beyond its due value for sale to the prior and convent of Friars Preachers of Berwick, in the diocese of St. Andrews, they are to moderate the value, and cause*

it to be sold to the said prior and convent at a fair price, to be paid in three years in an equal rate, and the money deposited in a safe place, in the name of the Roman church".(B9)(B9m)

The location of the Friars of the Sack, and later the Dominicans, is reputed to be near the end of the bridge existing at the time, although the map of around 1580, after the Elizabethan ramparts were constructed, does not show any buildings in the area adjacent to the bridge end.(E1) It is most likely on the site of the Chapel of Ravensdale on the north side of Love Lane, today covered partly by Tintagel House. Cowe identifies the site as the Chapel of Ravensdale on the north side of Love Lane, once the extreme western end of Bridge Street (formerly named *Briggate*). [see map on page 9].(C12) Northern Archaeological Associates carried out evaluation and excavation work on a site to the east of Tintagel House which recovered evidence for medieval structures and associated human burials. [see Chapter 2].(C27)(C25)(C12)

The first authenticated reference to the Chapel of Ravensdale is at the Dissolution when listed in 'Lands of Dissolved Religious Houses'. It must therefore, at this date, have been in the hands of an existing religious house in the town. The Trinitarians had left by 1488 and the only remaining houses in the late 15th century were Franciscans (on the Greens), Carmelites (on the Ness) and Dominicans. Information from Francis Cowe indicates that a second document dealing with the Dissolution indicates the chapel was property of the Dominicans.(C12)

The Chapel of Ravensdale is noted by Scott in 1888 as having been 30 yards (27.4m) long by 26 yards (23.8m) wide.(C30) By 1811 the site contained a complex of granaries constructed around a yard; and on the 1852 Ordnance Survey 25 inch map it is identified as a timber yard.(C25) There was a variety of religious houses in medieval Berwick at the north end of the existing timber bridge and the site of the Chapel of Ravensdale, to the north of the present Love Lane is most likely that of the Friars of the Sack and later the Dominicans. The chapel (recorded variously as Ravendale, Ravensdale, Ravensdonne, and Ravensdell) in Briggate North (Bridge Street) in 1562 is reported as '*in the Queen's Majesty's possession and occupied as a storehouse for her Majesty's provisions, and not rented*'.(C31) In the same Survey, mention is made of a "John Goodale, prior of Ravensdale":

"[15]. George Robinson holdeth there one ten[enemen]te conteininge in length XVII yardes and in breath V yardes, it is worthe by yere XIII s[hillings] And conveith title by the right of Johann, his wief, Doughter and heire of Jennet Davye, to whome the same was granted in fe fferme by John Goodale, prior of Ravensdale, by dede dated ultimo M[ar]eii anno XXIIVII [31—3-???] and paith by yere to the Quene for Borowmale VII d [pence] And rente reserved to the said late priorie. XII d [pence], XVIII [l or d ?]".(C31)

As John Goodale is not listed as a Minister of the Trinitarian house in Berwick in the years before it ceased to exist in Berwick,(A35) perhaps it adds strength to the argument that the Chapel of Ravensdale belonged to the Dominicans; but the link has yet to be proved conclusively!(C6)(C6c)(C6b)

There are fragile documents relating to the Chapell of Ravensdell or Ravensdowne from 1614 and 1647 in the Berwick Archives, so the chapel clearly survived until at least the mid-seventeenth century. In 1614, the chapel '*then or late used or employed as a store house for his Majesty's service on the North side of Briggate Street*' was rented out by the borough.(C6c)(C30) A subsequent lease of 1647 refers to '*that old chappell & waste Tenement called Ravens[d]ale*'.(C6c) A plan of about 1810 by Richard Todd shows the area "formerly known by the names of Ravens, or Ravens Dale, the old Chapel and waste grounds adjoining"; this area corresponds to the present Tintagel House and the spare land adjoining.(C11) By 1811, the site was owned by one Ralph Forster and contained a complex of granaries constructed on the site around a yard, which on the 1852 Ordnance Survey 25-inch map was identified as a timber yard.(C30) It was also recorded that '*one lady averred she played in the timber yard as a child, and her father, a servant to Forster, had told her not to go to a certain place where a chapel had been, lest she should see skulls*'.(C30)

Archaeological Investigations in Berwick-upon-Tweed

See Chapter 2 for archaeological investigations on the site of the Chapel of Ravensdale, the Friars of the Sack and the Dominicans.

Other Friars of the Sack in the vicinity

There was another short-lived house of the Friars of the Sack in Newcastle-upon-Tyne, which dated from 1267 until 1307. There were only three friars remaining in 1299, and in 1307 the Carmelites were allowed to transfer their priory from Wall Knoll to this site, west of the castle, provided that they supported the sole remaining Friar of the Sack.(Q2).

Work, education, architecture of the Friars of the Sack

The friars sought agreement with the local secular clergy and obtained their permission to preach in their area. One of their duties was to remind people to pay their tithes and dues to the church. They were to show hospitality to others, especially Franciscans and Dominicans. They generally enjoyed the support of local people, but not necessarily the writers of the time!(A1)(H1)

The Order saw the need to be educated in universities in order to be a professional preacher. Their constitutions refer to *studia generalia* in Montpellier, Paris, Oxford, Cologne and Bologna, to which each Province could send two friars; it is not clear whether, given the short time of the Order's existence, all these *studia* were ever formed. There were eight men left in Paris house in 1293 when it was finally closed.(A1)

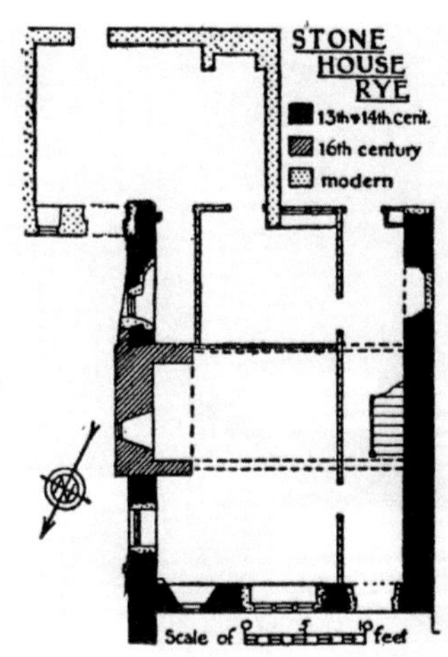

Plan of the Friars of the Sack house, Rye, Sussex.
By kind permission of the Sussex Archaeological Society

The site chosen by the Friars of the Sack, and later used by the Dominicans, is very restricted in Berwick-upon-Tweed, being sandwiched between Love Lane (was *Briggate*) in the south and, to the north, the hill that rises up eventually to the High Street/Marygate. There would not be sufficient room for the normal arrangement of church, cloister, claustral buildings etc. - but then, according to their constitutions, their houses were to be 'small and humble'. The only building of the Order that remains in England is part of their convent in Rye in Sussex (see illustration), a rubble-walled construction which was turned to secular use after the friars left.(G5) "*The existing house was apparently the north-west wing of a larger structure of c. 1265; probably the chapel and other buildings lay to the south of it*".(H2)

CHAPTER 4

The Dominican Order

Origins and Early History of the Dominican Order

The *Dominicans* are an Order of friars named after their founder, St Dominic. They are better known under their alternative name the *Order of Preachers* - this name is more likely to be used in medieval documents and indeed is used to this day.[(G10)] They were also known as *Black Friars* because of the black cloak they wore over a white habit; modern day illustrations of their habit can be found on the Order of Preachers website.[(G10)] Other alternative names were *Friars Preachers, Preaching Friars* and *Jacobin Friars*. The Dominicans are a mendicant Order, spending most of their time outside their convent or house, preaching and teaching, and are thus called "*to make the world our cloister*".[(G10)] The Order follows the Rule of St Augustine.

> "*At the heart of the Order of Preachers is the conviction that belief in God – and in the Christian Faith in particular – is rational and perfects the human person and completes the fundamental human desire for truth and goodness. Since our origins in 1216 members of the Order have, following the example of St Dominic, devoted their lives to the quest for truth, and to sharing the Christian Faith in a reasoned and loving way, with a great concern for individuals and their particular needs and circumstances*".[(G10)] The Order of Preachers was founded by St Dominic de Guzman (c.1174 - 1221) from Castile, who, as a young priest in arguing against the Albigensian heresy, realised that there was a need for prayerful, educated preachers to go out and teach the true faith and combat ignorance.[(G10)]

The Dominicans held the three basic tenets of monasticism: poverty, chastity and obedience, and to this they added asceticism. The friars vowed to conduct the ministry of preaching and confession following the example of the Apostles in zeal, poverty and holiness of lifestyle.[(G10)] In 1215, Bishop Fulk of Toulouse approved the foundation of the new religious order; and later the same year Dominic travelled with Bishop Fulk to Rome where on 22 December 1216 Pope Honorius III approved the foundation of St Dominic's community and took them under papal protection. On 21 January 1217, Pope Honorius III issued a second bull completing the confirmation of the Order, which would be known as an order of preachers: "*An Order which would be called and would be an Order of Preachers.*"[(G10)] By the end of the thirteenth century there were 404 priories and almost 15,000 friars including a province in the Holy Land.[(G10)]

Like other orders of friars, the Dominicans established themselves in urban centres and, as distinct from monks, preached the Gospel to city-dwellers. As Fr Anthony Ross OP said, "*the Black Friars lived in contact with the bustle of life in towns and cities, although some monastic elements of prayer and silence were retained in the domestic life of their communities*", thus combining the Dominican elements of contemplation and apostolic ministry.(G10)

The primary patron of the Dominican order in Scotland was the crown. Eight of the thirteen houses were founded by the crown, nine when Berwick is included.(C30) The crown's finances were split into the Exchequer, which dealt with the royal lands, and the Treasury, which covered more ad hoc income and expenditure; it was from the Treasury that spontaneous alms were given. The sum of 14s was the most regular payment for a priest's first mass, or a donation to a convent, or a gift of that kind.(C30)(G5)

Dominicans in Berwick-upon-Tweed: foundation, location and early history

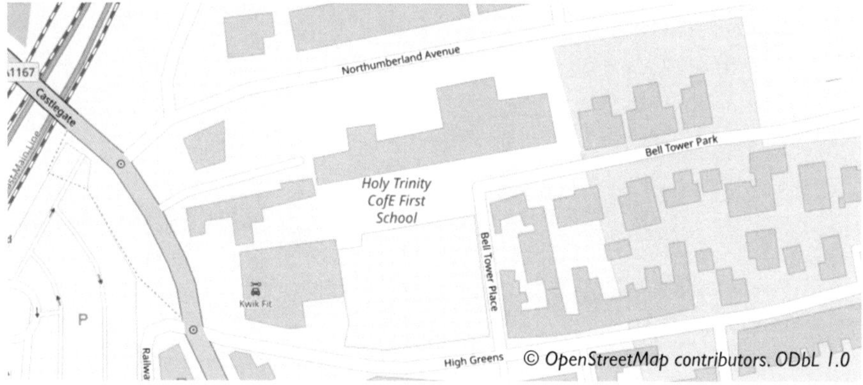

© OpenStreetMap contributors. ODbL 1.0

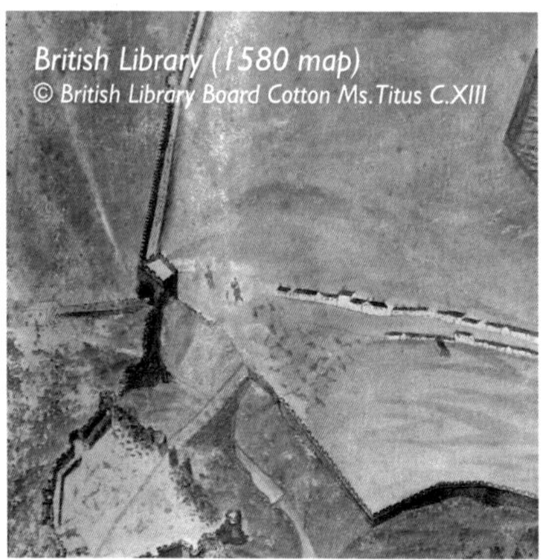
British Library (1580 map)
© British Library Board Cotton Ms. Titus C.XIII

The house of the Friars Preachers was established in Berwick-upon-Tweed sometime before 1240 - *Monasticon for Scotland* gives the date of 1230(A25); there is reference to this community in March 1240/1 in the *Calendar of Documents relating to Scotland*: "*.....a certain friar Siward, who was once professed in the Order of Friars Preachers, has to the scandal of the Order, retired from their house of Berwick, and like an apostate does not blush to serve laymen and others against the honour of his religion...*".(A7)(B8)

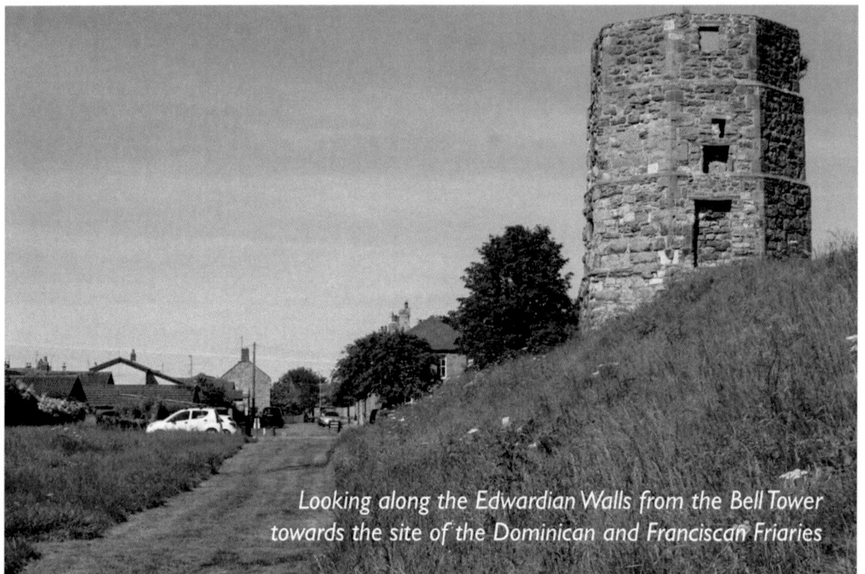

Looking along the Edwardian Walls from the Bell Tower towards the site of the Dominican and Franciscan Friaries

This house was founded by King Alexander II of Scotland, who reigned from 1214 until 1249; he also gave the house an endowment.[B23] "*In St Dominic's time King Alexander the Second founded the places of the Friars Preachers of Berwick, Perth, Ayr, Stirling, Aberdeen, Edinburgh, Inverness and Elgin…*"[A7][B24] The house in Berwick was dedicated to St Peter (Martyr) of Milan.[A7]

British Library (1725 map)
© British Library Board Maps K.Top.32.46

The friary was originally situated close to the castle just within the town boundary, on or near the site of the present Holy Trinity school in Northumberland Avenue and the adjacent garage premises. The north wall of the friary formed part of the defensive walls after 1296.[C27][C17] The 1580 map of Berwick shows open space, but this is so for the whole area of the Greenses, which doesn't mean there were no buildings, either in use or abandoned, at that time.[E1] Although much later, the 1725 map of Berwick[E2] shows blocks of buildings which may have supplanted the Dominican and Franciscan friaries of the medieval era. In the present day view along the Edwardian walls from the Bell Tower looking west [see photo], both the Dominican and Franciscan friaries would have been located on the left (south) side of the Edwardian walls, the Dominican friary being closer to the castle. The houses on the north side of Bell Tower Park, and the Holy Trinity School, were built on the line of the Edwardian walls. It is possible that archaeology could help

From Castle Hotel, showing current garage on site of Dominican Friary (with permission)

in the grounds of the school (and perhaps help in the teaching of local history and archaeology!)

As we have seen in Chapter 3, the Friars of the Sack were disbanded by the Pope in 1274, so their property reputed to be near the bridge in Berwick became available; on 17 June 1285 the Pope gave a mandate to the bishop of St Andrews to sell this house to the Friars Preachers. Although the Dominicans wanted to be nearer the main centre of population, the site of the Friars of the Sack building was probably very constricted compared with the open space of the Greenses from where they had moved. The community must have moved to their new premises near the bridge soon after 1289 as by 1292 their church adjacent to the castle was described as 'deserta' when it was used by several persons to swear fealty to Edward I. Previously, on August 13 1291, this same Dominican church by the castle was used for the meetings Edward I called to debate the claims of the rivals to the throne of Scotland.[C30][B8] Due to the size and relative neutrality of the friars' buildings, they were often used for large meetings.[G5] Abandonment of the site by the castle was confirmed by a reference in 1313 to 'the old place formerly of the Friars Preachers'.[D7][C10]

British Library (1580 map)
© British Library Board Cotton Ms.Titus C.XIII

Once purchased, the site on Love Lane was owned by the Dominicans until the

Dissolution. In 1436 the Friary is said to have been completely burnt by accident, but is named in a poem in the late fifteenth century so it was presumably restored.(C13)(C14) It is most likely on the site of the Chapel of Ravensdale on the north side of Love Lane, today covered partly by Tintagel House.

On the evidence of grants of pittances made by Edward I it would appear that there were four and six friars in this house, on separate occasions in December 1299, the 28th year of King Edward I.(A7)(B36) The 'Wardrobe Account' lists four religious communities in Berwick at this time, namely Friars Preachers, Friars Minors (Franciscans), Carmelite Friars and Friars of St Austin (Augustinians) (although there is doubt about that last one - see Chapter 14). In 1336 the number of Friars Preachers was stated at different times as fifteen and twenty(B6a)(A7)

Archaeological Investigations of the Dominicans in Berwick-upon-Tweed

See Chapter 2 for archaeological investigations on the site of the Chapel of Ravensdale, the Friars of the Sack and the Dominicans. There are no known archaeological investigations on the site near the castle.

Other Dominican Friaries in the vicinity

In Edinburgh a Dominican Friary was founded in 1230 and survived until dissolution in 1556/7.(A7)(G4) In England, there was a substantial Dominican Friary in Newcastle - incredibly many of the claustral buildings have survived and the friars' refectory is now a restaurant! The layout of the site, which is approximately 50m by 50m, is delineated and is free to visit - in Friars Street, not far from the main railway station and Grainger Street. A Berwick house of similar dimensions would have fitted happily in the Greenes, but not so by the old bridge. In Newcastle there were apparently 33 friars in 1299 and 1300 and 38 in 1310. Prior Richard Marshall fled to Scotland

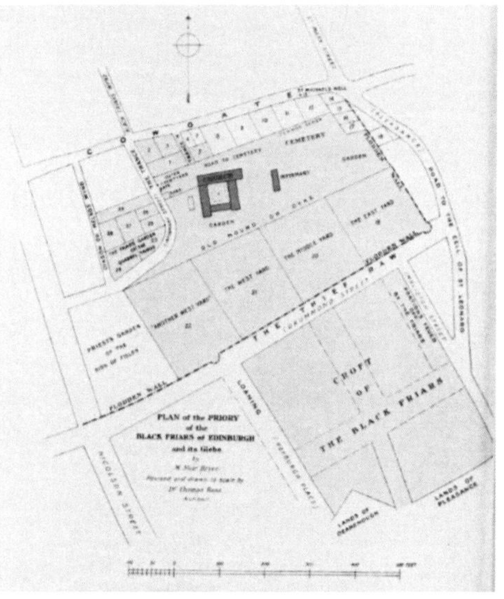

Plan of Dominican Friary, Edinburgh.
Reproduced under a Creative Commons Attribution 4.0 International (CC-BY) licence with the permission of the National Library of Scotland

Remains of Dominican Friary, Newcastle (and below)

in 1536, as he was in danger for preaching publicly against the royal supremacy. There were 12 friars besides the prior Roland Harding at the surrender on 10 January 1539.[(G1)(G9)(G8)]

Nearer to Berwick, there was a house of the Dominican Friars in Bamburgh; the house existed from before 1265 until 1539; there are a few remains, on private land. Henry III granted 7 acres to the friars for enlarging their site in August 1265. There were 10 friars in 1300. A monk of Durham obtained permission around 1450 to become a friar in Bamburgh, but joined the Dominicans at Berwick instead; but because he found the discipline too severe he returned to the Benedictines![(B30)] Ryder has produced a plan of the Friary in *Archaeology in Northumberland*.[(G12)(G2)(A17)] The convent of York was head of one of the four visitations into which the English province was divided. The visitation of York included the houses of York, Lincoln, Newcastle-on-Tyne, Lancaster, Scarborough, Yarm, Carlisle, Beverley, Pontefract, Bamburgh, and probably Berwick.[(G13)]

Berwick-upon-Tweed Dominicans: later history

On 30 July 1302 there is recorded an Inquisition concerning 40 acres of land "*extending from the old place formerly of the Friars Preachers of Berwick*". Payments from the Scottish Exchequer are recorded in the year 1329-1333.[(B23d)] On 10 August 1333, Edward III instructed the Provincial of the English Dominicans to remove the Scottish friars in this house to English houses south of the Trent and to substitute English friars.[(B51)(A7)] "*On March 2nd 1334 the King ordered his Receiver of Victuals to deliver them victuals to the value of 20 marks*". This was a general order to most of the religious orders in the town. We learn further, concerning the Black Friars, that the 40 marks paid annually out of the ferm of Berwick, with which the kings of Scotland had endowed their convent, were continued to be paid by Edward III; the Chamberlain was ordered to pay this sum annually to the prior and his brethren. Frequent alms were given to this house directly from the King. On 25 September 1335, he gave 6s 8d to John de Rodiard, the companion of Nicholas Herle, coming to Berwick from Perth, to remain in company of the friars. On 12 October of the same year he gave fifteen friars 5s to those who met him in procession on his arrival in Berwick, for their maintenance for one day.[(B6a)] In May and December 1337 various payments were made from the Exchequer, including to "*the Prioress of South Berwick, old alms of the Scottish Kings, 40 marks; Thomas de Baumburgh warden of St Mary Magdalene's Hospital, near Berwick, an annual rent of 25s.; the Friars preachers of Berwick, 40 marks ; the Friars minors, 20 marks ; the Carmelite friars, 8l....*" [(B17)(B17b)] On 16 December 1336, he had given 6s 8d to twenty friars on his arrival at Berwick, for the same purpose, by the hands of Thomas Deyncourt, who was prior of this house in the year 1337.[(C30)(B51)]

An indulgence for the rebuilding of the house, following its accidental destruction by fire, was granted 25 February 1436.[(B47)(A7)] The Friary is said to have been completely burnt by the accident, but the Dominicans are named, along with the Franciscans, Carmelites and Augustinians, in the poem "*The Friars of Berwick*" by Dunbar in the late 15th century so it is likely to have been restored.[(D9)(C13)(C14)] In 1450, the prior is mentioned several times in a History of Durham: "*....et adduxit eundem Robertus Erghowe ad Priorem domus Fratrum Praedicatorum de Berwico....*"[(A7)(B30)] On 25 April

1461, the Scots regained possession of Berwick. Brockie[B37] gives a charter (from the collections of Father Richard Augustine Hay) of James III to the sheriff of Berwick, but it is thought that this document is almost certainly not genuine.[A7]

Berwick was retaken by the English on 22 August 1482. The friars were loyal subjects of the Scottish crown, and this could be expressed in an active manner, such as the Scottish friar who, in March 1494, plotted along with others to take Berwick castle from the English and let in a company of Scots via the postern gate, using High Mass as his cover; they were, however, 'discovered and taken'[B8ar][G5] After this, there is no definite evidence that this friary survived until the general Dissolution of the English monasteries, but, as mentioned above, it is highly likely that the chapel of Ravensdale, a house of friars surrendered in 1539, belonged to the Dominicans.[B39][A7] A letter written by Richard, Bishop of Dover to Thomas Cromwell on 10 March 1539: "*Sinon…has received 16 convents of friars into his hands to the King's use. There are still standing about 10 houses in these parts, besides three or four in or near Barwyke…*"[B35]

Work, Liturgy, Education, Architecture of the Dominicans

The ethos of the Dominicans was both active and contemplative. Some of the active roles taken on by the Scottish Dominicans were perhaps a little unusual, such as munitions expert or clockmaker! The ideals of study, asceticism, poverty, obedience were common to all friars preachers everywhere.[G5]

Dominic legislated for his brethren begging but also allowed them to earn their keep. The odd jobs which friars did were all jobs of skill, presumably requiring some education. The town clock of Aberdeen was broken in the 1530s and Alexander Lindsay OP [Order of Preachers] was commissioned to mend it. His skill in clock making and mending must have been well known as Calderwood referred to him as 'a great mathematician and maker of horologes.' This was a task which involved knowledge of mechanics and science and the friar was well paid.[G5] Other jobs included: keeping the lawns at Stirling castle, whisky distilling, carpentry work, etc. [G5] It was common for documents of importance to be signed and witnessed within Dominican houses or churches.[G5]

Labour was not part of the Dominican's day in the same way as it was for Cistercians or Benedictines. The Dominicans did keep gardens, orchards and even work croft land but they did so together and were not to allow these labours to be detrimental to the primary aims of study and preaching. In an economy such as Scotland's it would have been difficult for the friars to purchase all their dietary requirements at market. The towns were still sufficiently spacious for a vegetable plot to be more convenient than the market-place. There is evidence that most of the Dominican houses, whether a place or a convent, had gardens. It seems reasonable to suppose that most did [but possibly not Berwick through lack of space]. The friars also kept fruit trees. In Glasgow the three lands of the Paradise croft, the Coal house croft and the west yard had fruit trees on them.[(G5)]

By far the most prominent duty which the Dominicans did for their communities in terms of parish service was their burial of the dead and the prayers and pastoral support which accompanied it. They must also have visited the sick, although as Moir Bryce emphasised; '*In their statutes the friars were strictly forbidden, when visiting the sick, to solicit the granting of legacies either in their own favour, or in that of their priories*'.[(G5)] Inside the convent, when peace and quiet prevailed, the day was divided by the canonical hours, which the Dominicans were to say briefly in order to be free to study and to preach.[(G5)]

The beginnings of St Andrews University in 1411, followed by Glasgow in 1451, and Aberdeen in 1495, were very important to the Order in Scotland. The friars preachers were naturally attracted to St Andrews because of the university and a small oratory or hospice was set up by the Order; it is recorded as having a prior in 1464 and was given sanction by a bull of Pope Sixtus IV, on 18 March 1477. When Glasgow University was founded, the friars' buildings became the core of the university on the High Street.[(G5)] Glasgow was the second to be founded but the first Scottish University to have a clear Dominican connection.[(G5)] A grant by Sixtus IV in 1477 shows the sorts of buildings that the friars would be expected to have: a church, cloister, a cemetery, a dormitory, refectory, a bell tower, a bell, a yard or garden and any other necessary offices.[(G5)] All convents would have had a library.[(G5)]

CHAPTER 5

Maison Dieu Hospital

Medieval Hospitals

For general information about medieval hospitals, see Chapter 2.

Maison Dieu hospital: foundation, location and early history

The hospital called 'Maison Dieu' in Berwick was founded by Philip de Rydale in the reign of Alexander III (1249-1286), prior to 1281. Philip de Rydale, Mayor of Berwick, was listed as one of the signatories to the oath of fealty to Edward I in 1291 - "*Rydale, Philippus de (major ville de Berewico)*".(B44) In the documentary records, as well as *Maison Dieu*, the hospital's name appears as *Domus Dei, House of God, God's House,* and various corruptions of the name Maison Dieu, for example, Masondue, Mesoun Due, etc.

In 1281 there was confirmation of the existence of the hospital on 6 July that year:

> "*..confirmation of grants to Philip de Ridale, burgess of Berewyk...to the master and brethren of the Domus Dei on the bridge of Berewyk, of 11 marks 6s 8d of rent receivable from the mill of Hedreslawe and from Robert Air of Hedreslawe*".(B11)(A7)(B51)(B8)

There is further confirmation of the foundation in *The Patent Rolls* for Edward I, 24 Nov 1300:

> "*The King confirms the donation by Philip de Rydale to the master, chaplains and poor of the Hospital of 'Domus Dei' of Berwick-on-Tweed, of all his lands and possessions in said town, and adjacent crofts, and in the vills of Chirneside, Wederburne and Quitusum* (Whitsome) *in Scotland, and likewise in the vills of Tweedmuthe, Bollesdune, Gateswyke, and Hedereslawe with its mill, within England; to be held in pure almoigne* [alms]".(B11)(B8)

Earlier, in 1287 and 1291, the master was engaged in a suit concerning the hospital's lands:

> "*...he also held another vill called Wedreburne of the earl by same service, containing*

6 carucates of land and meadow, from which the Domus Dei of Berwick has 20 marks yearly".(J1)(B8)(B10)

There is also an entry in the Papal Registers for October 1290 where is granted

"*...relaxation of one year and forty days of enjoined penance to penitents......... who visit the chapel of the House of God at Berwick, in the diocese of St. Andrews, on the Assumption of the Blessed Virgin, and the feasts of St. Andrew, St. John Baptist, and St. John the Evangelist, and their octaves*".(B9b)

Scott, writing in 1888, notes that

"*This house was undoubtedly situated at the corner of the present bridge, where the National Bank now stands, of which Mr Stephen Sanderson, a lineal descendent of the tenant in 1610, is a gent, and where he occupies premises as a Solicitor and the Clerk of the Peace for Berwick and Northumberland. The quay in front of the building long continued to be called the 'Mason Due', and everyone on becoming free was bound to pay 3s 4d for repair of this quay.*"(C30)

As we saw above, the confirmation of its existence in 1281 names it "*Domus Dei* on the bridge of Berewyk"; that it was adjacent to *Bridge House* (the Trinitarians and *St Edwards Hospital*) is confirmed in 1355-1357 by details of a brattice constructed "*.... between the Maison Dieu and the Bridge-house for £5*".(B39c)(B23) - see Chapter 2. The detailed plan of Berwick around 1580 is not of much help, but there are buildings shown to the east of the north end of the old timber bridge which might be the former *Maison Dieu*, as the name was still in use then.(E1) The photo shows the building on the site before the National Bank was built in 1869, presumably the building that replaced the *Maison Dieu* of medieval times.

Site of Maison Dieu medieval hospital
© Berwick Record Office

British Library (1580 map)
© British Library Board Cotton Ms. Titus C.XIII

Maison Dieu Hospital: later history

It appears, in 1328, as having its Scottish possessions restored after the recent war.

> "*Order to cause to be delivered to the master and brethren of God's House, Berwick-on-Tweed, their lands and possessions, which were taken into the late king's hands by reason of the Scotch war.....*"(B8)

At the end of 1333 a petition of the "*Master, brothers and sisters of the House of God, Berwick-upon-Tweed*" to the English king and his council shows that "*....their church and houses were utterly cast down by the engines during the siege, and the master has spent so much in repairing them that he has pledged his chalice and vestments; but the work is so unfinished that they cannot endure the winter without being utterly 'perished'.*" (B8) Scott gives information about some of the masters of the hospital.(J4)(C30)

There was a further confirmation of its foundation in 1334(B51b) and in a Petition to the King in 1335 about his late uncle's estate, Adam of Corbridge mentions the hospital among other possessions in and around Berwick:

> "*.....the third lying between the land of the Mesoundeu to the East.....the third croft lying between the road leading from the Kougat to the Snoke on the North and the Mesondue croft on the South....*"(B8)

On 20 November 1347 in a grant from the King "*...the vill...of Wetherbourne is charged with 20 marks sterling per annum to the Hospital of the 'Domus Dei' of Berwick..*"(B8) This is further confirmed by the King on 26 May 1348.(B8au)

According to Scott, after 1350 there is "*no further history of this hospital in olden times*", but since he wrote in 1888 other records have come to light.(C30) The Exchequer rolls for January 1355 to January 1357 include some details of work done in the vicinity of *Maison Dieu* and the '*Bridge House*' of the Trinitarians: Master John of Allerton was the chief carpenter, and John of Morpeth, described as 'carpenter of the Baron of Greystock' (then keeper of the town), made a long brattice(D17) - a temporary structure of timber erected on battlements - round the *Maison Dieu* by task for £10, and another between the *Maison Dieu* and the *Bridge-house* for £5.(B39c)(B23) This may be evidence to confirm the Trinitarians and St Edwards hospital, *Bridge House,* were sited on the south side of Love Lane. There was further mention of the *Domus Dei* in May/June 1362 in connection with the carriage of goods from the river, via *Domus Dei* to the castle.(B8)

There is in the British Library a manuscript dated 20 June 1395 relating to the grant of a tenement by "*John de Derby, master or warden of the House of God of Berwick-upon-Tweed*".(B5) "In December 1405 Henry [IV] made a grant of 1000 marks (£666 13s 4d) out of the customs to the citizens of Berwick to help them to restore their public and private buildings, many of which had been burned.(B51k)(B39b) The *Domus Dei* and the Tollbooth were among the buildings repaired or rebuilt.(B41)(B39c)(B23)

A grant to 'The House of God' by James I to his chaplain, Thomas de Lawedre, is provisionally dated 8 June 1425.

> "*Charter under the great seal, granted* [apparently by James I] *in favour of the King's chaplain 'Thomas de Lawedre' of the House of God or Hospital lying in the burgh of Berwick upon Tweed; to be held to him for the whole time of his life with all lands, teinds, rents and profits, etc.…*"(J7)

On 24 August 1482 Alexander Lye was granted custody of '*Mesuneue*' within the town of Berwick, "*with all rights and profits*"; and on 28 August 1484 a William Norton is named as master of the Hospital of Our Lord God at Berwick-upon-Tweed".(B11d)(J2) The Maison Dieu gets a mention in the poem *The Friars of Berwick,* written in the latter part of the fifteenth century:

> "*Of all the goodly towns where I have been*
> *This was the best and fairest to be seen:*
> *Town, towers, sea, river, castle, good green land,*
> *And the high walls above the town that stand -*
> *The Church of the Great Cross - the Maison Dieu -*
> *And Houses of the Friars of every hue;*
> *White Jacobins, Franciscans Gray and White,*
> *The Augustinian and the Carmelite,*
> *With black Dominicans and Minor sleek..*"(C13)

It is difficult to estimate the size of the hospital, but at different times there are references to the 'Master and brethren', the 'master, chaplains and poor', 'master, poor brethren and sisters', and 'their church and houses'.

After the Dissolution, a further appointment to the Meason Dieu of Berwick, 17 May 1543, probably concerns disused hospital buildings or nearby quay to which the name Maison Dieu long applied after it ceased to be a hospital.

> "*Griffin Lloyd, one of the grooms of the Chamber. To be master of the Bridge and of the Meason Dieu of the town of Berwick, with all profits which the captain, officers and soldiers there have been accustomed to pay to the said Bridge.…*".(B35c)(C30)

On the 1564 map and in 1603 the buildings were in use as a forge and bullet yard taken over by Mayor and Burgesses from the Crown.(C10)(D7h) In January 1586 the name is still in use and applied to the adjacent Quay or wharf: "*Barwicke uppon Twied xxiijmo Januarij 1586, anno regni Elizabethe regine xxixno* ."— Certificate of sundry most needful repairs to be done presently:

> *"The Masondue keye or wharfe, greatly fallen down, and more ready to fall every spring tide, will cost, 100l.....the Mary gate, the gate at the tower of the bridge, the Masondue gate, and Shore gate, will cost 1000l".*

Later mentions include:

> *"Gates: the Mary, two bridge gates, shore and Maison Dieu, of Berwick, in complete decay, 10th Aug, 1596;...the six iron, of Berwick: the Mary, the bridge, the Masendue and shore, and the new cost of restoring, by survey, 1st April, 1597".*[(B7a)]

Scott writes that in 1603 it became the property of the Corporation, and was let shortly afterwards to Michael Sanderson, a leading member of the Guild at the time; thus

> *"The Mason Due, now in possession of Henry Reveley, it's lots and cellars, its years and forge, and the bullet-yard, is let to Mr. Michael Sanderson for 21 years, he paying 40s yearly, and to keep it all in good repair, and leave it in the same state".*[(C30)]

This description clearly means that it was no longer a hospital.

There are in existence images of the *Maison Dieu* building [see page 42] which existed prior to the present building (originally a bank which dates from 1869) - the building shown prior to 1869 is not the original hospital.[(J3)(C26)] There is nothing known about the architecture or design of the medieval hospital, other than it consisted of a "church and houses".

Archaeological Investigations of Maison Dieu in Berwick-upon-Tweed

There are no known archaeological investigations on the site.[(C2)]

Work of the Maison Dieu Hospital

"It is supposed to have been a hospital for lepers"; but is this likely when the location was so near a populated area?[(C30)(A27)] Leper hospitals would normally be located away from town and villages to minimise the spread of infection. Or maybe because it's near to the entry to town from England? There was a leper hospital in Tweedmouth.[(A19)] The hospital could have accommodated mariners; the Middle Ages saw a growth in the network of hostels for travellers, pilgrims and seafarers; they were known variously as hostels, hospitals, hospices, *domus dei* or *maison dieu*.[(B38)]

CHAPTER 6

Bondington:

Church of St Mary the Virgin (21 Castle Terrace(?)), Church of St Lawrence (48 Castle Terrace(?))

© OpenStreetMap contributors. ODbL 1.0

The latest information about these sites is derived from recent archaeological investigations in the medieval village of Bondington; these investigations are excellently described in full reports: *Putting Bondington on the map. Report on the History and Archaeology of Bondington*, 2004, ISBN 0954920902, and *How Bondington was put on the map. Phase 2. Second Report on the History and Archaeology of Bondington*, Steering Group of the Bondington Project, 2007. ISBN 0954920937;

both reports[(K10)(K5)] are available to view in Berwick Archives.[(C6)] These reports also detail the documentary evidence for the sites. An important report prior to these is: Cambridge, Eric, Gates, Tim, and Williams, Alan. 'Berwick and Beyond: Medieval Religious Establishments on the North Western Margin of Berwick-upon-Tweed—Problems of Identity and Context', *Archaeologia Aeoliana* 5, 29, 2001, 33-94.[(K3)] A shorter booklet was published in 2005: 'Putting Bondington on the map: Berwick and its Lost Northern Suburb'. The Steering Group of the Bondington Project, 2005. ISBN 0-9549209-2-9.[(K11)]

Discoveries have been made at both 21 Castle Terrace and 48 Castle Terrace (Cheviot House) with evidence of two churches, which are known from documentary evidence as St Mary the Virgin and St Lawrence (Laurence), in the diocese of St Andrews;[(A8)] no definitive evidence has emerged to say which of the two sites is which church, but in some quarters it is thought that the former "*may be tentatively identified as the church of St Mary, Bondington....and Cheviot House.... tentatively identified as the parish church of St Laurence*".[(C27)] One or both probably served Berwick as a parish church prior to the foundation of Holy Trinity.[(K10)] On 10 May 1253, "*from the King [Henry III] to Prior and monks of Durham, of all the lands, tithes, churches etc.....belonging to the Priory...; Coldingham, with its church and pertinents,,; the church of Berewik, with its pertinents...*".[(B8as)] This church is most likely to be St Mary the Virgin. Cowan suggests that '*of the three churches associated with the town, St Laurence, St Mary and Holy Trinity, the first two (in Bondington) appear to antedate the last which became the parish church of the burgh only on or after its foundation by Earl David between 1119 and 1124*'.[(A6)(A8)] The remains of a church at 21 Castle Terrace were found by chance in June 1998; it was later identified as a Romanesque structure dating from the early to mid-twelfth century.[(C27)] The village of Bondington itself is thought to have been abandoned shortly after 1296. The dedication of St Mary's was transferred to a new church, close to the current Scots Gate; this church was demolished to make way for the Elizabethan ramparts.[(C10)] Holy Trinity Church, located just south of the present church, is documented from around 1120. [See Chapter 10].

Church at 21 Castle Terrace (St Mary the Virgin?): history

In 1130-1133 King David I of Scotland gave the church of St Mary to the monks of St Cuthbert in exchange for the church at Melrose.[(B20b)] St Mary's was probably always more important than the Church of St Laurence. It was mentioned in taxation records.[(B55)] Protection was given to the church by Edward I, dated 8 March 1296.[(B18)] "*Simple protection...for Alexander de Norham, chaplain of the chapel of St Mary, Bonyngton, and celebrating divine service there for the soul of Alexander, sometime King of Scotland*".[(B11c)] The church is thought to have been abandoned shortly after 1296, the dedication of St Mary being transferred to the new church close to what is now Scots Gate.[(C23)(C30)]

According to Chalmer's *Caledonia* a hospital was founded in Berwick which was dedicated to the Virgin Mary....in 1340 Edward III gave Robert de Burton the government of this hospital.[(B15)] As the church in Bondington had by this time been abandoned, it seems that this would most likely be the church near Scots Gate which was later demolished to make way for the Elizabethan ramparts.

Archaeological Investigations at 21 Castle Terrace

Decorated grave slab excavated at 21 Castle Terrace.

Excavations took place in July 1998; what was discovered on this site was a church built before the mid-twelfth-century, with a graveyard with 'at least 400 burials' which was found to have ceased in use after about 1350 - the graveyard must have continued in use some years after the church itself was abandoned. The church was of Romanesque design, the layout including an apse, a square chancel and a nave without aisles. Unusually, it had a narrow (0.75 m and 0.8m wide) wall with no foundations longitudinally down the centre of the nave, which may suggest part of the nave was partitioned off for use as a hospital, or possibly a chantry chapel. Further details and artist's reconstructions can be found on information boards at the site itself, and in the detailed published reports mentioned above. [See the photograph of a decorated grave slab uncovered at No 21 Castle Terrace][(K2)(D7b)(K10)(K5)(K11)(K3)]

Church at 48 Castle Terrace, 'Cheviot House' (St Lawrence?): history

The Church of St Lawrence (often spelt 'Laurence') was given to the monks at Durham. Around 1113 to 1119 a charter granted to the abbey of Selkirk referred to an existing church (which could refer to either St Mary's or St Lawrence's church) - "*et in Berewyce unam carrucatam* [a carrucate is a measure of land, generally of 120 or 80 acres.[(D17)]] *et unam maisuram* [Maisuram is a tenement or dwelling house[(235)]] *sub ecclesia usque...*"[(B31)(B20)] But a charter issued in 1159 by Malcolm IV identifies the church as that of St Lawrence.[(G11)] It is 'generally assumed' St Lawrence was founded in 1128 when the monks from Selkirk resettled in Kelso. Historic England Research Records link Cheviot House with St Lawrence, as does Scott; *'the Chartulary of Kelso (1128-1158) mentions that Roger Fitz William, probably the founder, gave the Church of St Lawrence to the monks of Kelso. When Cheviot House, in Castle Terrace, was built, the foundations of a church, 90 feet in length, with a 25 feet square tower at the west-end, were found together with several graves'.*(D18)(C30) *Coldingham Priory held the churches of Edrom, Berwick, Ednam* etc.(A25) *R[obert], bp of St Andrews: conf. of grant by abb. and conv. to ch. of St Laurence at Berwick of teinds, other rights, lands and fishery: poss. 1150, more prob. 1151. At Edinburgh. Date:Abb. Osbert of Holyrood].*(K14) The Kelso Chartulary may have been a forgery.(K13) 'Early Scottish Charters' confirms the addition to the endowment of the church of St Lawrence at Berwick, A.D. 1147-1153: confirmation by Robert, Bishop of St Andrews, of the increase to the endowment of St Lawrence at Berwick made by the Abbey of Kelso granting the tithe of a ploughgate of land at Berwick, and the fishings and toft in the burgh. Date between 1147 and 1150.(B20c)

The last known reference to St Lawrence is in the period 1188-1202, when Walter FitzRobert sought to lease land belonging to the Church of St Lawrence; Prior Bertram (of Convent of Durham) agreed to the lease, with the rent 4s per annum, payable half-yearly.(K10)

Archaeological Investigations at 48 Castle Terrace

A church and graveyard were exposed in the nineteenth century when building Cheviot House.(C30) Human bones were discovered in August 2000, and one ornate grave slab. There was an investigation in a field north of Cheviot House in September 2002, with finds associating it with the church at Cheviot House; and other archaeological work at West Hope Farm, which was probably associated with the Cistercian Nunnery [see Chapter 7]. There were further investigations at Cheviot House in 2006, the results of which have yet to be published.(K10)(K5)(K3)(C2)

CHAPTER 7

Bondington:

Cistercian Nunnery of St Leonard

Origins and Early History of the Cistercian Order of Nuns

Cistercian convents for nuns were usually dedicated to St Mary, with the number of nuns at least 13. A number of the convents began as Benedictine establishments, but later many changed to Cistercian to claim the privileges of the Order, such as the exemption from the payment of tithes. The Cistercian Chapter General tried to prohibit the founding of further nunneries from early in the thirteenth century.[A17]

Cistercian Nuns in Bondington: foundation, location and early history

Site of St Leonard's Cistercian Nunnery, Bondington

The Cistercian Nunnery of Bondington/Berwick-upon-Tweed was named St Leonard's, or St Mary and St Leonard's; in documents it is also referred to on occasions as the Nunnery of South Berwick (to distinguish it from North Berwick). It figures as "[the house] of the Blessed Mary and St Leonard of South Berwick" around 1284, when Henry, Bishop of St Andrews, confirmed the union of the possessions of the Nuns of South Berwick to Dryburgh Abbey.[A7][K6] It is evidently identical to the nunnery of "St Leonard outside Berwick" - "*Priorissa & conventus St. Leonardi extra Berewyk...*" mentioned 12 April 1296.[B51n][A7] It is said to have been founded by King David I who was responsible for founding many religious establishments around the mid-twelfth century; he died in 1153, so it would have been founded before that date. Key sources for the detailed discovery and background for this priory are those mentioned in Chapter 6 above, references K3, K5, K10, K11. *Putting Bondington on the map. Report on the History and Archaeology of Bondington*, 2004, ISBN 0954920902.[K10] includes a detailed documentary history of the Nunnery on pages 26-39.

According to Cowan and Easson, the nuns appear on record before 1177.(A7)(K7) The foundation may have begun life as a Benedictine house: *Rolment of Courtis* (and others) speak of black nuns here, *"The abbay or priorie of the Nunrie of South Berwick of the ordoure of Sanct Benedict foirsaid [of blak habit] founded by the said King David the First…"*,(B50)(A7) Others, such as the fourteenth century chronicler John of Fordun, state it was for Bernardines or Cistercians:"*…a monastery of Holy nuns close to Berwick…the monastery at Berwick was founded for Bernardine's or Cistercian nuns*".(B26c) A list of around 1207 given by Gervase of Canterbury(B2) has white [Cistercian] monks: "*Gervase of Canterbury…The Priory of South Berwick (White monks)..*"; but in Henry of Silgrave's list of around 1272, in Scalacronica(B52), "*…Prioratus, Suthberewik; moniales albae*", in Haddan & Stubbs(B28), and in Edinburgh University Manuscripts(B21) it appears as a house of white [Cistercian] nuns. In later records of 13 May 1420(B12b), the nuns are designated Cistercian; Masters of brethren associated with this house are found in office in 1204 and 1232.(K6d)(K7b)(A7)

The convent was mentioned in a papal document of 28 September 1219(K6b) "*… priorissa et moniales de Suthberwyk Cisterciensis ordinis..*", and in 1221 and about 1230 there were disputes about tithes at Gullane and Dirleton respectively, where the decision was in favour of the Prioress who, around 1221, was named as Froelina.(A35) There was further mention in a papal document of 2 June 1232.(K6c) In 1291, Lady Agnes de Bernham, prioress ["*Bernham, Domina Agnes de (prioriffa de Berewyco*"] was one of those swearing fealty to Edward I, and again in 1296 ["*South Berewyk, prioreffe de, Agneys (et le couent de mefme le lu*"].(B8)(K10) Edward I used the nunnery as his headquarters in 1296.(K10)(B4) In 1302-4, when Bondington was given as part of the King's demesne, the nunnery had over 600 acres. Scott details two separate convents: 'The Nunnery of St Leonard, nr Halidon Hill', (p343-344) and 'The Convent of Cistercian Nuns of South Berwick', (p345); this may be accounting for the fact that the Nunnery owned some land in the town itself, as well as the convent near Halidon Hill.

There is an exact location for the convent [NT 98445402], as recent archaeological excavation work has revealed the foundations of the buildings. It lies on the Duns Road beyond the fork in the road at the north end of Castle Terrace where the old road to Paxton branches off to the left, in the field beyond the modern houses 2-4 Duns Road; when these Ministry of Defence houses were being built on an area of land taken from the Nunlees, a number of skeletons were located.(K10)(E4)(E3) It is close to the modern A1 bypassing Berwick; horseless carriages thundering past at 60 miles an hour would have been unimaginable to the nuns cloistered here and the disturbance to the peace and quiet of the convent would not have been appreciated. The Castle Terrace/Duns road is probably on an ancient route from the north and the west, including from the abbeys of Kelso, Melrose, Dryburgh and Coldingham.

Two pilgrim badges were found during excavations at the nunnery which suggests that maybe pilgrims to and from Holy Island and St Andrews may have sought accommodation in the convent, conveniently sited between Halidon Hill [from where the destination of Holy Island is in sight] and the town of Berwick.(K10)

Archaeological Investigations of the Cistercian Nunnery

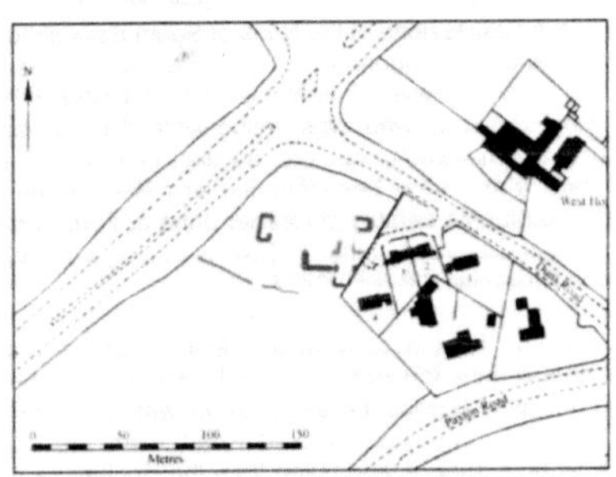

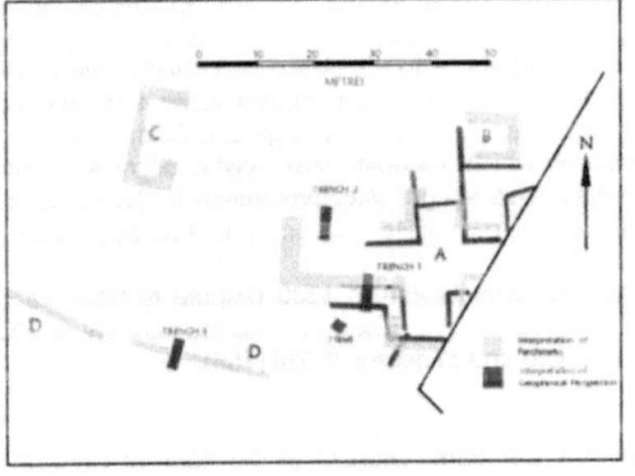

Alan Williams

Plan of St Leonard's Cistercian Nunnery, Bondington.
Courtesy of Steering Group of the Bondington Project

We are fortunate that much information about the nunnery has been obtained from recent archaeological investigations on the site, in 2002 and 2003; the findings are detailed in two publications: *Putting Bondington on the map. Report on the History and Archaeology of Bondington,* 2004. ISBN 0954920902;(K10) and *How Bondington was put on the map. Phase 2. Second Report on the History and Archaeology of Bondington*, Steering Group of the Bondington Project, 2007. ISBN 0954920937.(K5)

The site of the Cistercian nunnery of St Mary and St Leonard comprised a church on an east-west alignment measuring 36 metres by 22 metres. In addition, the investigations revealed two other rectangular buildings and other remains. There is a very good 'artist's impression' of how the priory buildings would have looked on Page 66 of *How Bondington was put on the map;*(D18)(K5)(K10) and is used, with permission, on the cover of this book.

As mentioned, two lead pilgrim badges were found during excavations which suggests that pilgrims may have sought accommodation at the convent.(K10) As well as the pilgrim badges, initial field-walking and geophysics rediscovered a medieval grave slab previously exposed in 1954. In the excavations in 2003 [see plan page 87 of Ref K10], part of the church was revealed, as were some of the conventual buildings.(K10) A rare surviving contemporary plan of a nunnery at Coldstream may indicate the extent of St Mary & St Leonard's.(K10) Other archaeological work at West

Hope Farm (on the other side of Duns Road), where twelfth to fourteenth century pottery was found, located a boundary ditch and outbuildings possibly associated with nunnery.(K10) Further excavations took place in 2006.(K5)(D7d)(K8)

Part of pillar from Cistercian Nunnery, Coldstream.
From the collections of Scottish Borders Council. (Coldstream Museum) Copyright: administered on behalf of Scottish Borders Council by Live Borders.

Other Cistercian Nunneries in the vicinity

For over 400 years there was a Cistercian Nunnery in Coldstream. This was situated on high ground north of a tributary to the river Tweed. There are no remains, but a sketch plan of the site used in a legal case survives from 1589 and shows the layout.(K12)(K10) There were other foundations of Cistercian nuns at Elbottle, Gullane, St Bothan's (Abbey St Bathans), Haddington and North Berwick, where there are some remains on Highfield Road/Nungate Road.(B14) It is possible, but not definite, that a foundation existed also at Trefontain Priory.(A7) The Cistercian Nunneries in the border area were relatively prosperous; in the assessment for papal tithes Haddington's contribution [£221] was more than that of Melrose Abbey [£217]; Coldstream's was £119, and Berwick's £121.

Berwick-upon-Tweed Cistercian Nunnery: later history

An allowance was given to the Prioress in 1301: "*Monialibus ejusdem ville (Berwick-upon-Tweed) ad unam pitanciam sibi emendam, per manus domine Isabelle de la Chamber ibidem, 15th Julii, ...6s 8d*".(B8ac) Scott states that in 1303 the Receiver for Scotland sanctioned a donation to the Prioress of 8 quarters of flour (worth 56 shillings) and a tun of wine (worth £4) for her own use!(C30) Records indicate in 1304/5 that Edward had holdings around Berwick..."..*farms of the King's lands in Eddington, Bondington and Latham*...". At the time of Edward III's battle success at Halidon Hill, March 1333, the Nunnery was burned and seriously damaged; lead shot has been found on the site. There were promises by Edward III after the battle to restore the buildings, make restitution for loss of possessions, erect a new altar and grant an annuity of £20 payable by the Sheriff of Berwick.(K10)(B51u) In 1335/6 Edward gave 5/- to the Prioress and nuns(C30) but by 1337 the nunnery had received only a small part of restitution; it seems that the nunnery never recovered from the ravages of war. The King was petitioned to grant a Charter to confirm 40 marks rent in Berwick etc.(K10)(A7)(K9)

That the nunnery existed as early as the reign of David I is borne out by references, in 1334 and 1336, to an annual grant of 40 marks made to it by King David from the ferme of the burgh: " *[pro] priorissa et moniales de Berewico super Tweedam … quadraginta marcis annuis ….David quanda regis Scotie…*".(B51p)(B51q) In December 1337: "*To the treasurer and barons of the exchequer. Whereas the king ordered Thomas de Burgh, chamberlain of Berwick-upon-Tweed, by divers writs under the great and privy seals, the seal used in Scotland, and by other letters under the seals of Robert de Ufford and Henry de Ferariis, to pay….. 40 marks to the prioress and nuns of Suthberewyk, of the anciently appointed alms of the kings of Scotland, …….9l. to the prioress and nuns of Suth Berewyk,…*".(B17b)

On the 15 December 1337 the Prioress received 40 marks from Thomas de Burgh, Chamberlain of Berwick.(B8ad) In the following year, 1338, Edward seems to have changed his mind about rebuilding the nunnery when he declared his intention to found a new monastery for a Prior and 12 Benedictine monks in Oxford "*in fulfilment of the vow made when the Scots were in battle against him at Halidon Hill near Berwick in Scotland*"; there is no mention of the nunnery.

Later in the century, a long-drawn-out dispute with Dryburgh Abbey began. In 1385/6, during raids, the abbeys of Dryburgh, Melrose and Newbattle were damaged, and King Robert III of Scotland, in compensation to the canons of Dryburgh Abbey, granted them the lands and revenues of the nunnery of St Leonards in a deed of 1390/91; there were only two nuns in residence at the time.(B49b)(A7) "*Following a petition by the Prioress and convent, a papal mandate to confirm the foundation of the convent of South Berwick made by King David was issued 16 Sept 1391 but was ineffective*".(B46) The Nunnery was supported by other Cistercian houses in South East Scotland.

In 1410 the Bishop of St Andrews issued a charter confirming annexation of the nunnery to Dryburgh Abbey. By 1420 the Prioress and nuns had disappeared and in their place Agnes Bron (Broun), a nun from St Bothan's and 'aged forty years or more', petitioned the Pope for possession of the nunnery; Agnes' predecessor as Prioress was Joanna de Ramsay.(A35) Later that year, on 13 May 1420, the Pope confirmed that Dryburgh Abbey obtain possession.(B12b) Agnes felt so strongly about it that in 1429 she travelled to Rome "*with the greatest perils of roads and dangers of seas*" [For details of dangers etc of travelling to Rome in Medieval times, see *Pilgrimage to Rome in the Middle Ages*(B66)] and petitioned the Pope on 31 July that year.(B12c) Dryburgh countered with petitions for confirmation of the union, 30 Dec 1429 and 7 Aug 1432.(B12d) The dispute dragged on until at least 1466 when it was heard in the papal court; Dryburgh Abbey still held it when, 23 July 1466, the Pope appointed mandatories, on the petition of Alexander Lumsden, clerk of St Andrew's diocese, for the administration of the priory, 'since all that region in which the nuns' monastery is situated, was returned to the obedience and fealty of James, King of Scots'.(B9f)

It is not certain that the dispute was ever resolved satisfactorily. The nunnery would have been dissolved by 1539.(K10) This house has sometimes been confused with Holystone: the Prioress of Holystone appeared on the Ragman Rolls - "Halifton, prioreffe de, Mariorie (del counte de Berewyk)".(A7)

The nunnery was clearly not prosperous in its latter days. It's possessions at the beginning include 6 carucates or plough lands close to its site; each of these will have been roughly 104 acres, or 40 hectares. (a Coldingham survey of 1300 found the size of the 8 oxgates which formed a carucate varied from 8 to 14 acres, although 13 was the accepted norm).(B19) This represented about a square mile of arable land. The nunnery fields presumably lay to the west of the village, a location that would fit well with the 'Nunlees'. It also owned property in Berwick itself - on the Ness around the present Palace Green, and in Uddyngate (Hide Hill). It was probably not an attractive place for the daughter of the well-to-do, mainly because of border wars; there were five other Cistercian nunneries in Berwickshire and Lothian away from the border.(K10) The National Records of Scotland, [Ref GD157/368], has several references to the priory of South Berwick: from the years of Pope Innocent IV [1243-54] - where the notetaker utters the familiar complaint *"whereof the date cannot be read!"* - and from 1279, 1337 and 1359.(K9) Known Prioresses of the Nunnery are included in Watt, D. E. R. and Shead, N. F., *The Heads of Religious Houses in Scotland from Twelfth to Sixteenth Centuries.*(A35)

CHAPTER 8

The Franciscan Order

Origins and Early History of the Franciscan Order

St Francis was born at Assisi in 1181/2, and the Rule of the Franciscan Order he founded was approved by Pope Honorius III on 29 Nov 1223. In medieval documents the Order was more usually called the Friars Minor, Grey Friars or Minorities. They were a mendicant Order, following the founder's decision to cast themselves on divine providence and their reliance on alms. They wore a grey habit initially (hence Grey Friars), but later, in the fifteenth century, a brown frock girded with a knotted rope, and a black hood; some went sandalled, but the rule required bare feet; the cord around the waist had three knots signifying poverty, chastity and obedience. Illustrations can be found on the Franciscans' website.[(L13)] They were not to own anything personally or collectively, so did not own churches (e.g. the new church at Assisi was not 'owned' by the friars), fields, vineyards, houses, animals, etc. They were required to work in return for their sustenance (Chapter 5 of the Rule), as well as preaching and ministering to people e.g. weaving, copying & binding, manuscripts, building, work with paupers, prisoners and the sick.[(L11)]

Around the time of its approval by the Pope, the Order expanded into Britain in 1223/1224, led by Agnellus of Pisa. Within the British Isles, there were soon convents established before 1240 in the cathedral cities of Canterbury, Carlisle, Chichester, Exeter, Hereford, Lichfield, Lincoln, London, Norwich, Salisbury, Winchester, Worcester & York. They had reached Scotland by 1231/2, with the convent in Berwick founded around 1231 (see below); Roxburgh was established before 1233, and Haddington before 1242. Scotland lost its 'provincial' status in 1239, probably due to the low numbers of foundations - until 1329 during this time it came under the jurisdiction of the minister provincial of England. The Order settled in most of the major urban centres, then larger boroughs, such as Stamford, Beverley, Boston & Lynn. From the 1230s they adopted more ambitious building plans, which sometimes brought them into conflict with nearby monastic houses. "*The quasi-monastic stability of place was becoming the norm for some friars*", and some of their churches were enlarged to house the large numbers wishing to attend sermons. They offered burial to all, which sometimes brought them into conflict with secular clergy.[(L11)]

Within a century of the founder's death, 1,421 friaries had been established, their ministry taking them to almost every parish and city. Their architecture was designed to accommodate large crowds for sermons.(L11) The size of a conventual friary was normally a minimum of 13 friars, with non-conventual friaries having less.(L11)

Franciscans in Berwick-upon-Tweed: foundation, location and early history

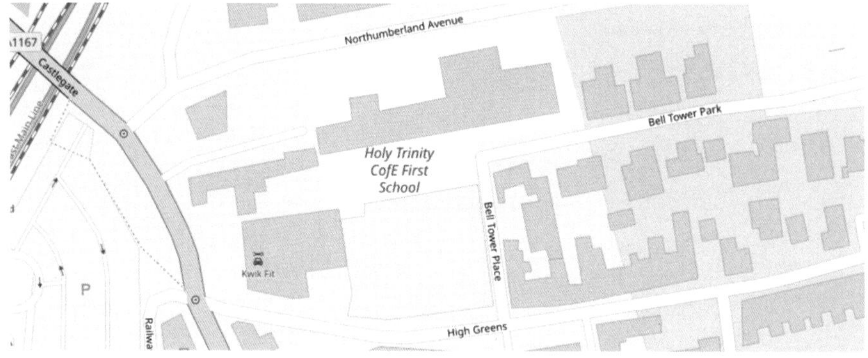

© OpenStreetMap contributors. ODbL 1.0

As mentioned above, the Franciscan convent in Berwick was established around 1231, and thus may have been in place shortly before the Dominican friary near the castle. Both of these friaries would have been built before Edward I instructed that stone should be used for the walls; before this the fortifications were most likely wooden. In 1296 Edward I ordered another ditch around the town; probably a wooden palisade, which was gradually replaced with a stone wall. The wall's two-mile length was defended with 17 towers, and pierced by 6 gates.(C17)

According to Cowan & Easson, sources place the foundation of the Franciscan convent in or about 1231, the year in which the friars entered Scotland: "*Hic primo ingrediuntur fratres Minores Scotiam*"(L4): "*Anno Domini millesimo ducentesimo trigesimo primo... hoc anno ingrediuntur primo fratres Minores Scotiam...*"(L7)(A7) "*An informal habitaculum was at once established at Berwick, and the year 1231 may be accepted as the date of its foundation, although it was not transformed into a regular friary until the month of May 1244, when its church and cemetery were consecrated by David de Bernhame, Bishop of St Andrews*".(L3)

It would appear that there were between five and seven friars in this house in December 1299 - "*Fratribus minoribus eusdem ville [Berewico super Twedam] pro eodem, per manus fratis Walteri de Wynterburn... 7s*".(B36b)(A7) The Friars Minor of Berwick were also listed, along with Carmelites, Dominicans and Augustinians, in the same year in the 'Wardrobe Account' of the King.(B36c)

The location of the Franciscan friary is not known for sure, but as we saw above

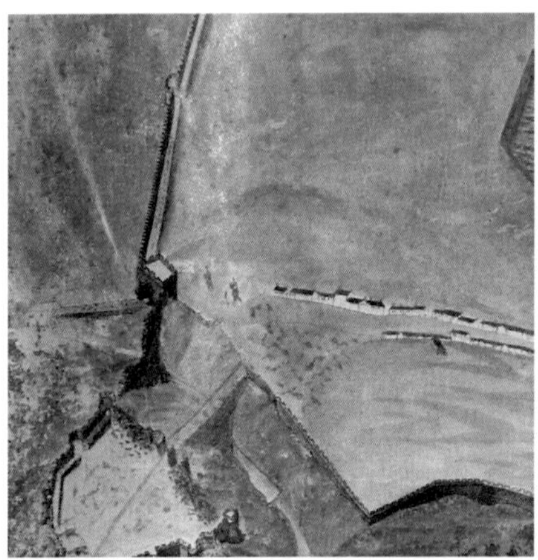

British Library (1580 map)
© British Library Board Cotton Ms.Titus C.XIII

when discussing the Dominicans: "*The [Dominican] friary was originally situated close to the castle just within the town boundary, on or near the site of the present Holy Trinity school in Northumberland Avenue and the adjacent garage premises. The north wall of the friary formed part of the defensive walls after 1296*".[(C27)(C17)] It is generally thought that the Franciscan Friary was adjacent to the Dominican Friary; photographs of the line of the Edwardian wall would indicate that the Franciscan Friary would be located within the walls and covering at least some of the area of present day housing in High Greens and possibly the south side of Bell Tower Park.

British Library (1725 map)
© British Library Board Maps K.Top.32.46

The farm of the chapel is recorded as located on the 'Grene' called house of Friars Minor.[(D7t)] The 1562 survey and 1564 map of Berwick show only the west side of Greens built up, so the friary was possibly on that side. [(B31b)(C10)]. The Army Plea Roll of 1296 includes the following description of Matthew de Forneys' visit to Berwick who dismounted his horse '*..at the gate next to the (house of the) friars minors..*' - "*Matthew de Forneys was attached to answer Lawrence de Preston on a plea of trespass. Whereon he complains that when he came on Friday in Easter Week [30 March] to Berwick with the king's army and his groom dismounted from his barbed and harnessed horse, value 8 marks, at the gate next to the [house of the] Friars Minors, the horse ran away from the groom. Later he found the horse in the custody of Matthew and asked for it. ....*".[(L2)] Other evidence from 1314 indicates the gateway being situated between the present location of the Bell Tower (NT95SE 34) and Lord's Mount (NT95SE 3). The Heritage Environment Record gives the location as NT 95 SE 28.[(D7t)]

Stones at Lord's Mount thought to have originated in Franciscan Friary

Archaeological Investigations of the Franciscans in Berwick-upon-Tweed

Altar slabs and a cross slab, which are thought to have come from the Berwick Franciscan Friary, were used in the building of Lords Mount; and the head of a medieval cross was used in the wall between Low Greens and Bell Tower.[(G2b)] The altar slab forms the front slab of the latrine box itself; one might ask if this was accidental or done on purpose? If the latter, surely the ultimate sacrilege!

Other Franciscan Friaries in the vicinity

Other friaries existed locally at Newcastle-upon-Tyne, Haddington and Edinburgh. It was thought that John Duns Scotus (see below) was in the Newcastle convent, founded 1237, for a time before 1300;[(A17)] there were 34 friars in 1299 and 1300, and 24 in 1322. At it's dissolution on 9th January 1539: "*Johannes Crayforth dive gardianus comus conventualis Fratum Minorum be Novo Castro super Tynam*", there were 11 friars, including the warden, John Crayforth, and 2 novices.[(A17)] Haddington Greyfriars existed from the mid-thirteenth to mid-fourteenth century;[(L5)] and Edinburgh Greyfriars from around 1483 to 1562.

John Duns Scotus

In the public park of Duns, a town in the Scottish Borders about fifteen miles west of Berwick-upon-Tweed, there is a sculpture in memory of the town's famous son, John Duns Scotus, a philosopher and theologian. The sculpture of the head of a Franciscan friar, by a German artist and presented to the town by the German Franciscans in 1966 on the 700th anniversary of the birth of John Duns Scotus, has been described as showing the friar "looking intently beyond and upward with a fixed gaze, as if 'seeing him who is invisible'".[(L12h)]

John Duns Scotus was born in Duns in 1265 or early 1266. Not much is known for definite about his early life; there's no known record of his visiting Berwick [at the time one of the foremost towns of Scotland], but it's not inconceivable that he could have visited the Franciscan friary there, the nearest friary of that order to his home town. Some Newcastle historians claim he received part of his education at the Franciscan house in that town.(D5)(C19)(C20)(C21)(A17) By 1281 he had made his profession within the Order; and on March 17th 1291, aged about 26, he was ordained priest at St Andrew's Priory, Northampton, and continued his studies at Oxford. Later he lectured at both Oxford and Cambridge universities on the *Sentences* of Peter Lombard, the four books of which, covering the main aspects of Christian belief, constituted the basic textbook of the course in theology at the time. In 1301/1302 he was appointed lecturer in Paris - not for long, as he supported Pope Boniface VIII in a dispute with Philip of France and had to leave Paris in June 1303; he returned to Oxford.

In 1304 he was able to resume academic life at Paris, where, a few months later, he attained his Master's degree in Theology. In 1308 he was lecturing in Cologne at the Franciscan house of studies [Studium]. He died there on 8 November 1308 at the age of 43; he is buried in the Minorite [Franciscan] Church near Cologne Cathedral. His remains were venerated; and within a few years his doctrines were widely adopted, especially by his order.(L12)

John Duns Scotus, the "Subtle Doctor," was beatified by the Catholic Church in 1993. "*The whole of Scotus' theology is dominated by the notion of love. The characteristic note of this love is its absolute freedom. As love becomes more perfect and intense, freedom becomes more noble and integral both in God and in man*".(L12d)(L12a)

Berwick-upon-Tweed Franciscans: later history

There is a reference to the guardian of the Friars Minor of Berwick, Adam de Neuton, reporting in December 1317 to the Cardinals about a failed mission to the Scots.(L10) In 1331-1332 there was a Mandate issued by the Pope to the bishop of St Andrews

> "*to ascertain the facts touching the complaint made by the guardians and convents of the Friars Minors of Berwick and Roxburgh, in the dioceses of St. Andrews and Glasgow, that Adam Hanupli, Thomas de Irwy, and Adam de Adigton, at the suggestion of William de Dalgernoc, abbot, and the convent of Kelso, left the Friars Minors, carrying off from their churches and dwellings bibles, and other books, chalices and ornaments, and handing them over to the said abbot and convent. Restitution is to be made, and the said friars, abbot, and monks are to be corrected.*"(B9j)

A mandate of Edward III on 10 August 1333 ordered the Scottish friars to be removed and English friars substituted for them.(A7)(B51r) Two friars were introduced to the friary in Berwick; while the newcomers were being entertained, the Scottish friars broke into the book cupboard and collected books, chalices and vestments and carried them off!

> *'Note, that when the Scottish friars had to leave the convent of Berwick and two English friars were introduced, the Scots provided them with good cheer ; and while some of them entertained them at dinner with talk, others broke open the wardrobe, collected all the books, chalices and vestments, packed them in silken and other wrappings, and carried them off, declaring that all these had been gifts from my lord Earl Patrick.'*(A5)

> "*After this incident* [replacement of Scottish friars with English in 1333] *the annual bounties to the Franciscans of Berwick from the Scottish Exchequer naturally ceased; and their English successors found it necessary to apply to Edward III for payment of the 'old alms' of twenty merks, which had been sanctioned by the Bruce....its friary passes out of the history of the Scottish Franciscans at this date*".(L3)

In October 1335 the number of friars is stated as thirty, but in January 1336 there were only fifteen friars of this order in Berwick.(B6d)(A7) On 12 June 1337 "*Berwick-on-Tweed. To the same. Order to cause Thomas de Burgh to have due allowance for what he has paid to John de Lenne,......[to] the guardian and brethren of the order of the minorites of that town...and Thomas de Burgh, chamberlain of Berwick, having viewed the king's writ and the acquittances made in this respect, as the king lately ordered Thomas de Burgh to pay to John de Lenne, 22l. 0s. 8½d. for divers works in the castle and town of Berwick...to the guardian and Friars Minors of that town 20 marks of like alms....to Thomas de Baumburgh, 40s. to the prioress, 40s. to the prior and brethren, 26s. 8d. to the guardian, 20s. to the prior of Mount Carmel, 50s...*".(B17)

On 15 December 1337 a payment from the English Exchequer to the friars is authorised:"*Warrant on Exchequer for allowance to Thomas de Burgh clerk, chamberlain of Berwick-on-Tweed, in his compotus, of various payments, viz. John Crabbe, for works in the town, 100s.,,,the Friars minors, 20 marks...*"(B8)(A7) The Close Rolls for 15 December 1337 describe it thus:"*To the treasurer and barons of the exchequer. Whereas the king ordered Thomas de Burgh, chamberlain of Berwick-upon-Tweed, by divers writs under the great and privy seals, the seal used in Scotland, and by other letters under the seals of Robert de Ufford and Henry de Ferariis, to pay 20l. to John de Lenne, late clerk of the king's works in the castle and town of Berwick, for divers works there....40 marks to the Minorites dwelling there, of a like alms granted to them,....*".(B17b) No further evidence for this house appears in record sources for two centuries, but it is mentioned in the fifteenth-century poem, *The Freiris of Berwick.*(see Chapter 5)(A15)(A7)

In 1347-8 Europe faced the Black Death - it is estimated that scarcely one-third of the friars survived - around 13,883 died in total in Europe.(L11) Earlier, in the 1330s, the stricter 'Observant' reforms began; after initial problems of acceptance, Pope

Gregory IX in 1374 instructed the bishops of Orvieto to protect Observants. In the years 1400-1446 the Observants (the "Friars Minor of the Strict Observance") gradually divided from Conventuals. By around 1460, the Observants had reached Ireland and in the same decade reached Scotland. The Vicar General (North of the Alps) was licensed to erect, found and build 3 or 4 friaries and receive 2 or 3 from Conventuals. In 1481 they founded a friary in Greenwich. The formal division between Conventuals and Observants occurred in 1517. There was further reform in 1525-9, with the founding of the Capuchins.(L11)

The house in Berwick was suppressed between 10 March 1538/9 and Michaelmas 1539.(B35b)(B39)(A7)

Work, Education and Architecture of the Franciscans

The friary ministered to the local urban population: visiting hospitals, and the sick in their own homes; visiting prisons; often a mediator in disputes; a ministry to travellers. The friars could be involved not only in their religious obligations but in weaving, copying & binding, manuscripts and building; in 1322, in Richmond, Yorks, they supplied the town with drinking water, as they did in many other English towns and cities.(L11) They acted as trusted messengers for kings and cardinals.(L8)

As well as preaching, they helped with wills, prayers, intercessions for the dead and at funerals. The friars' church was a place of devotion and instruction; on death they were buried in tombs in a common grave or the cloister; non-friars were also buried within the precincts of the convent - in Preston Lancashire, according to John Leland, several members of the 'Preston' family were buried within the precincts of the friary of the Grey Friars; an archaeological investigation concluding in 2007 uncovered 25 graves, four of them of children, inside a north chapel and nave of the main church. The extent of the site of the church and claustral buildings was about 60 metres by 60 metres, not including the cemetery, garden, gatehouse etc.(L15) Friaries were also places where locals gathered for civic as well as religious purposes.(L11)

As regards the sacramental life of the convent, the friars would recite the Divine Office, participate in the sacraments etc., and Mass would be celebrated several times daily, depending on the number of priests. They would not all be able to participate in all the services, as much of their work took them out of the friary to serve the urban population.(L11)

Education was important for the friars; the Order and new universities grew side by side and their histories were closely entwined in the 13th & 14th centuries. [See above for John Duns Scotus' education]. The Order pioneered a form of study to equip men for the apostolates of preaching and hearing confessions.(L11)

Like the Dominicans, the Franciscans inspired new forms of architecture designed to accommodate large crowds for sermons. They would include a large nave designed to maximise the space for those attending sermons; they would have more side altars than parish church, so all the priests could say Mass during the day. The range of buildings generally consisted of: bell-tower, cellar, cemetery, Chapter House, Church, cloisters, dormitory, gardens, granaries, infirmary, kitchen, library, refectory and school of theology.[(L11)]

CHAPTER 9

Hospital of St Mary Magdalene

For general information on medieval hospitals, see Chapter 2.

Hospital of St Mary Magdalene: foundation, location and early history

© OpenStreetMap contributors. ODbL 1.0

According to Cowan & Easson, the first mention of the Hospital of St Mary Magdalene was in 1296, when the Master of this hospital had restitution of lands from Edward I - *"Magister hospital' Be Mar' Magdalene ex Ber' vic' de Berewyk"*; so it existed before this date.[(A7)(B51c)(D7k)] As we saw in Chapter 2, the choice of St Mary Magdalene for the name of a hospital was quite common in Scotland. It may have been a leper hospital as it was located outside the fortified walls.[(A27)] The founder of the hospital is not known.[(A26)]

According to old Ordnance Survey maps, the hospital was located at the corner of the current golf course where it meets Northumberland Avenue - NT99895363 - and was marked on Ordnance Survey maps up to at least 1938, but was not included on the OS map for 1954.[(D7k)] There is nothing shown on the 1580 map of Berwick-upon-Tweed, but by that time it would have been abandoned for approximately 130 years.

There are no visible remains, but in 1910, as reported in the *Berwick Advertiser* on 12 August that year, a coffin, missing its lid, was found when cutting a drain towards new houses 200 yards north of the Edwardian fosse; this sandstone sarcophagus has been dated as no later than 1100 and was 90" x 30" in size.[(B40)(B60)] 200 yards north of the Edwardian Wall/Fosse reaches roughly to Percy Terrace - the houses there were being built around this time, and some occupied by November 1911. Many other coffin lids and ecclesiastical architectural fragments had been found from

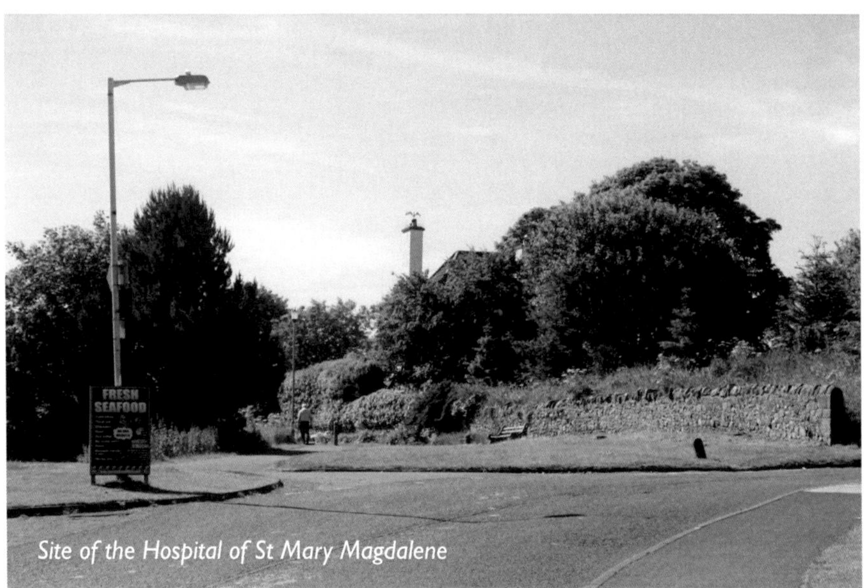

Site of the Hospital of St Mary Magdalene

time to time near the same place, which indicates the existence of a chapel and/ or cemetery, with a date probably around 1272-1377.(C30)(D7k)(B16)(B40)(C10)(D7k) If both the newspaper report and the OS maps are correct, the hospital and its cemetery must have occupied a very extensive site. The name has been perpetuated to this day in the surrounding fields - Magdalene (sometimes in the past named Maudlin) fields, which include the Magdalene Fields Golf Club and the Holiday Park.

Hospital of St Mary Magdalene in Berwick-upon-Tweed: later history

On 15 June 1334 restitution was made to the master of the hospital of St Mary Magdalene near Berwick upon Tweed.(B51f)(A28)

In June 1337, Thomas de Burgh, Chamberlain of Berwick-upon-Tweed, was ordered to pay certain allowances to religious foundations in the town, including to '*Thomas de Baumburgh, master of the hospital of St Mary Magdalene, near Berwick.....to Thomas Baumburgh 25s, which he ought to receive yearly from the said issues, as of the right of his hospital;...*'.(B17c) This was further confirmed on 15 December of 1337: '*....25s to Thomas de Baumburgh, warden of the hospital of St Mary Magdalen, near Berwick, of a yearly rent anciently due to the hospital...*' (B17d)(B8) On 19 August 1347 there was further reference to payments to the hospital and again in July 1348.(B51g)(B51h)

There was mention of the hospital again in 1356; on 6 June that year it is described as a hospital for the poor which had been destroyed by the Scots; Edward III, who has it in his gift, restores it.(B51d)

The Hospital of St Mary Magdalene from this time on is connected with another establishment at Segden, about two miles north. In July 1365 there is mention of Segden in Petitions to the Pope: "*John de Peblis, M.A. bachelor of canon and civil law, and advanced in theology. For the deanery of Glasgow on its voidance by the obtaining of the canonry and prebend of the same, formerly held by William de Rupe, by William de Grenlaw, papal collector in Scotland, notwithstanding that he has the treasurership of Glasgow, and the hermitage of Segden, in the diocese of St. Andrews, which he is ready to resign. Granted. Avignon, 5 Kal. July.*"(B42)

© OpenStreetMap contributors. ODbL 1.0

Segden, about two miles north of Berwick, was a previous name for what is now Follydean, a short valley down to the sea from near what is now the A1. Some of the variations of its name in documents are Segdon, Seggeden, Seggedene, Segdene, and Segeden. It seems that there was an Augustinian hospital and hermitage here, possibly founded by one of the Lindsays of nearby Lamberton in the thirteenth century. The hospital may have been moved to a site near Holy Trinity Church in Berwick in the following century; the Northumberland Urban Survey suggests "there are grounds for a further hospital in the area of the Parade and Berwick Barracks to be identified".(C12)(C27) The earliest reference to the hospital occurs in a thirteenth century taxation roll where it appears simply as Seggeden, under 'Papal Taxation of Churches'.(S5)

When Scott was writing [1888] it was thought that there were no further records of the hospital after 1395, and that author gives details of the masters of the hospital in the fourteenth century, and Edward III's restoration of tithes to the hospital.(C30)

There are, however, further documents relating to the site, even though it may have ceased to function as a hospital by about 1431/1432, when, on February 6 1431, it was called a 'free chapel': four local men, including the Mayor of Berwick, were to '*..enquire by inquest of the said town…as to the persons of the said town and county who are stated to be in occupation of lands belonging to the free chapel of St Mary Magdalene and the hospital of St Mary, Segden, which was about one and three-quarter miles from St Mary Magdalene's hospital., and to have taken the rents thereof and other rents of assize belonging to the said chapel or hospital*'.[(B11k)] On 16 February 1434 '*The King commands the Chancellor to issue a presentation in favour of John Bekson, clerk, to the free chapel of St Mary Magdalene juxta Berwick*'.[(B8)(B8ap)]

By 1437 the hermitage of Segden [see Chapter 14] was annexed to the free chapel of St Mary Magdalene: on November 4th, there was a '*Grant to Nicholas Neuton, king's clerk, of the wardenship of the free chapel of St Mary Magdalene by the king's town of Berwick and of the hermitage of Segden annexed to the same*'.[(A7)(B11m)] The free chapel with the hermitage annexed is last noted in 1453; on 16 May of that year: "*Petition to the King by William Bolton, chaplain, one of the clerks of his Chancery, to present him to the free chapel of St Mary Magdalene near the town of Berwick-on-Tweed and the hermitage of Segden annexed, void by the death of Nicol Neuton, clerk, late possessor*".[(B8)(B8aq)]

Appointments to the mastership are recorded until 1448[(A7)]; in May 1395, in the reign of Richard II, Richard Clifford was given custody of the hospital[(B51t)(B25)]; and in 1411 there is a reference to the church of the hospital of St Mary, the sanctuary of which had been violated before 8 Aug 1411.[(M1b)] This may relate to this foundation, or possibly to St Mary's on Castlegate.

Scott gives a summary of the holders of the land from after the Dissolution until it passed into the hands of the Duke of Northumberland in 1829.[(C30)] For Masters of the hospital 1319 to 1448, see *Fasti Dunelmensis* [(C35)]

CHAPTER 10

Church of Holy Trinity with St Mary

Church of Holy Trinity: foundation, location and history

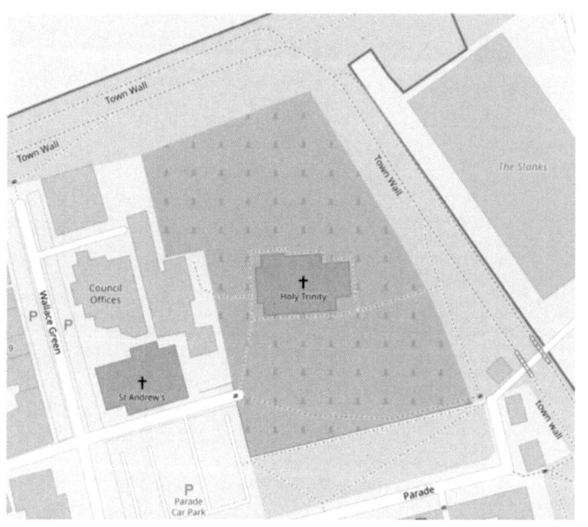

© *OpenStreetMap contributors. ODbL 1.0*

British Library (1580 map)
© British Library Board Cotton Ms. Titus C.XIII

The present parish church of Holy Trinity with St Mary, "a building of quite exceptional architectural interest",(B43) was built between 1650 and 1652, during the Cromwellian Commonwealth. It replaced a medieval church of *Holy Trinity* founded in the twelfth century, which it is believed was situated to the south of the present church - NU 0045317.(D18) The '*True Description…*' plan of about 1580 shows a narrow, aisleless church with probably slate roof, very close to the site of the present church; it shows a large cross at the east end, but no tower or spire.(E1)

In June 1584 the Mayor of Berwick petitioned Queen Elizabeth thus: "*That it might*

Site of medieval Holy Trinity Church

please her Majestie to grant some money to the building of a new church in Berwick, the old being very small and in utter ruin ready to fall, not able to hold the sixth part of the inhabitants, so that in tyme of Godes devine service, the greater sorte of people do bestowe themselves in alehowses and other places—and when they are taken and presented, they altogether excuse themselves for lacke of roome in the churche".[B7a] When the stone bridge was built in the time of James I, the money given was for a bridge and a church, but by the time the bridge was finished and paid for there was only £39-18-6 left for a church, hardly enough for a wayside cross! When *St Mary's* Church in Castlegate closed in 1989, the congregation joined with *Holy Trinity*, which was then renamed *Holy Trinity with St Mary*.[C11]

There is no mention of the Church of Holy Trinity in Berwick in *Early Scottish Charters prior to 1153*, whereas it does mention the churches of St Mary and St Laurence in Bondington (see Chapter 6).[B20] However, Menuge states that '*Holy Trinity Church, also an early foundation, documented from c 1120, just south of present church*'.[C23]

There is uncertainty over the location of the earlier Holy Trinity, but it is generally believed to be just south of the current church. Cowan indicates an early foundation for the first church of Holy Trinity, which lay to the south of the existing seventeenth century structure.[C27][P1] He further suggests that '*of the three churches associated with the town, St Laurence, St Mary and Holy Trinity, the first two (in Bondington) appear to antedate the last which became the parish church of the burgh only on or after its foundation by Earl David between 1119 and 1124*'.[A7][P1] The status and relationship of the three church sites have acquired a greater degree of importance after the archaeological discoveries in Bondington detailed above in Chapter 6. Scott writes that *Holy Trinity* was a twelfth century church, and probably in existence in 1156.[C30][A8]

It is not certain whether the church came under Durham or St Andrews in the early days. It belonged to Kelso Abbey in twelfth century. A church, not named, in Berwick belonged to Durham in 1156, and the Prior of Coldingham was bound to pay five marks annually to the perpetual vicar.[(B54)(N1)]

Early Sources of Scottish History 500-1286 gives a list of churches dedicated by the Bishop, including '*The Church of Holy Trinity was reconciled, after the effusion of blood… on 15th April 1242….The Church of the Friars Minor at Berwick on 6th May 1244'.*[(K1b)(A21)] In 1267 Roger, the Prior of Coldingham, granted to the Friars de Penitentia Christi (Friars of the Sack - see Chapter 3) that they might build and have edifices and an oratory in the town of Berwick and '*within our parish church of the Holy Trinity of South Berwick'.*[(A7)(B45b)] In 1296 among those swearing fealty to Edward I was "*William vicaire del eglise de la Trinite de Berwyk*".[(B8at)] Scott lists the early vicars of Holy Trinity, from about 1227 to 1536, as does *Fasti Dunelmensis* from c 1299.[(C30, p 337;C35)]

Cowan, in his *Parishes of Medieval Scotland*, states that "*a medieval settlement took place in 1368 and was maintained in the fifteenth century. During this period the parsonage revenues, which seem to have now included those of the other churches of Berwick, accrued to either Coldingham or Durham dependent upon the actual possession of the town itself, these falling permanently to the latter after 1482*".[(A8)]

As we saw above, towards the end of the sixteenth century the church was in a poor state; the Petition of June 1584 continues: *…in tymes past, the towne had as fayer and large a parishe churche as most was in Englande, which was taken downe for the use of the fortificacions in the tyme of Kinge Henrye the eight, and the stones, tymber, leade, iron and other thinges therof were wholie employed to the affayers and services of her Majesties said late father of famous memorie."*[(B7b)] This makes reference to the church of St Mary, probably the successor to St Mary in Bondington, that was destroyed to make way for the Elizabethan fortifications. No demolition date is known for the previous *Holy Trinity* church, but the present church was begun in 1650 and opened in 1652.

Architecture of Holy Trinity Church

As mentioned and illustrated above, the '*True Description…*' plan of about 1580 shows a narrow, aisleless church with probably slate roof, very close to the site of the present church; it shows a large cross at the east end, but no tower or spire.[(E1)(C2)]

CHAPTER 11

Church of St Nicholas

Church of St Nicholas: foundation, location and history

Site of St Nicholas' Church

St Nicholas' Church (or chapel), named most likely after St Nicholas of Myra, in Greece, Patron Saint of Sailors (among others), stood near or above the site of the Malthouse on Pier Road, with the churchyard extending back towards the Walls as far as the later cricket ground. It overlooked the river, not unlike other maritime towns and cities where churches are named after St Nicholas - such as in Newcastle and Liverpool. On the formation of the cricket ground, before 1849, a row of boulder stones was found - maybe the church foundations? One of the towers on the medieval wall near King's Mount was called 'St Nicholas Tower', which is suggestive of the general location. Between September 1575 and March 1579, among other works at Berwick, 75 shillings was spent on "mending St Nicholas' tower" (B7b) According to Scott: '*St Nicholas is given as last mount of old walls, which corresponds to the King's Mount. So called in survey of Henry VIII*'.(C30) Scott continued that there were the remains of a churchyard, or burying ground, where the coastguard houses were built above Pier Road; this burying-ground stretched back towards the old walls as far as the cricket ground. Named in the 'Laws of the

© OpenStreetMap contributors. ODbL 1.0

guild' as the place where some of the later orders of that code were framed in 1281. From Stevenson's 'Transcripts', David, Bishop of St Andrews, dedicated the chapel of St Nicholas of Berwick to Holy Trinity in Berwick, which the monks of Durham held. As it is sometimes called a 'chapel', maybe it was deemed of less important than other churches?(C30)(C11)(D7f)

The Church of St Nicholas is mentioned in the *Calendar of Documents Relating to Scotland* in September 1301 when

> "*The writer [the constable of Berwick], informs the K. that Sept. 14....That morning he caused Sir Walter to proclaim that all the men-at-arms and others should meet them at St Nicholas's church. And there, in presence of Sir Peres de Maulee, Sir Robert his brother, and Sir Walter, he asked each gentleman by name, knight or esquire, if he would mount guard...*"(B8ae)

Ellison cites Scott and Hutchinson as sources for the mention of a '*large church built by Bishop Bec in Berwick c.1301*'(C10)(C27) The name of St Nicholas' Tower was still in use in 1560.(P1)

CHAPTER 12

The Carmelite Order

Origins and Early History of the Carmelite Order

The order of Carmelite Friars originates from Mount Carmel, near modern day Haifa, in the Holy Land. Some of the alternative names include the Order of St Mary de Mont Carmel,(C30) the White Friars or Whitefriars,(C30) Friars of the Blessed Virgin and the Hermits of the Blessed Virgin of Mount Carmel.(A1) It was a mendicant order and the friars were often referred to as White Friars after the colour of their habit adopted in 1284; illustrations of the habit can be found on the Carmelites' website.(Q17)

In the Holy Land the Order began as an informal gathering of hermits. After a few decades, they began preaching and contributing to pastoral care in some urban areas. The first documentary evidence dates from the early thirteenth century. Their 'vita formula' gave guidance on how to live: to fill their time in solitary prayer and contemplation; no personal possessions, all to share property in common; to fast from 14 Sept to Easter, except Sunday and if anyone was ill; meat to be avoided unless for convalescence; to work; and to observe silence ('with discretion').(A1)

The order received papal approval from 1229; and in 1242, because of unrest in the Holy Land, some of the order moved out to such places as Cyprus [1238], Sicily [1240-42], and England [1242]; in that year, convents were established in Aylesford and Hulne [see below], the latter being founded by John de Vesci for the hermits he had brought to England - at first there were as many as 24 brothers, and by 1301 there were 28.(A1)

In 1247 a convent was founded close to Fleet Street in London, thus indicating a change in role towards the new urban and pastoral concerns of the Order. By this year there may have been three 'Provinces' in the West - Sicily, England and Provence; the Berwick foundation would later become answerable to the English 'Province'. For the organisation of the Order, each Province sent a Provincial Prior to the General Chapter of the Order which was overseen by the Prior General.

This change in role to a more outward-looking and itinerant form of life, focused on the mendicant ideals of the active life, the 'vita activa', in contrast to the 'vita contemplativa' of the hermit. The Order sanctioned houses in urban and suburban areas; in this change in their role they were more like the Franciscans and Dominicans, including a common refectory, the recitation of Office in common, chastity, and renunciation of property. To accommodate a more mobile community, there was a reduction in the overnight silence, they were allowed the use of donkeys or mules, and food when travelling.(A1)

In 1252 a request was made by the Pope to the bishops asking them to protect the Carmelites and allow them to build cells and churches and to have cemeteries and bells. From 1253 they could preach and hear confessions, and from 1261 the laity were allowed to frequent their churches - this was met with some opposition from those brothers who wanted to revert to being hermits; and there was some discord with the local secular clergy. By 1293 the Carmelites had 28 foundations in England and 5 in Scotland. In May 1298, Pope Boniface VIII removed any uncertainty about the Order and instructed bishops to protect the friars, their rule was given papal approval and thus confirming their right to exist.

By 1294 there were 12 'Provinces', and the English houses were further subdivided into four '*distinctiones*': London, Oxford, Norwich and York. Until the 1290s the Scottish convents were included with English convents but in 1294 they joined Ireland as a separate 'Province'. Scotland had their own Province from 1324, with 6 foundations. To improve the education of the Carmelite friars, in 1294 other '*studia generalia*' (in addition to Paris already in existence) were founded in Toulouse, Montpellier, London & Cologne; and there were Carmelite houses in Oxford & Cambridge where students attended the universities.(A1) By 1357 there were 18 provinces.(A1)

Carmelites in Berwick-upon-Tweed: foundation, location and early history

There is a reference in John Speed's *Historie of Great Britaine under the conquests of the Romans, Saxons, Danes and Normans* that a house, dedicated to St Mary, of the Order of 'Whyte Friars' was founded in Berwick in 1270 by Sir John Grey (or Gray).(B53) This gentleman had been mayor of Berwick in 1253,(B45) but according to Cowan and Easson "*is known, however, to have been a major benefactor of the Franciscans here*(A5)*, and it may well be that Speed's source confused the tradition of the two houses*".(A7) The Carmelites were definitely founded in Berwick some time prior to August 1296 when the friars swore fealty to Edward I;(Q8)

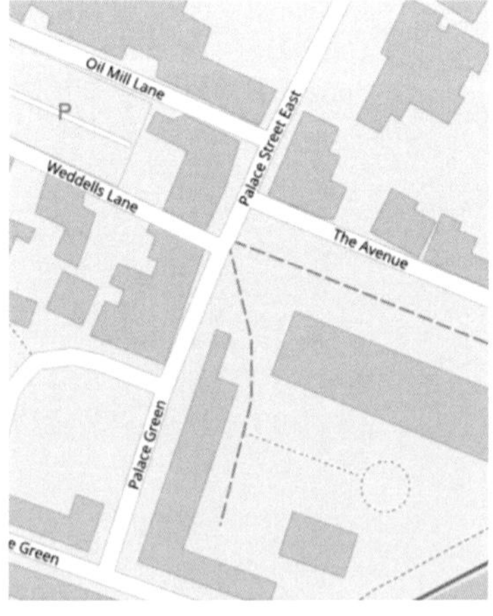

© *OpenStreetMap contributors. ODbL 1.0*

and on 25 Sept the same year they were granted land by the said King contiguous to their existing site in Berwick.[(B51j)] The land contained in length 19.5 predicates and in breadth 5 predicates, one of which places was rented by John the Plumber from the Prioress and Convent of South Berwick, and for which the prior was to pay 8s by the year. Also another piece adjoining their said area on the east, containing 13 predicates in length and 3 in breadth, for the enlargement of their area.[(C30)] They were granted 4 shillings in alms in December 1299.[(B36b)] The community received 40s from the same king, Edward I, on 5 January 1300 in recompense for damages inflicted on their houses during his stay in Berwick in December 1299.[(B36c)]

The location of the friary, traditionally, is a site on the Ness close to, or part of, the present Governor's house and Gardens in Palace Street East, with Grid Reference NT9999 5264 - at the junction of Palace Street East and Oil Mill Lane.[(D7m)] '*The True Description of Her Majesties Town of Barwick*" map of around 1580 shows a few prominent buildings (e.g. Holy Trinity Church) with roofs coloured grey, as if covered by slate; there was a group of such buildings in the Ness, which may have been those of the former Carmelite Friary, dissolved about 40 years earlier; or possibly the medieval Palace after which the street was named.[(E1)]

The 'Partial Survey' of Berwick for 1297 tails off at the end of a list of large plots on the 'western side of Fisher Street' (Vicus Piscatorum), but nothing is listed for the much larger eastern side - where the Friary may be expected to have been located [(C28)] The 1562 survey of the town records that "*John Wetherington holdeth one Stable and yerde con[aining] in length X yardes and in bredth IIII yardes, it was parcell of the possessions of the late frieries of Nes*".[(C31)] According to the plan recently displayed in the Main Guard museum, this lot would be the third building up Ravensdowne from Silver Street; either this contradicts the above re Oil Mill Lane or the friary's stables were located outside the bounds of the friary.

Other Carmelite Friaries in the vicinity

There were several other Carmelite foundations in the vicinity including, as we have seen, Hulne, near Alnwick, an early foundation for England in 1242; there were other convents in Linlithgow in West Lothian, South Queensferry near Edinburgh, and Newcastle. There are substantial remains of Hulne - on a hilltop, perhaps recreating the original site on Mount Carmel - about two and a half miles to the north west of the town of Alnwick. Modern day Carmelites are allowed once a year to say Mass in the remains of the church. The location is more suitable for hermits as it is a good distance from the urban centre to serve the community; maybe because it's an early foundation before the role of Carmelites changed? It seems to have been built for about 24 friars. There were 28 friars in 1301, and some 10 friars at the Suppression. The priory was surrounded by a fortified curtain wall.[(Q4)]

There are also remains of Carmelite convents in Linlithgow[(Q3)(Q12)] and South

Queensferry, where the chapel of the Friary is still used as a place of worship.(Q10) In Newcastle-upon-Tyne, Carmelite Friars were situated firstly [before 1262] at Wall-Knoll; and from 1307 until the Dissolution west of the Castle. There were 24 and later 27 friars in 1299. In 1307 the Carmelites moved to the site of the defunct Friars of the Sack, to the west of the castle, and later on the Wall-Knoll site passed to the Trinitarians. There were 30 Carmelite friars in 1335. Their house was surrendered on 10 January 1538 by the prior, 7 brethren and 2 novices.(Q4)(Q2)

Hulne Priory (and above)
(Courtesy of Northumberland Estates)

Archaeological Investigations of the Carmelites in Berwick-upon-Tweed

There are no visible remains of the friary, but there have been several archaeological investigations in the area, but with no definitive result regarding the location of the friary. There was an investigation by Pre-Construct Archaeology Ltd in 2001 which located considerable medieval structures and deposits below ground; five trenches were excavated in advance of proposed development, recording medieval features possibly belonging to the Carmelite Friary, as well as post-medieval activity. The investigation was funded by McCarthy & Stone.(C1)(C29)(D7p)(D7q) A report in *Archaeology in Northumberland* states that "*on the comer of The Avenue and Palace Street East which revealed the remains of series of sixteenth century or earlier buildings and cobbled surfaces. Due to health and safety considerations it was not possible to fully investigate any earlier remains below the sixteenth century structures. However, limited investigation revealed a number of walls and further cobbled surfaces of medieval date, which may be associated with the Carmelite Friary.*"(C4) A small-scale excavation, funded by McCarthy and Stone Ltd, within a group of outbuildings close to the Governor's House was reported in 2002 as having revealed medieval walls of the Carmelite friary at map reference 399000, 653000.(Q9b)(C5)(C24a) Around the same time there was an investigation at grid reference 400050, 652550 [east end of The Avenue/Governor's Gardens] by Briden where there was an opening-up and investigation within a group of outbuildings on the site.(C24b)(C9) There was an earlier investigation in the 1970's reported in NMR Excavation Index in Palace Street East; Grid Reference NT 99990 52638: "*Below a thick 15th and 16th century garden layer were the remains of a large stone-walled building which had had a thatched roof. Destroyed by fire, sealing 14th-15th century pottery. Beneath the front of the house was a boundary wall. To the west lay hearths, areas of burning and trodden earth interspersed with blown sand layers - may date to 11th century. The excavated area lay in the 'Palace' area, the buildings may have been part of a larger complex. 13th and 14th century imported wares found*".(C24c)(C5b)(D7n) Medieval and post-medieval remains at the former Blackburn and Price Garage, Silver Street, were reported in 2007.(62h) Groundworks in 2014, at NU0001852536 and NU0001152543 in Governor's Gardens, "*revealed a NNW-SSE orientated wall constructed of unbonded, roughly-shaped limestone blocks; it measured 0.86m x 0.42m x 0.22m. This wall was truncated by another wall aligned NE-SW which comprised irregularly-coursed facing stones and a 0.45m thick rubble core; mortar was present in places. Deposits that abutted the walls were indicative of deliberate medieval dumping events, interpreted as an attempt to consolidate and raise ground level. The presence of mid-15th century pottery within deposits abutting the first wall suggests it may pre-date the 1450s*".(D7s) The same Index has a reference to 'Land at Palace Green' [400050, 652550 - Governor's Gardens] where an assessment of proposed development within the medieval core of the town took place.(C24d)(C8)

Berwick-upon-Tweed Carmelites: later history

On 18 June 1310, Isabella, countess of Buchan, was ordered to be removed from her place of imprisonment in Berwick Castle to the Carmelite friary: "...*in domo fratrem ordinis Blessed Marie de Monte Carmeli in eadem villa*..."(B51k) The friars housed the wardrobe in their buildings at some time in the winter 1310-1311, as that department paid them 5s for the damages sustained there on 31 July 1311.(B6b)

On 17 November 1317 Edward II granted the request of these friars that they might be allowed to minister in the Royal Chapel in Berwick Castle as friars of their order formerly did:

> "*The King, on account of the 'eminent devoutness' of the friars of the order of the Blessed Mary of Mount Carmel of Berwick-upon-Tweed, grants their petition to serve his chapel in the castle there as heretofore, receiving from the Chamberlain of Scotland the same stipend as the secular chaplains who used to serve it*".(B8)(B11e)

They had an annual grant of £8 from the fermes of Berwick which was paid in part in the year 1327-1328 and in full in each of the five years following.(B23b) Edward III on 29 July 1333 gave 20s to the twelve friars of this house through Friar Richard de Cockermouth.(B62) On 10 August 1333 Edward III gave mandate to the prior provincial of the order in England to remove the Scottish friars here to English Houses and to substitute English friars.(B51m) The expulsion of the friars of Scottish birth did not diminish the number; in March 1333-4 the King gave victuals to the value of 10 marks to the Carmelites. In August 1335 he gave alms to fifteen Carmelites of Berwick, and in October of the same year to ten.(B6)(Q8)

In October 1335 the number of friars was stated to be 10 and by January 1336 it had risen to 15.(B6c) In 1337 Simon de Karl was prior of this house (Pipe Rolls) and an annuity of £8 had been settled upon it from antiquity, and that this year 20s of this sum was allowed them out of the Exchequer accounts.(C30) The English King continued the annual grant to the friars at irregular intervals and often in curtailed form at least to 1341.(B17e)(B8)(C30) For example: in June 1337, under Berwick-on-Tweed:

> "*To the same. ....the king lately ordered Thomas de Burgh to pay to... the prior and friars of Mount Carmel of that town, 8 marks of like alms appointed of old, to be received from the issues of the said town;..... and from the said day of October until Michaelmas...20s. to the prior of Mount Carmel*".(B17)

On 15 December of the same year, 1337, there was a warrant on Exchequer

> "*for allowance to Thomas de Burgh, clerk, chamberlain of Berwick-on-Tweed, in his compotus [account], of various payments, viz....the Carmelite friars, 8l.....*"(B8b)(B17c)

The friary was named in the late 15th century poem by Dunbar, *The Friars of Berwick*'.:

"*The choice of the walled city of Berwick as the background for the friars' adventures provides a good deal more than a few initial descriptive passages and the sort of detail, which gives an impression of realism. The fact that it is a walled city provides the necessary motivation for the friars' appeal for shelter. They are outside the walls and fear that the gates will be closed before they reach Berwick (lines 46-50). That town is also an ideal setting for a work which derives much of its comic effect from the intense rivalry between the orders of friars. As Easson has indicated, Berwick alone of all Scottish towns did house each of the major orders. In all probability Carmelites, Augustinians, Franciscans and Dominicans were represented there from 1270 until 1436 and Berwick's reputation as a centre for friars lasted long after that time*".[(A15)]

There is a record from c.1539 of six burgage plots in Berwick belonging to '*the chapel by Nesse*'.[(D7m)] A second document relating to the Dissolution names this as the property of Carmelites.[(D7m)] Between 10 March and Michaelmas 1539 the 'chapel next to the Nesse' in Berwick was dissolved.[(B35b)(B39)] That this was the Carmelite friary is shown by an account of 1547.[(B35)]

In a letter to Thomas Cromwell on 10 March 1539, it was stated that "...*Cromwell has received 16 convents of friars into his hands to the King's use. There are still standing about 10 houses in these parts, besides three or four in or near Barwyke. Does not know whether Mr Lawson has received them or not. Does not wish to go himself, as it is 100 miles out of his way and he would not be home before Easter*"![(B35d)] It is not clear from this if the Carmelite's convent was one of the 'three or four'.

After the Dissolution, a survey of 1562 records that "*John Wetherington holdeth one Stable and yerde con[aining] in length X yardes and in bredth IIII yardes, it was parcell of the possessions of the late frieries of Nes*".

Later history of the Carmelite Order

By 1462 there were 25 provinces, with much expansion created by division of provinces into 'vicariates'. The Order was founded by, and it's survival depended on, lay patronage; in return, the Carmelites provided services: they had secure buildings and so were entrusted with valuables; their houses were used for signing treaties and their churches for places of sanctuary. The friars were often present in entourages - John of Gaunt had Carmelite confessors, and Edward II was a substantial supporter of the Order, and acted as royal chaplains elsewhere in Europe.

Cities and towns often agreed payments to the Carmelites in return for expecting them to participate in public devotions and to help in maintaining both social order and health. They said Mass and led processions against war and epidemics. There was a flood of brother- and sisterhoods or confraternities linked to Carmelites' churches. The mid-15th century saw the incorporation of Carmelite women; there was no question of Carmelite nuns following the mendicant preaching life of the male Carmelites. For the nuns, statutes emphasised enclosure, strict poverty, and a common life of work, prayer and the liturgy. The convents included both 'incluse' or cloistered nuns, and 'non-incluse' who might go out on errands.(A1)

The male Carmelites' convents were often sited outside walls, but later incorporated within the walls; in Berwick the convent was always well and truly inside the Edwardian walls. In Newcastle they had to move from the original site because of the building of a tower and extension of the town wall on the site of their church. The choir of the Newcastle convent was probably 20m long, similar in length to those at Hulne, Sandwich and Aylesford. The cloister also was of a similar size in these three. An inventory for Newcastle at the Suppression in 1539 lists: the choir with 4 altars, 2 lecterns and stalls, vestry, kitchen, cloister with 'lavatorium' of tin and lead, a frater, brewhouse, buttery, porter (with partitions replacing the original hermit cells), a Lady Chapel, rood chapel and a chapel 'next the dore'. The churches did not have as large a nave, if any, as the Franciscans. The extant choir and crossing of the church at South Queensferry is the only building of the Order still standing in Scotland. Its long narrow church seems to follow the pattern of the English Carmelites house at Hulne, but is also typical of rural churches in medieval Scotland. At Linlithgow (near the Forth, west of Edinburgh) there was a passageway between the nave and the chancel connecting the cloister with the cemetery and the 'outside world'; it was similar to the English Carmelite houses of Aylesford and Hulne.(A1)

1562 saw the foundation of the first community of the discalced (barefoot) Carmelite nuns by Teresa of Avila, based on the observance of the rule of Albert of Jerusalem. The modern day convent at Quidenham in Norfolk states

> *"We are a community of Catholic women who have come together from many different backgrounds and previous religious experience to live together the Teresian Carmelite vocation. We endeavour to witness to the gospel through a complete gift of ourselves to God in a life of love and service. Inspired by the spiritual way marked out for us by Saint Teresa of Avila, our primary mission in the Church is one of contemplative prayer and intercession".*(Q11)(A1)

Work, Liturgy, Education and Architecture of the Carmelite Order

The papal document *Super Cathedram* of 18 February 1300 restricted the work of mendicant friars: they might preach in their own churches and public squares but not in parish churches; to hear confessions or conduct burials they required the permission of the local bishop; they were to avoid times when local churchmen were accustomed to preach; any revenues for work authorised by the bishop were to be shared with parish clergy. They were to do good works and help the poor. Most ordinary Carmelites divided their time between contemplation, study, pastoral care and preaching. (For a collection of sermons see Ref [A1], p 44.) By 1378 they also found themselves hearing confessions. In that year Thomas Hatfield, bishop of Durham, authorised a Carmelite of Hulne, Ade Clyffe, to hear the confessions of 100 persons in a year.[(A1)]

From the late thirteenth Century, each Province was to have a prison; and by 1343 every house was to have its own prison. When a friar or nun died, after it was made explicit by the Pope in 1262, he or she was to be buried in the house's own cemetery.

Regarding the liturgy, as the role of the Order changed from that of hermits to pastoral care, the recitation of the Office changed from individual to communal, in choir. From 1312 there was an Ordinal for whole Order, with chants, prayers, readings and feasts to be celebrated etc. The Virgin Mary was claimed as its special patron; devotion to the Virgin Mary became the focus of spirituality for the Order, which was named 'Hermits of the Blessed Virgin of Mount Carmel".

The friars needed to be educated in order to preach, and the Order followed the Franciscans and Dominicans in their scholastic organisation. A *'Studium Generale'* was established in Paris, with *'Studia Particularia'* in each Province teaching basic logic, grammar and philosophy. The convents had libraries, the best documented being Florence. There is a surviving book list for Hulne from 1365: the collection comprised some 60 books and 20 others for the church, nine volumes of the Bible, works by Bernard, Augustine, Gregory, John Chrysostom, Aquinas, and nine collections of sermons.[(A12)(A9)]

One would normally expect the convents to be based on the usual monastic layout, with church, cloister and conventual buildings, but in the town probably on a smaller scale than priories and abbeys. There is no information about the Berwick convent but it is possible to get some idea from Hulne which has substantial remains. The choir in Newcastle was probably 20m long, similar to those at Hulne, Sandwich and Aylesford; the cloister also of a similar size to these three. At Hulne, the gothic remains of church, cloister and conventual buildings cover a site about 52m square; in addition, there is a curtain wall, inside which would have been the convent cemetery, gardens, stables etc. In an inventory for Newcastle at the Suppression in 1539, the following are listed: choir with 4 altars, 2 lecterns and stalls, vestry, kitchen, cloister with 'lavatorium' of tin and lead, frater, brewhouse, buttery, porter (with partitions replacing the original hermit cells), a Lady Chapel, rood chapel and a chapel 'next the dore'.

CHAPTER 13

Hospital of St Bartholomew, Spittal

Hospital of St Bartholomew, Spittal: foundation, location and history

The Hospital of St Bartholomew, at Spittal by Tweedmouth, for lepers and sick poor was founded before 1234; the endowments of a leper hospital were confirmed by Bishop Poore in that year.(B16)(A17) A tower or pele, referred to in 1612 as Bathes Tower, was erected for protection in 1369.(B45c) The tower was last mentioned in 1753.(R1) It is claimed by Rev L O Henderson that the lands of the hospital extended from Spittal Hall [NU 00165185] eastwards along the Tweed estuary to NU 00055200 (near the Lifeboat Station) and that the buildings of the hospital were in the area of Spittal Hall. Jim Walker has reproduced 'an artist's impression' of what the hospital and surrounds may have looked like on page 76 of *Berwick-upon-Tweed Through Time*. C36

The name 'Spittal' is derived from this hospital, a similar derivation to many other places in the country, such as 'Spital' in Chesterfield.

In 1365,

> "*...John is master of the lazar-house of St. Bartholomew, Twedunth (Tweedmouth), from which he has got no fruits, save those which he has applied to the uses of the said house*".(B42) In the following year, 1366, the hospital is mentioned again when the following Petition is granted by the Pope:

> "*The hospital for poor and lepers of St. Batholomew, Tweedmouth, in the diocese of Durham. Whereas it has been devastated by incursions of the Scots, and its rents and profits are no longer enough to repair the buildings, the master, John Lowyck, has provided of his own goods a little fishing vessel to fish in the sea, on whose shore the hospital stands, for the sustenance of the brethren and the infirm; and whereas the masters of the hospital have not paid tithes to any other church of the lands of the hospital, nor of their other goods, nor of oblations offered in their oratory, nor have any been demanded, and whereas the prior and convent of Halleland (Lindisfarne),*

> *pretending that the hospital is in their parish, now demand tithes of the fisheries, though they do not presume to exact them on other goods, the pope is prayed to grant them exemption".*(B42)

The hospital is mentioned again in August and September 1366, when John de Lowyk was "*master of the lazar-house of St. Bartholomew, Tuedu [Tweedmouth], a benefice in the same [Durham] diocese*".(B42) By March 1391 John de Lowyk had died:

> *"To John de Scremerston. Provision of the poor hospital of St. Bartholomew, Twedemowthe, in the diocese of Durham (to be assigned, by its foundation ordinances, to secular clerks), value 8 marks, void and reserved to the pope by the death at the apostolic see of John de Lowyk, rector, called warden; notwithstanding that he is expecting, under letters of the present pope, a benefice with or without cure in the common or several gift of the bishop, prior, and chapter ….."*

According to Tanner, at the time of Richard II (1377-1399) the mastership of St Bartholomew's hospital was with the Bishop of Durham.(A33)

The hospital survived until the dissolution of the monasteries.

CHAPTER 14

Other possible establishments with unknown locations

The Augustinian Order of Friars

Origins and Early History of the Augustinian Order of Friars

The Augustinians were another mendicant Order of friars that may, or may not, have established a house in Berwick. They were variously known as Austin Friars, Augustinian Hermit Friars, Order of Hermit Friars of St Augustine, or Augustines. "*The habit was white garment and scapulary when they were in the house; but in the choir, and when they went abroad, they had over the former tta sort of cowl and a large hood, both which were girt with a black leather thong*".(C30) For illustrations of the habit, see the Augustinian website.(S2) To begin with, in Northern Italy, they were hermits, but by the end of the Middle Ages they were "*closely linked to the world of university and deeply engaged in city life*" - in 1268 Oxford became the first of two *studia generale* of the Order in England, followed by Cambridge before 1289.(A1)

The Order arrived in England around the middle of the thirteenth century, and a house was founded in London before 1256. From that year the Order was to follow the Rule of St Augustine, and the habit to be black, with a belt covering a tunic, the belt being of black leather at least one and a half fingers wide. The Augustinians would be defined by their pastoral, mendicant role (*vita activa*), their closest model now being the Franciscans and Dominicans rather than desert hermits. Their principal duties were teaching, preaching, giving examples of holy life and deeds and hearing confessions.(A1)

A house was established in Newcastle around 1290.(S6) By 1300, there were at least twenty houses in England, mostly in the north and east.(A1) Around that time there were 10 provinces in Italy, and also in France, Germany, Hungary, Provence, Spain & England; by 1329 there were 24 provinces. The English Province was later further subdivided into *limits (limes)* for ease of administration: Cambridge, Oxford, Lincoln, York & Ireland. There was a 'Mother House' - the central mechanism of government was the *General Chapter*, attended by *provincial priors;* then *convent* or *priory.*(A1)

By 1303 the Order was safe from the suppression [see Friars of the Sack in Chapter 3] and with the same privileges relating to preaching, confession and burial as Franciscans and Dominicans. Unlike Benedict's Rule, the Augustinian Rule is a collection of exhortations....on shared life, to 'have one heart and one soul seeking God'; built on the idea that common life, based on shared property and common prayer, will promote fraternity and love. The Rule was supplemented by *constitutions* or *institutes*, giving the mechanics of daily observance.(A1)

Augustinians in and around Berwick-upon-Tweed: foundation, location and early history

There is no evidence that the establishment in Segden was in any way connected with a friary of that order in Berwick. [See Chapter 9]. Cowe suggests that the south side of Silver Street might have been the location of an Augustinian Friary but, at the moment, there is no evidence for this. There were excavations reported in 2007 which found medieval and post-medieval remains at the former Blackburn and Price Garage, Silver Street, but with no conclusive evidence of a religious building. (D7r)

On 28 August 1296 *"Friar William 'mestre de la meson de Seint Austyn' of Seggedene,"*, swore fealty to Edward I.(B8z)(B44) Also a writ was issued for the return of the house's lands.(B51s) In this source, the Augustinians and Segden are linked, and there doesn't seem to be any other Augustinian friars from Berwick swearing fealty.

In the *Liber Quotidianus Contrarotulatoris garderobae* for the year 1299 there is a '*List of Religious Communities mentioned in this Record'* which received alms from the King, and included, for Berwick: Friars Preachers, Friars Minors, Carmelite Friars and Friars of St Austin; the detail for the Augustinians reads: "*Fratribus Sancti Augustini ejusdem ville* [Berwick-upon-Tweed] *pro eodem, per manus dom' Henrici Elemos' ibid' 18 die Decemb'....6 shillings*". On the 24th December: "*Fratribus Sancti Augustini ejusdem ville pro eodem, per manus fratris Willi' de Goseford ibid' eodem die....2 shillings 8 pence.*"(B36b)(A7) "*From the grant of these pittances it would appear that there were six friars in this house on 18 Dec, 1299, and four at Christmas*".(A7) Could these be two different houses, as the alms were given to two different people?

Later History of the Augustinians in and around Berwick-upon-Tweed

In 1300-1301, further alms were given to several Orders in Berwick-upon-Tweed and included "....*Fratribus Sancti Augustini ejusdem ville pro eodem, per manus Fratris Willelmi de Goseford ibidem, eodem die,.. iiij s.....Fratribus Sancti Augustini ejusdem ville pro eodem, per manus Fratris Willelmi de Goseford ibidem, . . iij s. iiij d. ....Fratribus Sancti Augustini ejusdem ville pro eodem, per manus Fratris Willelmi de Goseford ibidem, eodem die, . xvj d.*"(B8an)

In March-June 1311, Edward III gave the hermit of Seggedene 100s in alms to glaze the windows of the chapel:"*13th June :—Friar Roger of Wateby the hermit of Seggedene, by the K.'s alms to glaze the windows of his chapel there, 100s*".(B8aa) Cowan & Easson write that in the period 1328-1331, from the Scottish king, the Augustinians had a special grant of £20 for the fabric of their church, paid in three unequal instalments between 1328 and 1330/1(B23c) Later, on 10 August 1333 Edward III gave mandate to the prior provincial of the Augustinian hermits in England to remove the Scottish friars here to English houses and to substitute English friars.(A7)(B51m) In October 1335 the number of friars was stated as fifteen and in January 1336 it was twelve.(A7)(B6e)

An inquisition of 1333 mentioned property in Narrowgate (of which there may have been two in Berwick): "*Randolfe de Holme....was seised of 3 tenements in Narugate.... two of the tenements he had of the gift of the king's grandfather; the third he acquired from the brethren of Seggedene.*"(S3a) A confirmation of a grant of 1335 shows that the advowson of the chapel of Segdene had belonged to the Lindsay family: "*The King to the Chancellor. As William de Coucy has given by charter to William de Coucy his son, and his heirs, the whole barony of Lyndeseye within the vill of Berwick-upon-Tweed, in Scotland, with appurtenances, the manor of Lamberton....with the 'avowesons' ....of the chapels of Segdene and Bodikan, which barony and others were lately in the hand of the King's cousin, the King of Scotland, by the death of Crestiene de Lydeseye, Williams' mother...*"] (B8ag)

In 1338 Edward III granted protection for two years to the master and brethren of the house, '*who depend for their subsistence on charity, collecting alms in churches*'.(B11f) Up to 1349, two chaplains 'of the order of the house of Segden in Scotland' had a chantry on an island on Windermere which was also part of the possessions of the Lindsays of Lamberton in the thirteenth century:

> "*Two chaplains of the order of the house of Segden in Scotland used to have a chantry on an island in Lake Windermere called Seynt Marieholm within the demesne lands, which belonged to William de Coucy, to which the island was appropriated for a residence; a close called Frerefeld, containing 10 acres and of the yearly value of 6s 8d, and a close called Monkbergh, containing 15 acres and of the yearly value of 13s 4d were appropriated to the chantry...The last chaplain died about All Saints 23 Edward III [Nov 1349/50] and the chantry has since been void.*"(S3c)

'Hermit brethren' were already established on the isle of St Mary, Windermere, by 1272(B10b), but it is not clear that they were then in any way connected with Segden.

A warden of the hospital was appointed by the English king in 1362(B11g), ["*June 14 Grant for life to the king's clerk Richard de Middelton of the wardenship of the hospital of Segden"*] John de Peblis was said to hold the administration of the hermitage in 1363 and 1365:

> "*1363 Petitions to Pope, Urban V Ibid. John, king of France. On behalf of John de Peblis, M.A. student of civil and canon law, and practising in law for five years in the court of the bishop of Glasgow, whose official he has been for three years, for a canonry of Dunkeld, with reservation of a prebend, notwithstanding that he is treasurer of Glasgow, value 20l. and has the administration of the hermitage of Segdon, in the diocese of St. Andrews, which he is ready to resign. Granted. Avignon, 3 Kal. May.*"[(B9k)] [(B42)] Also: "*1365.* Petitions to the Pope, Urban V. (f. 130d.)....*Granted. Avignon, 5 Kal. July*".[(B42)]

An inquisition into the hospital's possessions on 15 May 1367 contains a reference to land next to it '*in its enclosure within the cemetery of Berwick*', which seems to indicate that the hospital was actually in the town by that time. ["...*who find that the Master and friars of the hospital of Segdene have a tenement lying in 'cornerie' of Narwegate and Seynte Marie gate....there are 4 acres of land lying next said hospital, in its enclosure, within the cemetery of Berwick, lying waste.."*].[(B8c)(B8ah)] Also [" ...*inquire.. as to lands, rents, and services belonging to the hospital of Segeden, which is of the king's patronage. Westminster. 15 May 41 Edward III [1367] ......The master and brethren of the said hospital have a tenement in the corner of Narwegat and Seyntemarigat worth 10s yearly now held by William Sirr....there are four acres adjoining the hospital which belong to its inclosure and are within the churchyard of Berwick, and are empty"].*[(S3b)(B8aj)]

In 1379 Segden was described as the king's free chapel[(B51t)]: "*Warrant for letters in favour of Richard Clifford clerk, to the custody of the K.'s free chapel of Segden for life*".[(B8ak)] Although it was again termed hospital in 1431[(B11h)] ["*Feb 6, 1431, Commission to....as to the persons of the said town [Berwick] and county who are stated to be in occupation of lands belonging to the free chapel of St Mary Magdalene and the hospital of St. Mary, Segden near Berwick, and to have taken rents thereof and other rents of assist belonging to the said chapel or hospital*".] It seems probable that it had already ceased to function as a hospital before the earlier date. The hermitage of Segden was annexed to the free chapel of St Mary Magdalene (formerly the hospital) at Berwick by 1437[(B11j)] ["*Nov 4th 1437 Grant to Nicholas Neuton, King's clerk, of the wardenship of the free chapel of St Mary Magdalene by the King's town of Berwick and of the hermitage of Segden annexed to the same*"] and it is last noted in 1453[(B8)]: "*May 16 [1453] Petition to the King by William Bolton chaplain, one of the clerks of his Chancery, to present him to the free chapel of St Mary Magdalene near the town of Berwick-upon-Tweed and the hermitage of Segden annexed, void by the death of Nicol Neuton clerk, late possessor*".[(B8am)]

A document dated 1406-7 refers to the Prior of St. Austin at Berwick. Raine states that the account rolls of Lindisfarne Priory note that the Holy Island priory borrowed 26s 8d from the Austins in 1406-7.[(A7)(B45)]

Cowan & Easson note that the house does not appear to have survived the general Suppression of the friaries in England although it may have been one of the three or four houses of friars near Berwick reported as still standing, 10 March 1539.(A7)(B35a)

Archaeological Investigations of the Augustinians in Berwick-upon-Tweed

Archaeology Data Service gives the grid reference as 398000, 656000, which is on the opposite side of the A1 from Folly Farm, and slightly north. It appears there has been no archaeological investigation of the site.(C2)

There is therefore no doubt that an Augustinian house existed in Berwick-upon-Tweed, but not clear whether it referred to Segden and that that house was included under the town's religious communities.

Other Augustinian Foundations in the vicinity

There were Augustinian foundations in Linlithgow (1503), Haddington (1511) and Newcastle-upon-Tyne where the friary must have been fully established by 1291, when the brethren were assigned a messuage in Penrith for a new house; there were 25-28 brethren in 1299-1315, 19 in 1319-20 and 30 in 1333-45. After the surrender on 9 January 1539 the prior and his 13 brethren, including 3 novices, were each given a few shillings.

Later history of the Augustinian Order

Friars' communities had an area of land to use for begging, called a 'limit', 'limitation' or 'terminus'; 'limitors' ('questors') were authorised to preach and beg for alms within those 'limits'. From Chaucer's *Prologue*: *"A FRERE ther was, a wantowne and a merye, A lymytour, a ful solempne man…".*(B63) In the late fourteenth century new 'observant' congregations grew up, who focussed on an inner existence of prayer and meditation, and following the common life. They insisted on attending the refectory and canonical hours and the removal of special provisions, dispensation or the *peculium* (personal property). Friar Martin Luther was an Augustinian Observant.(A1)

At the time of the Reformation there were over thirty communities of Augustinians, or Austin Friars as they were known then, in England and Scotland. None of these survived and the order became extinct. But the order did survive in Ireland, and it was from there that the Augustinians returned to England in the second half of the nineteenth century.(S2)

After the Reformation, the order played a significant role in the great missionary thrust of the Church. They were the first to bring Christianity to the Philippines; many were martyred in Japan in the 17th century; and the first missionary to circumnavigate the world was a Spanish Augustinian. In 1977 an independent province for England and Scotland was formed. A significant step in this movement towards the reestablishment of the Augustinians in this country was the return to Clare Priory in 1953, when it became the first house in England to receive novices since the Reformation.[(S2)]

Today, Augustinians of many nationalities are to be found as parish priests, teachers, missionaries and servants of the Church in over forty countries.[(S2)]

Work, Education and Architecture of the Augustinians

Friars were much in demand as preachers and confessors, and friars of all orders organised processions and other festivities. The Austins, like other friars' orders, were asked to preach by royal patrons. They often helped out secular clergy, especially if they had a specialism, e.g. if they spoke other languages in the London house. Like other friars, they acted as executors, and offered burial in the friary church.[(A1)(B34)]

In 1268 Oxford became the first of two *studia generale* of the Order in England, followed by Cambridge before 1289.[(A1)] From the beginning, the Order saw the importance of education. The first *studia* in Paris dates from 1260; it was considered that the study of theology, together with regular observance, would lead to the growth and prestige of the Austins. As well as the *studia* there were schools where the friars studied logic, philosophy and basic theology - these schools were often referred to as *studia particularia.* By the middle of the fourteenth century, the Austins were playing a prominent role in universities.[(A1)]

Most friaries would possess their own library - a saying of the time was "a monastery without a library was like a castle without an armoury"[(S4)] - and acquired books of liturgical and theological works. The Augustinian Friary in York had Bibles, works of St Augustine and other prominent Austins, the Rule and constitutions, treatises on preaching, sermon collections, theological and philosophical *summae,* music, logic, geometry, classical history, and recent chronicles.[(A12)] By the late fourteenth century most friaries had separate collections of books for choir and of library books for borrowing by the friars and students. Scriptoria were present in many key houses, producing and illuminating both liturgical and secular books.[(A1)]

When the Order began they built small oratories, but these expanded as the Order grew. The layout became similar to other mendicant orders - church, cloister etc; there was no template for churches and cloister, chapels etc because the Order wasn't governed by a Mother Church; hence there was a great variety of buildings

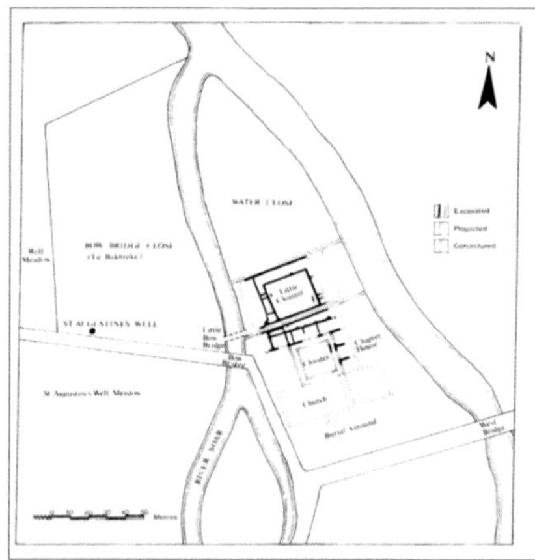

Plan of Augustinian Friary, Leicester.
Courtesy of the Council for British Archaeology and Leicestershire County Council, Historic & Natural

- large, small, sometimes used buildings previously used by others, such as at Warrington. Evidence from the relatively undisturbed site (under a garden) at Leicester allows us to reconstruct the form and evolution of a typical small friary. The cloister, measuring about 19.25m by 17m, seemed not to be enough so they built another 'Little Cloister'.(A1)(S1) It was on a triangular site, with rivers on two sides, measuring roughly 100m x 60m. In the friary in London the nave of church was 27m wide and 47m long; with the choir added to this the full length was about 90m. As there would have been plenty of space at Segden, the hermitage/hospital there could have been substantial; one wonders why there is no evidence of the foundation given that most of it has not been built upon since!

Leper House

According to Cowan and Easson this house was evidently founded by the gild of Berwick before the mayoralty of Robert de Bernham in whose term of office an ordinance was passed to the effect that no lepers were to enter the gates of the town, as alms were collected for their sustenance in a proper place outside the burgh.(A7)(T1) *"Hic incipient statuta Gilde apud Berwicum facia …..No leper shall come within the gates of the borough and if one gets in by chance, the sergeant shall put him out at once. If one wilfully forces his way in, his clothes shall be taken off him and burnt and he shall be turned out naked. For we have already taken care that a proper place for lepers shall be kept up outside the town and that alms shall be there given to them".*(C22)(T1)(C30) Robert de Bernham was mayor in 1238 and 1249, and possibly on other occasions.(A7)(C30) The location of this hospital is unknown, but by the nature of the hospital and by the fact the Mayor stated, it was located 'outside the town'.

Hospital of St Leonard

There seems to be just one documentary source for this hospital c.1297, according to Cowan and Easson, when the master and brethren petitioned Edward I and his council for the restitution of some land in Liddesdale, of which they had been dispossessed.[(A7)(J1)] *"The Master and brethren of the Hospital of St Leonard at Berwick laid claim to certain lands which they stated their predecessors had been seized of, viz. a carucate of land, with the appurtenances, in Val de Lydel. They presented a petition to Edward I, stating that the charter had been confirmed by each King of Scotland successively until the time of Master William Fuelers....".*[(B64)] No location is indicated and Ellison[(C10)] does not list the hospital site. Could this be the 'Unknown Building' on Walkergate? [See below]. Could the following be related - from the 'Ragman Rolls'? - *"Magister hospitalis St Leonardi de Louweder vic' de Berewico"?*[(B51)]

Unknown Building, Walkergate

In a report of 2010 into excavations at Walkergate in 2006, details were given of the discovery of a substantial stone building of 'probable thirteenth- to fourteenth-century date'. The building was *'evidently decorated with a green and cream plain mosaic tile floor'*. Referring to Stopford, the report notes that *'the sites with this type of flooring...are mainly monasteries, and particularly Cistercian monasteries'*.[(B65)] The fact that medieval painted window glass was also found - the nearest parallels for the three examples dated to the fourteenth century being found in the reredorter area of Battle Abbey. *'This building also had a tiled roof with green glazed ridge tiles from Ely, and peg tile from the same source, possibly with some or all glazed yellow, which themselves are indicative of high status, most likely ecclesiastical.'* Scorching and sooting of some tiles suggests that the building was destroyed by fire at some time in its history. *'From what is known of the plan the building does not immediately possess the characteristics of a church, although this cannot be ruled out. However the narrowness and lack of subdivision into aisles, and the presence of a north-south running drain, may be more indicative of a range of a monastic range, a hospital, or other religious establishment'.*[(C34)] Which establishment is it likely to be? Contrary to the report's statement that the Austin Friars (Augustinians) are not included in the late fourteenth century poem *The Friers of Berwick*, they were in fact included:

> *"...and Houses of the Friars of every hue;*
> *White Jacobins, Franciscan Gray and White,*
> *The Augustinian and the Carmelite,*
> *With black Dominicans and Minors sleek...."*[(C13a)]

There is the possibility therefore that this was the site of the Augustinian friary, if the friary existed at all - see above. It is unlikely that the 'Leper House' with unknown location was sited here as such hospitals would normally be located outside a town. Another possibility is that it was the Hospital of St Leonard - see above - or maybe an unrecorded ecclesiastical establishment.[(C34)]

POSTSCRIPT

From the time of the earliest known habitation of the Berwick and Tweedmouth area, the people have come together to worship God; and that continues to this day. As we have seen, in early medieval times there were short-lived churches in Bondington; but ever since churches were established in Berwick and Tweedmouth, there has been continuous worship down the centuries. From medieval times, as well as parish churches, there were friaries and hospitals and one priory; these were an integral part of life at the time - teaching, preaching, hearing confessions, burying the dead, and looking after the poor, the sick, seafarers and pilgrims. Many of these foundations had already ceased to exist in the area before the changes brought about by Henry VIII in the 1530s when he became head of the church in England; but by 1539, after he closed all the religious houses, large and small, all the remaining religious foundations, apart from the churches, were dissolved.

From around the same time, the Reformation became established in the country. The following centuries saw a different picture of Christian church foundations emerge in the area with the establishment of various nonconformist churches and chapels, as well as the Established Church; and once the years of intolerance had receded, the Catholics of the town were able to re-establish a chapel. All these churches and chapels bring their communities together to worship and pray. Today, the caring role of the medieval religious houses has been taken over largely by the state through organisations such as Social Services and the National Health Service, but as in the past, there is always a caring, as well as a spiritual, role for the various churches and chapels within the town, as they faithfully follow Jesus' words that the greatest commandment is "to love God and love your neighbour."

Religious establishments in existence in...

Numbers in first column relate to those on 'Trail and Map Key' on page 9.		12th Century	13th Century
1	Trinitarian Order	1198 Order Founded	< 1296
2	Hospital of St Edward		< 1234
3	Friars of the Sack		1267 Founded 1274 Abolished 1285 to Dominicans
4	Dominican Order		< 1240 1285 relocated to near bridge
5	Maison Dieu Hospital		< 1281
6	21 Castle Terr St Mary the Virgin ??	< 1113-1119	Ceased 13th C in Bondington
7	48 Castle Terr St Laurence?	< 1113-1119	Ceased early 13th C
8	Cistercian Nunnery	c 1150	
9	Dominican Friars (before relocation)	[See 4 above]	
10	Franciscan Order		c 1231
11	Hospital of St Mary Magdalene		< 1296
12	Holy Trinity	c 1120	
13	St Nicholas		< 1281
14	Carmelite Order		1270
17	St Bartholomew Leper Hospital, Spittal		1234
	Augustinian Friars ?		< 1300
	Leper House		c 1238-1249
	Hospital of St Leonard		1297 ?
	Unknown Building Walkergate		

Berwick-upon-Tweed & Bondington in Medieval Times

	14th Century	15th Century	16th Century	17th Century onwards
		1456 Ruinous 1476 To Peebles		
		1494 Last mentioned	1539/40 Dissolved	
		1484 ?		1603 To Corporation
	In town		Removed on building of ramparts	1857-58 New Church on Castlegate
	1390/1 Granted to Dryburgh Abbey	1467 - dispute still ongoing	1539 Dissolved ??	
			1539 Dissolved	
		1453 Annexed to Segden		
				1650-1652 New Church
	1335 < ?			
			1539 Dissolved	
			1535	
	Confusion with Segden ?			
	??			
	??			

REFERENCES AND BIBLIOGRAPHY

This 'References and Bibliography' section is arranged in a way that facilitates the location of sources under a particular subject or type of material.

A. Religious Houses, Hospitals - General

A1 Andrews, Frances. The other Friars : the Carmelite, Augustinian, Sack and Pied Friars in the Middle Ages / Frances Andrews. Woodbridge : Boydell, 2006. ISBN 1843832585.

A2 Blench, J.W. The Freiris of Berwik: a Late Mediaeval Scottish 'Merry Tale'. History of the Berwickshire Naturalists' Club, Vol 48, Pt 1, 1999, pp 47-60.

A3 Bradley, Edith. The story of the English Abbeys : told in counties. Vol 1, The Northern counties. Edition 1: The Northern counties. Hale, 1938.

A4 British Listed Buildings: St Leonard's Hospital, Denwick. www.britishlistedbuildings.co.uk/

A5 Chronicles of Lanercost. Chronicon de Lanercost. Maitland Club, 1839. p. 186, 275, 281-282. Online - archive.org.

A6 Cowan, Ian B The Medieval Church in Scotland by, Scottish Academic Press, Edinburgh, 1995 (see pp.40-41 for the churches of Berwick and Bondington).

A7 Cowan, I B and Easson, D E, 1976. Medieval Religious Houses in Scotland. 2nd Edition, Longmans, London. ISBN 0582120691.

A8 Cowan, Ian. The parishes of medieval Scotland / by Ian B. Cowan. Scottish Record Society. Edinburgh, 1967. xv, 226 p. ; 8vo.

A9 Davis, G. R. C. Medieval cartularies of Great Britain : a short catalogue. Longmans, Green, 1958. Updated 2010 - British Library, ISBN 9780712350389.

A10 Dugdale, William. Monasticon Anglicanum : a history of the abbies and other monasteries, hospitals, frieries, and cathedral and collegiate churches, New ed / by John Caley, Sir Henry Ellis and Bulkeley Bandinel. London : James Bohn, 1846.

A11 Friars, The : The Impact of the Mendicant Orders on Medieval Society / C.H Lawrence. I.B.Tauris, 2013. ISBN: 9780857732989 0857732986.

A12 *The Friars' Libraries*. Ed K.W. Humphreys. London : British Library in association with the British Academy, 1990. xliv, 281 p. ; 24 cm. ISBN: 0712300686.

A13 Friars' tales : thirteenth-century exempla from the British Isles / selected sources translated and annotated with an introduction by David Jones. 2011.

A14 'It would have pitied any heart to see': Destruction and Survival at Cistercian Monasteries in Northern England at the Dissolution. Carter, Michael. *Journal of the British Archaeological Association*. Volume 168:Issue 1(2015); 2015; 77-110. Online - tandfonline.com.

A15 Jack, R.D.S. *The Freiris of Berwik and Chaucerian Fabliau.* Studies in Scottish Literature, Vol 17 (1), 1982. Online - http://scholarcommons.sc.edu/ssl/vol17/iss1/12

A16 Kerr, Julie. Health and Safety in the Medieval Monasteries of Britain. *History,*

93:309, 2008, p. 3-19.
A17 Knowles, David. Medieval religious houses, England and Wales, by David Knowles and R. Neville Hadcock. Longman, 1971. 0582112303.
A18 Knowles, David. The religious orders in England. [Vol. 1, The old orders 1216-1340, the Friars 1216-1340, the monasteries and their world]. C.U.P, 1948.
A19 LEPER HOUSES AND MEDIÆVAL HOSPITALS. Author: Mercier, Charlesa. Is Part Of: *The Lancet*, 1915, Vol. 185(4766), pp.33-36. Identifier: ISSN: 0140-6736 ;
A20 The Leper in England: with some account of English lazar-houses. Hope, Robert Charles. 2009-08-19. Project Gutenberg.
A21 MacKinlay, J.M. Ancient Church Dedications in Scotland, Edinburgh: David Douglas, 1910.p 35. Online - archive.org/.
A22 The medieval hospital and medical practice / edited by Barbara S. Bowers. Ashgate, 2007. ISBN: 978-0-7546-5110-9.
A23 Medieval hospitals of England. Dainton C. *History Today*. 1976;26(8):532-38.
A24 The monastic contribution to mediaeval medical care. Aspects of an earlier welfare state. Furniss, D A. *J R Coll Gen Pract*. 1968 Apr;15(F1):244-50
A25 *Monasticon for Scotland*: the ancient church of Scotland, a history of the cathedrals, ….. churches, and hospitals of Scotland, by Walcott, Mackenzie E. C. (Mackenzie Edward Charles), 1821-1880 Publication date 1874 London, Virtue. Online - archive.org.
A26 "Nurseries of the Poore": Hospitals and Almshouses in Early Modern Scotland. McCallum, John. Oxford University Press, 2014. *Journal of social history* vol 48 issue 2 page 427. ISSN : 1527-1897
A27 Orme, Nicholas and Margaret Webster, The English hospital 1070-1570 New Haven, Conn. ; London : Yale University Press, 1995. ISBN: 0300060580 Bibliography: p289-298.
A28 National Archives: Petitioners: Thomas de Baumburgh (Bamburgh), clerk, keeper of the hospital of Mary Magdalene in Berwick. See Nat Archives Online Catalogue.
A29 Preaching, building, and burying : friars in the Medieval city / Caroline Bruzelius. Yale University Press, 2014. ISBN 9780300203844.
A30 Reading and writing during the dissolution : monks, friars, and nuns 1530-1558 / Mary C. Erler. Cambridge University Press, 2013. ISBN 9781107039797.
A31 The role of the hospital in Medieval England: Gift-Giving and the Spiritual Economy. Sweetingburgh, Sheila Dublin: Four Courts P., 2004, pp. 288. £55. ISBN 1-85182-794-3.
A32 Stevenson, W.B. The Monastic Presence, in 'Scottish Medieval Town', 1988, ed Lynch, M. ISBN : 0859761703
A33 Tanner, Thomas, Notitia Monastica: or, an account of all the abbies, priories, and house of friers…and also of all colleges and hospitals ……London, 1744. Online - archive.org.
A34 'Unto yone hospitall at the tounis end': the Scottish medieval hospital. Derek Hall.
Online - www.academia.edu.
A35 Watt, D. E. R.; Shead, N. F., eds. (2001), *The Heads of Religious Houses in Scotland from Twelfth to Sixteenth Centuries*, The Scottish Record Society, New

Series, Volume 24 (Revised ed.), Edinburgh: The Scottish Record Society, ISBN 0-902054-18-X, ISSN 0143-9448.

A37 Geltner, G. Mendicants as victims: scale, scope and the idiom of violence. *Journal of Medieval History*, Vol 36, Iss 2, pp 126-141, June 2010.

A38 Cowan, M. Death, life and religious change in Scottish towns, c 1350-1560. Manchester University Press, 2012. ISBN 9780719080234.

A39 Heale, MRV. Dependent priories and the closure of monasteries in late medieval England, 1400-1535. *English Historical Review,* Vol 119, Iss 480, pp 1-26, Feb 2004.

B. General Sources
[See also Section A above]

B1 'Access to Research'. http://www.accesstoresearch.org.uk. **B1a** Migration and mobility in a less mature economy: English internal migration, c . 1200-1350 by Postles, David *Social History*, 10/2000, Volume 25, Issue 3. **B1b** List of Publications on the Economic and Social History of Great Britain and Ireland. Published in 2007 by Matthew Hale Richard Hawkins. *The Economic History Review,* 11/2008, Volume 61, Issue 4. **B1c** Framework and form: burgage plots, street lines and domestic architecture in early urban Scotland by Still, Geoffrey Tai, Robin. *Urban History*, 02/2016, Vol 43, Iss 1. **B1d** Reconsidering the Scottish Town . McKean, Charles. *Architectural Heritage*, 11/2008, Volume 19, Issue 1. **B1e** Index of Architectural Heritage (Journals XI-XX) by Architectural Heritage, 11/2009, Vol 20, Issue 1. **B1f** A crisis of confidence? Parliament and the Demand for Hospital Reform in Early 15th and Early 16th century England. Radcliffe , Carole. (Univ of East Anglia) Parliamentary History, Vol 35, No. 2 (2016), pp 85-110

B2 Anderson *Scottish Annals, (Scottish Annals from English Chroniclers 500 to 1286),* ed. A.O. Anderson, London, 1908) 327. Online - archive.org.

B3 Anson, Peter F. Online - Amazon.co.uk/books/ Christ and the Sailor: A study of the maritime incidents in the New Testament. 1954.; The Church and the Sailor - A Survey of the Sea- Apostolate Past and Present. 1948. [A ROVING RECLUSE] 2008 [Paperback]. 1 May 2008.

B4 *The border-history of England and Scotland, deduced from the earliest times.......* By the late Mr. George Ridpath, published by Philip Ridpath, ...London : printed for T. Cadell; A. Donaldson; J. Balfour, in Edinburgh; and R. Taylor, in Berwick, 1776. Online - archive.org.

B5 British Library Manuscripts Catalogue (http://www.bl.uk/reshelp/findhelprestype/catblhold/all/allcat.html). Title: Grant. Reference: Wolley Ch v.5 Creation Date: [20 Jun 1395]

B6 British Museum. MS. Cotton Nero. **B6a** cviii, fos. 203-4 [Dominicans, Franciscans, Carmelites, Augustinians]. **B6b** viii, fo. 51 [Carmelites[. Edward II. 1311. **B6c** viii, fo. 203 [Carmelites]. Edward III. 1336. **B6d** c, viii, fo, 204 [Franciscans]. Edward III 1335-1336. **B6e** c, viii, fo…203 [Augustinians] Edward III 1335-1336.

B7 *Calendar of Border Papers: Volumes 1 & 2, 1560-1603*, ed. Joseph Bain (London, 1896). Online - british-history.ac.uk/; elelctricscotland.com **B7a** 'Volume 2, pp 896-904, Index: G' [Maison Dieu] [Holy Trinity]. **B7b** Volume 1, p. 12 [St

Nicholas Tower]

B8 Calendar of Documents relating to Scotland, ed J. Bain, Edinburgh 1881-8. Online - electricscotland.com/. **B8a** Volume 1, Paragraph No 1519; Year=1240-1 [Dominicans]. **B8b** Vol 3, Para No 1251; Year=1337 [Various]. **B8c** Vol 2, Para No 1176; Year=1300 [Maison Dieu]. **B8d** Vol 3, Para No. 962; Year=1321-1330 [Maison Dieu][Domus Pontis]. **B8e** Vol 3 , Para No 1105; Year=1330-1339 [Maison Dieu]. **B8f** Vol V, Para Nos 55 [Year=1287]; Paras 86 & 89 [Year=1291][Domus Dei]. **B8g** Vol 2, Para Nos 1176, 1178, Year=1300 [Maison Dieu] See 49b above. **B8h** Vol 3: Para Nos 1105 [Year=c 1333], 1193 [Year=c 1335], 1515 [Year=1347], 1532. [Year=1348]. [Domus Dei/Maison Dieu] See B8e. **B8j** Vol 4: Para No 68, Year=1362 [Domus Dei]. **B8k** Vol 4, Para No 1070; Year=1433-4, page 220. [St Mary Magdalene]. **B8m** Vol 3, Para No 1251; Year=1337 [St Mary Magdalene +]. **B8n** Vol 2, Para No 582; Year=1317 [Carmelites]. **B8p** Vol 3, Para No 1251; Year=1341 [Carmelites]. **B8q** Vol 3, Para No 962; Year=1328 [Domus Dei]. **B8r** Vol 3, Para No 962; Year=1328 [Brethren of Holy Trinity]. **B8s** Vol 2, Appendix III, P542, para 119; [Trinitarian seal description]. **B8t** Vol 2, Para No 507; Year=1291 [Dominicans]. **B8u V**ol 2, Para No 1608; Year=1302-4 [Bondington]. **B8v** Vol 2, Para No 508; Year=1291 [Fealty/Cistercian Nuns]. **B8w** Vol 3, Para No 1251; Year=1337, [Franciscans]. **B8x** Vol 4, Para No 135; Year=1367 [Segden hospital]. **B8y** Vol 3, Para No 1159; Year=1335 [Segden hospital]. **B8z** Vol 2, Para No 823; Year=1296 [Segden hospital]/ **B8aa** Vol 3, Para No 218; Year=1311 [Segden chapel glazing]. **B8ab** Vol 4, Para No 1251; Year=1453 [Segden]. **B8ac** Vol 4, Page 447; Year=1300-1301 [Cistercian Nuns]. **B8ad** Vol 3, Para No 1251; Year=1337 [Cistercian Nuns]. **B8ae** Vol 2, Para No 1223; Year=1301 [St Nicholas Church]. **B8af** Vol 3, Para No 1104; Year=1333 [Segden]. **B8ag** Vol 3, Para No 1159; Year=1335 [Segden]. **B8ah** Vol 4, Para No 132; Year=1367 [Segden]. **B8aj** Vol 4, Para No 135; Year=1367 [Segden]. **B8ak** Vol 4, Para No 278; Year=1379 [Segden]. **B8am** Vol 4, Para No 1251; Year=1453 [Segden]. **B8an** Vol 4, Para No 1300-1301; Year= [Segden etc]. **B8ap** Vol 4, Para No 1070; Year=1434 p. 220. [St Mary Magdalene/Segden]. **B8aq** Vol 4, Para No. 1251, p. 254. Year=1453 [St Mary Magdalene/Segden]. **B8ar** Vol V, Para No 1107; Year=1494. [Friar tries to take over castle]. **B8as** Vol 1, Para No 1924; Year=1239-1253. [Church at Berwick]. **B8at** Vol 2, Para No 823; Year=1296 p206. [Church of Holy Trinity][Ragman Roll]. **B8au** Vol. 3, Para No 1532; Year=1348 [Maison Dieu]

B9 Calendar of Papal Registers Relating To Great Britain and Ireland: Several Volumes ed. W H Bliss and J A Twemlow (London, 1902 -). Online - british-history.ac.uk/. **B9a** 'Regesta 297: 1386-1386', Volume 4, 1362-1404, pp. 252-254. [Trinitarians]. **B9b** Volume 1, pp 512-527, [House of God]. **B9c** 'Lateran Regesta, 429: 1446-1447', Volume 9, 1431-1447, pp. dlxv-dlxxii [Trinitarians]. **B9d** 'Lateran Regesta 434: 1447-1448', Volume 10, 1447-1455, pp. 287-294, [Trinitarians]. **B9e** Volume 11, 1455-1464, pp. 42-48, [Trinitarians]. **B9f** Volume 12, 1458-1471. p 256. [Cistercian Nunnery]. **B9g** Volume 13, 1471-1484, pp. 487-495, [Trinitarians]. **B9h** Vol 1, 1198-1304, pp. 479-491 [Friars of the Sack]. **B9j** Regesta 116: 1330-1332, Vol 2, 1305-1342, pp 498-506. [Friars Minor]. **B9k** Papal Letters. i, 482, 494-5.[Vol 1] Vetera. Monuments Hibernorum et Scotorum Historiam Illustrantia, ed A. Theiner, Rome, 1864;

nos 288, 309. 141 [Friars of the Sack]. **B9m Papal Letters.** pp 491-511. [1289. 7 Id. Feb. St. Mary Major's. (f. 68.) [Vol 1] Vetera. Monuments Hibernorum et Scotorum Historiam Illustrantia, ed A. Theiner, Rome, 1864; nos 141.

B10 *Calendar of Inquisitions Post Mortem:* ed. J.E.E.S. Sharp and A.E. Stamp (London, 1912). Online - british-history.ac.uk/. **B10a** Vol 3, Edward I, pp. 489-508. [Maison Dieu]. **B10b** Vol 1, Henry III, 1272, no. 829, pp 273-287. [Augustinians][Segden][Brethren on Lake Windermere].

B11 *Calendar of Patent Rolls preserved in the Public Record Office*. London: HMSO, 1891-. Online - catalog.hathitrust.org. **B11a** Edward 1, Vol 1. [Maison Dieu]. **B11b** Henry III, Vol 3, p484 [Hospital of St Edward]. **B11c** Edward I, Vol 3, p 186. [St Mary, Bonydyngton]. **B11d** 1476-85, 313. [Maison Dieu]. **B11e** Edward II. 1317-1321, 53. [Carmelites]. **B11f** Edward III. 1334-1338), 572. [Segden]. **B11g** Edward III. 1361-1364, 215. [Segden]. **B11h** Henry VI. 1429-1436, 131. [Segden]. **B11j** Henry VI, 1436-1441, 97. [Segden]. **B11k** Henry V (1429-36), 131. [St Mary Magdalene/Hospital of St Mary, Segden]. **B11m** Henry VI (1435-41), 97. - [St Mary Magdalene].

B12 Calendar of Scottish Supplications to Rome. [Hardcopy (6 volumes) available in National Library of Scotland]. Online - some vols available digital.nls.uk/. **B12a** 1471-1492. Scottish Record Society, Vol 42. [Cistercian Nuns]. **B12b** *1418-1422,* Scottish History Society, 1934 i, 96 (pp. 152, 159, 196)]. [Cistercian Nuns]. **B12c** *1428-1432,* pp. 30-31 [Cistercian Nuns]. **B12d** *1428-1432,* pp 66-67, 243-244 [Cistercian Nuns].

B13 *Calendar of Writs preserved at Yester House 1166-1503*, ed C.C. H. Harvey and J. Macleod. (SRS, 1930). Online - archive.org. **B13a** pp6-9, 33-34 [Trinitarians/Kettins]. **B13b** pp 6-8, Nos 9, 11 & 12. [Trinitarians/Kettins]

B14 CANMORE - National Record of the Historic Environment (Scotland). https://canmore.org.uk. The online catalogue to Scotland's archaeology, buildings, etc.

B15 Chalmers, George. *Caledonia*. Paisley: Alexander Gardner, 1887-. Online - archive.org.

B16 Clay, RM. Medieval Hospitals of England, 2013(Reprint of 1909 ed.). Online: books.google.com.

B17 Close Rolls, Edward III. Online - british-history.ac.uk/ **B17a** Volume 4, June 12 1337, Pages 59-71, Berwick-on-Tweed. [Various]. **B17b** Volume 4, Dec. 15 1337, Pages 223-225, Westminster. [Various]. **B17c** Volume 4, 1337-1339, pp. 59-71. [St Mary Magdalene]. [Carmelites]. **B17d** Volume 4, 1337, pp 68-69, 223-4. [Carmelites]

B18 Documents Illustrative of the History of Scotland (1286-1306), ed Stevenson, J, p. 24, 1870 Online - archive.org.

B19 Duncan, A. A. M. (Archibald Alexander McBeth) Scotland, the making of the kingdom . Edinburgh : Oliver & Boyd, 1978, c1975. xii, 705 p. : maps ; 22 cm. ISBN: 005003183X Series: The Edinburgh history of Scotland ; v.1 , p 310. [Cistercian Nunnery].

B20 Early Scottish Charters prior to 1153. Online - archive.org. **B20a** No. 39, pp 33-34. [Church of St Mary][Church of St Laurence]. **B20b** No 35, p 26-7, c 1113 [St Lawrence, Bondington/Berwick]. **B20c** No 99, page 79.[St Mary, Bondington/Berwick]. **B20d** No 185, page 404. [St Laurence, Bondington/

Berwick].
B21 Edinburgh University Manuscripts. Online - ed.ac.uk/information-services/.
B22 Edward I and the throne of Scotland, 1290-1296… E.L.G. Stones and Grant G. Simpson. Oxford University Press for the University of Glasgow 1977-1978. 2v. ISBN: 0197133088.
B23 Exchequer Rolls of Scotland (Rotuli scaccarii regum scotorum). Ed J. Stuart et al, Edinburgh, 1878-1908. **B23a** i, 208.[Dominicans]. **B23b** i, 63, 311, 312, 361,411. c 1327-1332. [Carmelites]. **B23c** i, 173-4, 279, 320, 1328-1331. [Augustinians]. **B23d** i, 208, 312-3, 361, 411. [Dominicans]
B24 *Extracta e Variis Cronicis Scocie*, p 249. Abbotsford Club, 1842. Online - archive. org.
B25 *Fasti Dunelmensis*, 188 - Edinburgh. 1926 (Surtees Society, 101)
B26 John of Fordun's Chronicle of the Scottish Nation. In: *The Historians of Scotland*: Edinburgh, Edmonton and Douglas, Volume 4, 1872. Online - archive.org. **B26a p**. 426 [Cistercian Nunnery]. **B26b** p. 238, App 3, p. 432 [Cistercian Nunnery]. **B26c** Vol 2, Book V pages 230, 426 - [Cistercian Nunnery]
B27 Google Scholar. https://scholar.google.co.uk. **B27a** Graves, C. P. (2002) 'The development of towns in the north.', in Past, present and future : the archaeology of Northern England : proceedings of a conference held in Durham in 1996. Durham: Architectural and Archaeological Society of Durham and Northumberland, pp. 177-184. **B27b** Lay Piety in later Medieval Lothian, c. 1306-c. 1513. HS Brown - 2007 - era.lib.ed.ac.uk. **B27c** Church and society in the medieval north of England. RB Dobson - 1996. **B27d** Poor relief in England, 1350–1600 MK McIntosh - 2011.
B28 Haddon, A.W. & W. Stubbs, *Councils and Ecclesiastical Documents relating to Great Britain and Ireland, Oxford, 1869-1878)* iii, 181. Online - archive.org.
B29 Historical Papers and Letters from the Northern Registers, ed J. Raine [Chronicles and Memorials of Great Britain, London, 1873, No cxi. pp177-178 Online - archive.org.
B30 *Historiae Dunelmensis Scriptores Tres* App 321-323.) Online - archive.org.
B31 History of the Berwickshire Naturalists Club. Online - biodiversitylibrary. org/. **B31a** Vol 22: p 151. **B31b** Vol 24 (1919-22), p. 461.
B32 History of the King's Works. Vol II. The Middle Ages HMSO, 1963. pp 568-569.
B33 Kverndal, Roald. Seamen's missions : their origin and early growth / by Roald Kverndal. Pasadena, W. Carey, 1986. ISBN 0878084401.
B34 Leland, John: The itinerary of John Leland in or about the years 1535-1543. Edited by Lucy Toulmin Smith. London, Centaur, 1964. Online - archive.org.
B35 Letters and Papers of Henry VIII. Online - british-history.ac.uk/. **B35a** xiv (1), p. 194, 1539, 10 March. [3 or 4 convents of friars still standing in or near Barwyke]]. **B35b** xiv, no. 494. [Carmelites[. [Franciscans]. **B35c** xviiii, 366, no. 72. [Meason Dieu]. **B35d** March 1539, 6-10' [Dissolution].
B36 *Liber Quotidianus Contrarotulatoris garderobae*, Society of Antiquaries, 1797. Online - archive.org. **B36a** p. xxxiv [Dominicans][Franciscans][Carmelites] [Augustinians] **B36b** p. 26. 1299. Edward I. [Dominicans][Franciscans] [Carmelites][Augustinians][Chapel in the Castle] **B36c** pp. 28-29. 1300. Edward I. [Carmelites].
B37 MS Collections of Fr Marianus Brockie, in Scottish Catholic Archives,

Edinburgh. **B37a** p. 1121. [Dominicans]; **B37b** p. 1274. [Franciscans].

B38 Miller, R. THE EARLY MEDIEVAL SEAMAn and THE CHURCH: CONTACTS. ASHORE. Author: Miller, R. Taylor & Francis Group. Is Part Of: *The Mariner's Mirror*, 01 January 2003, Vol.89(2), p.132-150. ISSN: 0025-3359 ; E-ISSN: 2049-680X ; DOI: 10.1080/00253359.2003.10659282.

B39 National Archives. Official archive and publisher for the UK Government, and for England and Wales. www.nationalarchives.gov.uk/. **B39a** P R O , Ministers Accounts, Henry VIII no 7364, m 11d. Nat Archives Reference: SC6/HENVIII/7364. Also 1539: no. 7364, m.11 d. Also 1547: Edward VI, no. 355, m. 54. 1547. [Carmelites]. **B39b** SC 6/HENVIII/7374. Northumberland, etc.: Monastic Possessions etc...of Newminster, etc. (as in SC 6/ HENVIII/7373), including Tynemouth, Hulpark [near Alnwick], Newcastle-on-Tyne, Bamburgh, Friars Preachers, Berwick-on-Tweed, Friars Minors. **B39c** E 101/482/16 SCOTTISH MARCHES: Particulars of the account of John de Boulton of repairs to the Douglas tower and other buildings at Berwick-on-Tweed. 29 and 30 Edw III. 2 membranes. Date: 1355 Jan 25-1357 Jan 24 [Maison Dieu/Trinitarians]. **B39d** E 101/483/9-10, enrolled as E 364/66, rot. D [Maison Dieu/Trinitarians]. **B39e** E 101/483/7, enrolled as E 364/47, rot C. [Maison Dieu/Trinitarians]. **B39f** Berwick upon Tweed, Northumb: Trinitarian House: seal of Brother Adam minister of the... Reference: SC 13/ D46B.

B40 Norman, F.M. *Proceedings of the Society of Antiquaries of Newcastle* 3 ser 4 1910 224.

B41 *O.P.C.*, ii, p.93.

B42 Petitions to the Pope. Online - british-history.ac.uk/

B43 Pevsner, N & Richmond, I. Northumberland. [*The Buildings of England* series]. Newhaven and London: Yale University Press, 2002. ISBN 978 0 300 09638 5

B44 *Ragman Rolls* [List of those who swore Fealty to Edward I]. Online - rampantscotland.com, electricscotland.com.

B45 Raine, J. *History and Antiquities of North Durham.* London, 1852. **B45a** Appendix. no. ccxxxviii. [Sir John Gray] [Carmelites]. **B45b** Appendix No dclii [Friars of the Sack]. **B45c** p 246-7. [St Bartholomew's Hospital, Spittal]

B46 *Registra Avinionensia* in Vatican Archives. 268, fo 366v.

B47 [Registra Supplicationum in Vatican Archives, 319, fo 210 (MS Calendar of Entries held by Dept Scottish History, Univ of Glasgow]. The following lists supplications but not text, and doesn't cover 1436 [or 1475-6]: http://asv.vatican.va/content/archiviosegretovaticano/it/attivita/ricerca-e-conservazione/progetti/strumenti-multimediali/registra-supplicationum--rs--1-265---479---509---961-1169.html. **B47b** 735, fo's 108, 200-200v. [Trinitarians, 1475-1476].

B48 *Registrum S Marie de Newbotle*, Bannatyne Club, 1849. Online - archive.org.

B49 *Registrum Magni Sigilli Regum Scotorum* ed. J.M. Thomson and others, Edinburgh, 1882-1914. **B49a** i, no 838. 1386. (Trinitarians and St Edward's Hospital). **B49b** i, No 832. (Cistercian Nuns). **B49c** *Registrum Secreti Sigilli Regum Scotorum,* ed M. Livingston and others, Edinburgh, 1908 -, ii, no 203] [Trinitarians, 1475/1476].

B50 *Rolment of Courtis, (Habbakuk Bisset's Rolment of Courtis,* ed. P. Hamilton-

Grierson, STS, 1920-26) ii, 128. Online - archive.org.

B51 *Rotuli Scotiae in Turri Londinansi et in Domo Capitulary Westmonasteriensi Asservati,* ed D. Macpherson et al (1814-19). 2 vols. Online - books.google.co.uk/. **B51a** Vol i, p. 258. Edward III, 1333 [Maison Dieu][Dominicans][Franciscans]. **B51b** Vol i, p.176, Edward I, 1296-7 [Maison Dieu]. **B51c** Vol i, p.25, Edward I 1296 [St Mary Magdalene]. **B51d** Vol i, p. 794, Edward III 1356 [St Mary Magdalene]. **B51e** Vol ii, p. 128, Richard II, 1395. [St Mary Magdalene]. **B51f** Vol i, p. 272, Edward III, 1334. [St Mary Magdalene]. **B51g** Vol i, p. 704, Edward III, 1347. [St Mary Magdalene]. **B51h** Vol i, p.719, Edward III, 1348.[St Mary Magdalene]. **B51j** Vol i, p.34, Edward I, 1296. [Carmelites]. **B51k** Vol i, p.85, Edward II, 1310.[Countess of Buchan and Carmelites]. **B51m** Vol i, p. 258, Edward III. 1333.[Carmelites][Augustinians]. **B51n** Vol i, p.23, Edward I, 12 April 1296.[Cistercian Nunnery]. **B51p** Vol i, p. 267, Edward III, 4 March, 1334[Cistercian Nunnery]. **B51q** Vol i, p. 416, Edward III, 20 April 1336. [Cistercian Nunnery]. **B51r** Vol i, p. 258, Edward III, 1333 [Scots replaced] [Franciscans]. **B51s** Vol i, p 25, Edward I, 1296 [Segden]. **B51t** Vol ii, p 15, Richard II, 1379.[Segden]. **B51u** Vol i, p. 257, Edward III, 1333 [Cistercian Nunnery]. **B51v** Vol i, p.39, Edward I, 1296 [Domus Dei]. **B51w** Vol i, p. 266, Edward III, 1333-1334 [Domus Dei]. **B51x** Vol i, p. 318, Edward III, 1334-1335 [Dominicans]. **B51y** Vol i, p. 399, Edward III, 1335-1336 [Dominicans]. **B51z** Vol i, p, 486, Edward III, 1336-1337 [Dominicans]. **B51aa** Vol i, p. 492-493, Edward III, 1337 [Domus Dei]. **B51ab** Vol i, p. 526-527, Edward III, 1338 [Dominicans]. **B51ac** Vol i, p. 608, Edward III, 1341 [Franciscans][Dominicans]. **B51ad** Vol i, p. 639, Edward III, 1343 [Dominicans]. **B51ae** Vol i, p. 698, Edward III, 1347 [Domus Dei]. **B51af** Vol i, p. 703, Edward III, 1347 [Domus Dei].

B52 *Scalacronica,* by Sir Thomas Gray of Heton Knight, Maitland Club, 1836) p. 241. Online - archive.org.

B53 Speed, John. *Historie of Great Britaine under the conquests of the Romans, Saxons, Danes and Normans.* London, 1611. Online - books.google.co.uk/.

B54 Stevenson, J. *Transcripts from the Treasury of Durham…..*

B55 *The Taxation of Ecclesiastical Benefices for Papal Tenths within the Southern District of Scotland*; an Appendix to *Correspondence, Inventories, Account Rolls and Law Proceedings of the Priory of Coldingham,* 'Surtees Society', ed Raine, J, 1840.

B56 Topographical Dictionary of Scotland, 1846. Online - british-history.ac.uk/.

B60 *Berwick Advertiser* newspaper. Some coverage online - britishnewspaperarchive.co.uk.

B61 Swain, Hedley. Introduction. *Archaeological Journal*, Vol 172, Suppl, pp 1-47, 2015.

B62 Exchequer Accounts, 386, no. 10, 1333.

B63 Chaucer, Geoffrey. The Canterbury Tales. New Translation by Gerald J. Davis. Insignia Publishing, 2016. ISBN 978-1533594600.

B64 Armstrong, Robert Bruce. The History of Liddesdale, Eskdale, Ewesdale, Wauchopedale, and the Debateable Land. Part I ... to 1530. [With plates.] Edinburgh : David Douglas, 1883. p.88.

B65 Stopford, J. Medieval Floor Tiles of Northern England, Oxford, Oxbow, 2005. ISBN 1842171429.

B66 Pilgrimage to Rome in the Middle Ages : continuity and change, by Debra J. Birch. Woodbridge: Boydell Press, 1998. ISBN 0851156363.

C. Local Sources (Berwick, Berwickshire, Durham, Northumberland, Newcastle, Lothian, Borders) [See also Sections A-B above]

C1 AN ARCHAEOLOGICAL EVALUATION AT PALACE GREEN, BERWICK-UPON-TWEED, NORTHUMBERLAND. Written and Researched by Jennifer Proctor Pre-Construct Archaeology Limited. April 2001.

C2 Archaeology Data Services: http://archaeologydataservice.ac.uk/archsearch/basic.xhtml.

C3 *Archaeology in Northumberland:* 1997-98, 8-9. [annual newsletter]. *Medieval archaeology* : journal of the Society for Medieval Archaeology, 42/1998, 148.

C4 *Archaeology in Northumberland:* 2001-2002, 21-22.

C5 *Archaeology north : the news bulletin of the Council for British Archaeology Regional Group Three.* 20/Summer 2002, p. 28. **C5b** 14/1976, p.6. [Also: /1977/142 for 1976 Excavations??]

C6 Berwick Archives. https://www.northumberlandarchives.com/about/. **C6a** Property between Western Lane & Bankhill, formerly known as Ravensdale, c 1810. U3/8. **C6b** Ravensdale. Property between Western Lane and Bankhill. U3/1-27. **C6c** Chapel of Ravensdale - lease. 1st February 1614. F32/8.

C7 Berwick-upon-Tweed Conservation Area. Berwick-upon-Tweed Borough Council, March 2008. Online - northumberland.gov.uk/

C8 Bourn R/2000/Palace Green, Berwick-upon-Tweed: archaeological desk-based assessment. Tyne & Wear Museums Archaeology Department; [assessment & evaluation reports].

C9 Briden C & Moore G/2001/Palace Green, Berwick upon Tweed, Northumberland: note on the results of opening-up and investigation within a group of outbuildings on the site.

C10 Clack, P A G and Gosling, P F, eds 1976. Archaeology in the North: report of the Northern Archaeology Group. 304p. Also, companion Volume: *Archaeology in the North: Gazetteer.* 1975.

C11 Convey, John. Berwick-upon-Tweed: a view from the walls. Berwick-upon-Tweed, John Convey, 2017. ISBN 0995462119; 978-0995462113.

C12 Cowe, F, Berwick-upon-Tweed: a short historical guide. Berwick, 1975. (Revised edition, 1998). ISBN 0 9533130 0 X.

C13 "The Friars of Berwick". [See A2 & A15 above, and C14 below]. **C13a** The Friars of Berwick. Freely adapted from a poem attributed to William Dunbar. A play in one act. John Meiklejohn Stewart MACCABE. Glasgow : Brown, Son & Ferguson, [1952]. **C13b** Article: 'The Freiris of Berwik and Chaucerian Fabliau'. *Studies in Scottish Literature,* Vol 17 (1), Jan 1982. R. D. S. Jack. **C13c** [Mediaeval Pageant (in modern English):
https://books.google.co.uk/books?id=3i8nmdU7ge8C&pg=PA55&dq=friars+berwick+Dunbar&hl=en&sa=X&ved=0ahUKEwiB5K_oxOTYAhXGJ-cAKHcPHBf0Q6AEIJzAA#v=onepage&q=friars%20berwick%20Dunbar&f=false]

C14 The friars of Berwick : a narrative poem in Scots / edited with an introduction by Duncan Glen. Kirkcaldy : Akros, 2002. ISBN : 0861421337
C15 Fuller, John. The History of Berwick-upon-Tweed. Third Edition. Newcastle-upon-Tyne: Frank Graham, 1973. SBN 902833081. [First edition 1799].
C16 Guild Books, Extracts from: Research Report Series No 7-2015, English Heritage, '2 Love Lane/64 West Street....etc', ISSN 2046-9799 (Print) ISSN 2046-9802 (Online)
C17 Herbert, Jim. Defences and fortifications. Archaeology in Northumberland 2006, pp 19-21.
C18 Historical Account of Newcastle-Upon-Tyne Including the Borough of Gateshead (Newcastle-upon-Tyne, 1827), pp. 134-137. Online - britishhistory.ac.uk/
C19 History of Newcastle and Gateshead Vol. I. Fourteenth and Fifteenth Centuries, Edited by Richard Welford, London: Walter Scott, 14 Paternoster Square. 1884. Online - archive.org.
C20 The history and antiquities of the town and county of the town of Newcastle upon Tyne: ....By John Brand, ...1789.. [pt.1] Online - http://ota.ox.ac.uk/text/5299.html
C21 The history of Newcastle upon Tyne: or, the ancient and present state of that town. By the late Henry Bourne, 1736. Online - http://ota.ox.ac.uk/text/5244.html
C22 Leper hospital at Berwick. In: 'English Guilds', ed Toulon Smith, Early English Text Society, os, xl (1870), p. 341. Online - books.google.co.uk/
C23 Menuge, A. Berwick-upon-Tweed: three places, two nations, one town. Swindon: English Heritage, 2009. ISBN 978 1 84802 029 0.
C24 NMR *Excavation Index.* http://archaeologydataservice.ac.uk/archives/view/304/. **C24a** *Land at Palace Green [Carmelites].* **C24b** *Palace Green [Carmelites].* **C24c** *Palace Street East [Carmelites].* HER 2502. Main source: DOE, 1977. Archaeological Excavations 1976. London: HMSO (142). **C24d** *Palace Green [Carmelites].*
C25 Northern Archaeological Associates, 1997. Land Next to Tintagel House, Berwick upon Tweed. Archaeological evaluation. (NAA 97/54).
C26 Northumberland Communities website: https://communities.northumberland.gov.uk
C27 Northumberland Extensive Urban Survey, 2009. Online - northumberland.gov.uk/
C28 'Partial Survey' of Berwick, 1297. (Berwick Archives)
C29 Proctor J/2001/An archaeological evaluation at Palace Green, Berwick-upon-Tweed, Northumberland. Pre-Construct Archaeology [reports].
C30 Scott, John. Berwick-upon-Tweed: the history of the town and Guild. 1888. Online - archive.org, and British Library Explore database.
C31 1562 Survey of Berwick.(Berwick Archives)
C32 TINTAGEL HOUSE, LOVE LANE, Berwick-upon-Tweed, Northumberland ARCHAEOLOGICAL WATCHING BRIEF DURING CUTTING OF FOUNDATION PITS FOR BALCONY. April 2003. Prepared for The Tintage/ House Partnership by: Alan Williams Archaeology.
C33 Pattinson, Tom. Saint Leonard's Hospital Alnwick: outline history and excavation report. Alnwick County Secondary School, 1975.
C34 Excavations at Walkergate, Berwick, 2006. Final Archive Report. John Mabbitt

Terry Frain Nick Hodgson. April 2010. Report Number: 673. OASIS Ref: Tyneandw3-22597.

C35 Fasti Dunelmenses - A Record of the Beneficed clergy of the Diocese of Durham down to the Dissolution of the Monastic and Collegiate Houses. Online - archive.org.

C36 Walker, Jim. Berwick Upon Tweed Through Time. Stroud : Amberley Publishing, 2009. ISBN 9781848685604; ISBN 9781445626888 (Electronic book (EPUB format));

D. Catalogues, Dictionaries, listings etc

D1 Alumni Cantabrigienses (Cambridge). Online - archive.org.

D2 Alumni Oxonienses 1500-1714. Online - british-history.ac.uk/

D3 British Library group of online catalogues, including the Integrated Catalogue 'Explore'. http://www.bl.uk/reshelp/findhelprestype/catblhold/all/allcat.html

D4 Dictionary of Medieval Latin. (http://www.dmlbs.ox.ac.uk/publications/online).

D5 Dictionary of National Biography. [Available online via several public library websites].

D6 Greek and Latin Dictionary. http://logeion.uchicago.edu

D7 Historic Environment Record Reports. **D7a** HER 2453 [Friars of the Sack]. **D7b** HER 2714 [21 Castle Terrace]. **D7c** HER 2452 [St Mary's]. **D7d** HER [West Hope]. **D7e** HER 4134 [St Nicholas]. **D7f** HER 4135 [St Bartholomew's Hospital][Leper House?]. **D7g** HER 2449 [Dominicans]. **D7h** HER 2712. **D7j** HER 2454 [Maison Dieu]. **D7k H**ER 2437 [St Mary Magdalene]. **D7m** HER 2450 [Carmelites]. **D7n** HER 2502 [Carmelites]. Main source: DOE, 1977. Archaeological Excavations 1976. London: HMSO (142). **D7p** HER 13332 [Palace Green/Carmelites]. **D7q** HER 14949 [Palace Green/Carmelites]. **D7r** HER 23697 [Palace Street East/Silver Street]. **D7s** HER 27443/27444 [Palace Street/Governor's Gardens] Main source: Lotherington, R, 2014. Interim Excavation Rpt - Governors Gardens, Berwick-upon-Tweed. **D7t** HER 2451 [Franciscans]. **D7u** HER 2392. [Segden]. **D7v** HER 2456. [Segden].

D8 Historic Environment Scotland. Historic properties across Scotland; archives and research; publications; advice and support etc. https://www.historicenvironment.scot. **D8a** Historic Scotland. https://www.historicenvironment.scot/visit-a-place/places/cross-kirk-peebles/history/

D9 Keys to the Past - Northumberland and Durham. http://www.keystothepast.info/article/8749/KeysToThePast-Home-Page.

D10 Listed Buildings in Scotland. https://www.historicenvironment.scot/advice-and-support/listing-scheduling-and-designations/listed-buildings/search-for-a-listed-building/

D11 Listed Buildings in England. https://historicengland.org.uk/listing/the-list/

D12 Martin, Charles Trice. The Record Interpreter: Abbreviations, Latin Words and Names used in English Historical Manuscripts and Records, 1892. Online - archive.org.

D13 National Library of Scotland - https://www.nls.uk/catalogues.

D14 National Records of Scotland (National Archives of Scotland). Online -

webarchive.nrscotland.gov.uk/
D15 Northumberland County Library Catalogue. northumberland.spydus.co.uk/
D16 Northumberland Archives Online Catalogue - northumberlandarchives.com/
D17 Oxford English Dictionary. Printed volumes available in large libraries; many public libraries make available digital versions: http://www.oed.com
D18 Historic England Research Records - over 420,000 records on archaeological, architectural and maritime sites held in the National Record of the Historic Environment (NRHE). https://www.heritagegateway.org.uk/gateway/
D19 Some notes of Medieval English Genealogy. http://www.medievalgenealogy.org.uk/index.html

E. Maps and Plans

E1 "*The true description of Her Majesties town of Barwick;*" about 1570-1580. See Cotton Ms. Titus C.XIII, Cotton Ms. Titus F.XIII. Article 36, and Harley Ms. 151.[Held in BL]
E2 1725 Map of Berwick, *A Plan of Berwick upon Tweed.* [Held in the British Library].
E3 Northumberland County Council Planning website, for recent (post-1974) planning applications etc. Has very useful current large-scale Ordnance Survey maps.
E4 Ordnance Survey Maps (Current). https://osmaps.ordnancesurvey.co.uk

F. Trinitarians and St Edwards Hospital

[See also Sections A-E above, including A7, A35, B8, B9, B11, B13, B15, B17, B39, B47, B49, C16, C27, C30].

F1 Bain. 'Notes on the Trinitarians or Red Friars of Scotland, etc' *Proceedings of the Society of Antiquaries of Scotland (PSAS)*, X, (1887-8), pp 26-32. Online - archaeologydataservices.ac.uk/
F2 Dubé, Steve. The Cross Kirk, Peebles. Kirklands Press: Peebles, 2016. ISBN 978-0-9956703-03.
F3 Event No 13187, Love Lane/Bridge Terrace, Tyne and Wear Museums, 1998.
F4 Gunn, Dr. The Manual of the Cross Church, Peebles. Alan Smith: Peebles, 1914.
F5 Kettins Church. http://www.ardler-kettins-meigle.org.uk/kettins-parish.html
F6 National Records of Scotland. Reference CH2/518. Title Records of Kettins Kirk Session. Dates 1682-1875
F7 National Records of Scotland. Reference DD27/3679. Title: Dovecot (Remains of Red Friars' Monastery), Dunbar, East Lothian. Departmental cipher 22772/1/A
F8 Renwick, Robert. *Aisle and Monastery,* Glasgow, 1897. pp 71-74.
F9 Trinitarians website (Modern day): http://www.trinitarians.org/index.html

G. Dominicans

[See also Sections A-E above, including A7, B6, B8, B9, B15, B17, B23, B24,

B30, B36, B37, B51, C16, C27, C30].

G1 Brand, John. *History and Antiquities of ….Newcastle-upon-Tyne*. 1789. An inside view of the Monastery of Blackfriars…..

G2 Bamburgh Dominican Friars [with plan]. *Archaeology in Northumberland*, 1993-1994, p 11.

G2b Berwick Franciscan Friary, *Archaeology in Northumberland*, 1993-1994, p. 24.

G3 Bibliotheque de Bordeaux. MS 780 fo.42r; *Dominican History Newsletter*, iv, 1996, 111.

G4 Black Friars of Edinburgh. [With a plate and plans.] Bryce, William Moir. 1911. R.234.a. Online - archive.org.

G5 Foggie, Janet P. *The Dominicans in Scotland*, 1450-1560. University of Edinburgh 1998.

G6 Foggie, Janet P. Renaissance religion in urban Scotland : the Dominican order, 1450-1560 / Leiden ; Boston : Brill, 2003. x, 343 p. : ill. ; 25 cm. ISBN:9004129294.

G7 Garrett F/2004/Love Lane, Berwick-upon-Tweed. Archaeological Watching Brief. Tyne & Wear Museums Archaeology Department [assessment & evaluation reports]. Report No 137.

G8 Harbottle, R.B., and Fraser, R. Blackfriars, Newcastle upon Tyne, after the Dissolution of the Monasteries. *Archaeologica Aeliana*, 5, 15, 1987, 23-149. Online - dropbox.com.

G9 Knowles, W.H. The Black Friars Monastery in Newcastle. *Archaeologica Aeliana* 3, 17, 1920, pp 314-336. Online - dropbox.com. Includes bibliographical references and index.

G10 Order of Preachers (Dominican) website: https://www.english.op.org/about-us.htm

G11 Regesta Regum Scottorum, ed Barrow, G.W., ch 131 pp 192-5, Edinburgh 1960.

G12 Ryder, Peter. Bamburgh Friary [Dominican]. *Archaeology in Northumberland* 1992-1993 p. 14. Includes a plan of the Friary.

G13 Victoria County History of the County of York, Vol. 3. (fn. 11) [Footnote 11 = 11. Cf. Worc. Cath. Lib. MS. Q. 93 (fly leaf).] pp 283-296. Online - british-history.ac.uk/.

H. Friars of the Sack

[See also Sections A-E & Q, including A1, A7, B9, B45, C16, C27, C30, Q2].

H1 Chettle, 'Friars of the Sack in England', *Downside Review*, 63 (1945), pp 239-57.

H2 Victoria County History of Sussex. Volume IX, 1937, p. 43.

J. Maison Dieu Hospital

[See also Sections A-E above, including A7, B7, B8, B9, B10, B11, B15, B16, B32, B39, B41, B51, C2, C10, C27, D7, C30, M1a].

J1 Documents and Records Illustrating the History of Scotland, ed F. Palgrave, London, 1837; i, nos xviii, cxii.

J2 Hodgson, *History of Northumberland*, II, ii, 503-4. Online - archive.org.
J3 Maison Dieu/Domus Dei/God's House. Sketches of Ord House and Maison Dieu….Miscellaneous Documents. Berwick Record Office Date. BRO17/6/c.
J4 Maison Dieu/Domus Dei/God's House. Petitions to the King 1333-1334 re destruction of buildings etc. Held at National Archives - Special Collections. Ref: SC 8/33/1608.
J5 National Archives: Writ of assise of novel disseisin to the sheriff of Northumberland for trial before the… C 47/22/1/27 Date: 1291 May 22.
J6 Petitioners: Brothers and sisters of the Houser of God of Berwick-upon-Tweed, Held at National Archives, Special Collections, 1333-1334. Ref SC 8/34/1659.
J7 Reports of the Royal Commission on Historical Manuscripts, London, 1870; 12th Report, App, pt, viii, 174. Online - babel.hathitrust.org/
J8 Unidentified ruins of church; on reverse Marygate Street looking up to Scotsgate; no dates. [pre-1869]. Berwick Record Office BRO 17/4/b.

K. Bondington, St Laurence, St Mary, Cistercian Nunnery
[See also Sections A-E above, including A6, A7, A9, A21, A35, B2, B4, B8, B9, B11, B12, B15, B18, B19, B20, B21, B26, B28, B31, B46, B49, B50, B51, B52, B55, B56, C10, C30, D7].

K1 Anderson, *Early Sources (of Scottish History, 500-1286,* ed. A.O. Anderson, Edinburgh, 1922). **K1a** ii [Nunnery, North Berwick?], 221 . **K1b** ii, 525. [Franciscans] **K1c** ii, 521 [Holy Trinity Church]
K2 Border Archaeological Society information panel, 21 Castle Terrace, Berwick.
K3 Cambridge, Eric, Gates, Tim, and Williams, Alan. Berwick and Beyond: Medieval Religious Establishments on the North Western Margin of Berwick-upon-Tweed— Problems of Identity and Context. *Archaeologia Aeoliana* 5, 29, 2001. 33-94. Online - dropbox.com.
K4 HER 2714 [21 Castle Terrace]. **K4a** Letter, A Williams, 25-Jul-1998. DCMS (IAM) Ams England SM32762 09-MAY-2001 Berwick Advertiser March 1941 Local Board of Health Plan, 1852. **K4b** The Archaeological Practice, 1998. Archaeological evaluation of a church and graveyard at 21 Castle Terrace, Berwick-upon-Tweed. Unpublished. **K4c** Langston, J, 2000. The Human Skeletal Material from Berwick-upon-Tweed (site code BCT98). Unpublished report. **K4d** [As Ref **K10**] Chappell, B, (ed) 2004. Putting Bondington on the Map: a report on the history and archaeology of Bondington (Steering Group of the Bondington Project) . **K4e** Unknown, 1999. Rescue Recording of a church and graveyard: 21 Castle Terrace, Berwick-upon-Tweed: Assessment Report and Updated Project Design. Unpublished The Archaeological Practice report.
K5 How Bondington was put on the map. Phase 2. Second Report on the History and Archaeology of Bondington, Steering Group of the Bondington Project, 2007. ISBN 0954920937.
K6 Liber S. Marie de Dryburgh. Registrum cartarum Abbacie. Online - archive.org. **K6a** Liber S. Marie de Dryburgh. Registrum cartarum Abbacie…… Page xv, note 5. **K6b** Cistercian Nuns of South Berwick. No 37 (1219). **K6c** Same….No 270 (1232). [Cistercian Nunnery]. **K6d** Master of same. Nos

35-36 (1204-1232).

K7 Liber Sancta Marie de Melros: munimenta vetustiora monasterii cisterciensis de Melros. **K7a** No. 142. Online - archive.org. **K7b** Same. No 144.

K8 Morrison J/2002/An archaeological evaluation at West Hope, Berwick-upon-Tweed, Northumberland. Headland Archaeology [assessment & evaluation reports].

K9 National Records of Scotland. GD157. Title 18th century notes on Dryburgh Abbey Charters. Dates 1166-1908. **K9b** Reference GD157. Reference GD157/368. **K9c** GD157/368 4. Instrument, 12 December 1465, anent acres in Berwick pertaining to priory of South Berwick.... **K9d** GD157/368 4. Instrument, (8th yr of Martin V, on day of Saint Margaret the virgin, 1424/5),........... property in Berwick owned by said priory. **K9e** GD157/368 6. Great seal charter by Edward, to prioress and nuns of Berwick ......20 April ar 10th. [1337?] **K9f** GD157/368 12. Papal bull of Nicolas III to prioress and convent of South Berwick [in Diocese of St Andrews] containing confirmation and indulgence, 1279. **K9g** GD157/368 12. Papal bull of Innocent IV [1243-1254] in favour of Prioress of South Berwick, "*whereof the date cannot be read*"! **K9h** GD157/368 13. Charter by William Spurr, burgess of Berwick, to Saint Leonard of South Berwick and monks, of a bovate of land in territory of Bandington. [In Latin]. Publication note: charter by William Spurr published by W W Scott in 'Eight Thirteenth-Century Texts', in 'Miscellany XIII' (Scottish History Society, 2004).

K10 *Putting Bondington on the map*. Report on the History and Archaeology of Bondington, 2004. ISBN 0954920902.

K11 *Putting Bondington on the map: Berwick and its Lost Northern Suburb*. The Steering Group of the Bondington Project, 2005. ISBN 0-9549209-2-9.

K12 Rogers, C: Chartulary of the Cistercian Priory of Coldstream, Grampian Club, 1879. Online - archive.org.

K13 Smith, Andrew, (2011) The Kelso Abbey cartulary: context, production and forgery. PhD thesis. (Univ of Glasgow). Online - theses.gla.ac.uk/

K14 SYLLABUS OF SCOTTISH CARTULARIES. Kelso Lib. (Bann.Cl., ed. C.Innes, 1846). Online - scottishmedievalcharters.files.wordpress.com

K15 Religious women and their communities in late medieval Scotland. Curran, Kimberly Ann. University of Glasgow, 2005. Thesis.

L. Franciscans

[See also Sections A-E, G, K including A5, A7, A12, B6, B8, B15, B17, B31, B35, B36, B37, B51, C10, C27, C30, D7, G2b, K1].

L1 Archaeological Excavations at Jedburgh Friary 1983-1992 [Paperback]. Piers Dixon (Author); Jerry O'Sullivan (Author); Ian Rogers (Author). ISBN: 9780951934470. Published by : STAR Scottish Trust for Arch.Research

L2 Army Plea Roll, Edward i. Online - deremilitari.org/

L3 Bryce, W. Moir: *The Scottish Grey Friars*, Edinburgh, 1909. i, 6. Online - archive.org/

L4 *Chronica de Mailros*, Bannatyne Club, 1835, 142. Online - archive.org/

L5 GD1 Miscellaneous small collections of family, business and other papers. GD1/39 Dates 9 Apr 1490. Access status Open. Location - on site: National

Records of Scotland.

L6 The history of the Franciscan Friary of Jedburgh, with some account of Adam Bell, its Historian Friar.. Author(s): Watson, George, 1876-1950. [S.l., 1906?], p. 82-88 ; 8vo.

L7 *Joannis de Fordun Scotichronicon cum Supplementis et Continuatione Walteri Boweri,* ed. Goodall, Edinburgh, 1759, ii, 59. Online - babel.hathitrust.org/.

L8 Mandate. 4th June 1334. 4 Kal. June. Avignon. (f. 138d.) Mandate to pronounce sentence of excommunication against Robert Brus.. Online - british-history.ac.uk/

L9 National Archives Refs C 47/22/2/33, C 47/22/2/32, 47/22/2/34 Writ to the Treasurer of Scotland.. 1296 Nov 23, CMR 474

L10 National Archives Ref C 47/32/1/3 Report to the Cardinals by Adam de Neuton, Date: 1317 Dec 20.

L11 Robson, Michael. *The Franciscans in the middle ages.* Boydell Press, 2008. ISBN 1843832216.

L12 **John Duns Scotus. L12a** Balic, Fr Charles, O.F.M.] (*New Catholic Encyclopedia,* Vol. 4, p. 1105). **L12b** Blessed John Duns Scotus : Friar Minor (1265-1305). 1980 HP2.93.6542. **L12c** Cross, Richard. Duns Scotus. [Great Medieval Thinkers series]. Oxford University Press, 1999. ISBN 0-19-512552-5 (Hardback). **L12d F**ranciscan Media: https://www.franciscanmedia.org/blessed-john-duns-scotus/. **L12e** Historia Maioris Britanniae, tam Angliae quam Scotiae, per Ioannem Maiorem, nomine quidem Scotum,…by Major, John, 1521. Online - archive.org/. **L12f** Medieval Christian philosophers : an introduction / Richard Cross. **L12g** Philosophy of John Duns Scotus / Antonie Vos. Vos, A. Antonie) 2006. **L12h** Torrance, James B & Walls. Roland C. John Duns Scotus in a nutshell. Edinburgh: The Handsel Press Ltd, 1992. ISBN 1871828 19 8.

L13 Website of Franciscans (Modern Day): http://www.friar.org

L14 Apostolic poverty at the ends of the earth : the Observant Franciscans in Scotland, c.1457-1560. Strauch, Christina Arja. University of Edinburgh, 2007. Thesis.

L15 Bradley, Jeremy and Rowland, Stephen. Brothers Minor: Lancashire's lost Franciscans; investigations at Preston Friary, 1991 and 2007. Oxford Archaeology North, 2020. ISBN 978-1-907686-35-1.

M. St Mary Magdalene Hospital

[See also Sections A-E above, including A7, A28, B8, B11, B15, B17, B40, B42, B51, C10, C30, D7].

M1a *Register of Thomas Langley, bishop of Durham.* Surtees Society, i, no. 90. [Register of Thomas Langley, Bishop off Durham 1406-1437, Storey, R.L. Ed, 6 vols, Surtees Society 164, 166, 169, 170, 177, 182 (1949-79). **M1b** i, no 210.

N. Holy Trinity

[See also Sections A-E & K, including A21, B8, B54, C2, C30, K1].

N1 [V, 7, 1 Faustina, A.V. 1, 12b] Holy Trinity.

P. St Nicholas

[See also Sections A-E above, including B7, B8, C30, D7].

P1 The National Archives, Kew. [St Nicholas' Tower] Reference: MPF 1/300: 1 item extracted from SP 59/2 (folio 127). Date: [1560]

Q. Carmelites

[See also Sections A-E above, including A1, A7, A9, A12, B6, B8, B11, B15, B17, B23, B35, B36, B39, B45, B51, B53, C1, C2, C5, C24, C27, C30, D7].

Q1 *Archaeologica Aeliana:* Knowles, W. H. Recent Excavations on the site of the Carmelites, or White Friars, at Newcastle. 2, 13, 1889, 346-350. Online - dropbox.com/

Q2 Brand, J. *Hist of Newcastle* (1789), i, 60-4. Volume i, pp 58-59.

Q3 Dennison, E Patricia & Coleman, Russel. *Historic Linlithgow: the archaeological implications for development.* Edinburgh: Historic Scotland, 2000. ISBN 1 84017 013 1.

Q4 Egan, Keith J. Medieval Carmelite Houses: England and Wales, pp 1-85. In: *Carmel in Britain; essays on the Medieval English Carmelite Province*, Volume 1: People and Places: Carmelite Provincial Office, Aylesford, 1992. ISBN: 88-7288-024-6.

Q6 English Heritage Archives. Photographs and documents on England's historic buildings and archaeological sites. Online - englishheritagearchives.or.uk/

Q7 Harbottle, R.B. Contributions by Gillam, J.P. et al. Excavations at the Carmelite Friary, Newcastle upon Tyne, 1965 and 1967, 4,46, 1968, 163-224. Online - dropbox.com/

Q8 Little, A.G. *The White Friars of Berwick.* Unpublished account in Bodleian Library. Ms. Eng. hist. c. 348/4. [More likely now [2018] under MS. Eng. hist. c. 972 folios 49r, 50r, 51r]

Q9 Northumberland Library Catalogue: Online - northumberland.spydus.co.uk/. **Q9a** Carmel in Britain: Essays on the medieval English Carmelite province. :Volume 2: Theology and writing LR255.73 Pub date 1992. **Q9b** Carmel in Britain :Volume 1: People and places LR255.73 Pub date 1992. **Q9c** Around the ruins of Hulne Priory. Maclean, Elsa. LR726.7. **Q9d** A handbook to Alnwick Castle, Hulne Park and Abbey : the dairy grounds, churches etc Author Ferguson, W.M. LR942.887 Pub date1911. **Q9e** Davison's new illustrated guide to Alnwick and North Northumberland.... Author Davison, John LR942.887 ALN Pub date 1910. **Q9f** A description of the hermitage of Warkworth. LR942.887 WAR Pub date 1888. **Q9g** A descriptive and historical view of Alnwick, the county town of Northumberland; Date: 1822.

Q10 Priory Church, South Queensferry. http://www.priorychurch.com/history.html

Q11 Quidenham Carmelite Convent, Norfolk. https://quidenhamcarmel.org.uk

Q12 Spearman, R.M. *Linlithgow Carmelite Friary: The documentary evidence.* Online - archaeologydataservices.ac.uk/

Q13 Three Scottish Carmelite Friaries....excavations at Aberdeen, Linlithgow and Perth, 1980-1983. J.A. Stones, editor. Edinburgh : Society of Antiquaries of Scotland, 1989.

Q14 White Friars. An outline Carmelite history, with special reference to the English-speaking provinces, etc. [With a portrait.] Maccaffray, Patrick Romaeus. 1926 R.20.d [

Q15 Woodhorn Archives catalogue, References to Carmelites in: https://www.northumberlandarchives.com/catalogue/

Q17 Web of British Province of Carmelites (Modern day): *http://www.carmelite.org*

R. St Bartholomew's Hospital, Spittal

[See also Sections A-E above, including A17, B45, C30, D7].

R1 Scott, J, 2010. Spittal Point, Spittal, Berwick-upon-Tweed, Northumberland: archaeological desk-based assessment. (Unpublished TWM Archaeology report 1047)

S. Augustinians

[See also Sections A-E above, including A1, A7, B6, B8, B9, B10, B11, B23, B36, B42, B51, C27, C30, D7].

S1 *The Augustinian Friary, Leicester.* CBA Research Report, 1981. Online - archaeologydataservices.ac.uk/. Also: Jean E. Mellor & Terry Pearce, *The Austin Friars, Leicester,* Leicestershire Archaeological Field Unit Report, Leicestershire Museums, Art Galleries and Record Service, 1981. Online - archaeologydataservices.ac.uk/

S2 Augustinian website: http://www.stjosephsbroomhouse.org.uk/the-augustinians.html See also: http://www.osa-oae.org/Provinciae/ANG.html

S3 Calendar of Inquisitions Miscellaneous (Chancery). Volumes 1, 2 (1916) & 3, 1916. Online - archive.org/. Volume 3 (1348-1377) Online - babel.hathitrust.org/. **S3a** Segden, Volume 2, 1333, no. 1402. **S3b** Segden, Volume 3, 1367, no. 647. **S3c** Segden (and island on Windermere), Volume 3, 1349, no. 167

S4 Chetham Society. Remains... [1st series], Vol. 30 : Documents relating to the Priory of Penwortham and other possessions in Lancashire of the Abbey of Evesham, edited by W.A. Hulton. Publisher Manchester : C.S, 1853.

S5 The Correspondence, Inventories, Account Rolls and Law Proceedings of the Priory of Coldingham, ed J. Raine (Suretees Society, London, 1841). page cxvi.

S6 The English Austin friars, 1249-1538 / by Francis Roth. Francis. Roth. New York: Augustinian Historical Institute, 1961-1966. 2 Vols (Volume 2 = Sources).

S7 Gorleston Augustinian Friary. [http://www.heritage.norfolk.gov.uk/record?tnf435]

T. St Leonard's Hospital & Leper House

[See also Sections A-E above, including A7, C30.

T1 Ancient Laws & Customs of the Burghs of Scotland, SBRS 1868-1910, i, 72. Online - archive.org/

Adam, Friar 18-19, 25
Ancrum
Trinitarians 26
Augustinians 66, 84-90
Bamburgh
Dominicans 37-38
Bell Tower Park 13, 34, 58-59
Bell Tower Place 13,
Black Friars (See Dominicans)
Bondington 11-13, 46-55, 69-70
bridge 10-11, 5, 19, 22-23, 29, 35, 41-45, 69
Bridge End 11, 22, 29
Bridge House 10-11, 19, 22-23, 42-43
Bridge Street 10, 22-23, 29
Briggate (see Bridge Street)
Buchan, Isabella Countess of 78
Carmelites
Berwick 15, 73-81
Hulne, [nr Alnwick] 73, 75-76, 80
Linlithgow 75, 80
Newcastle-upon-Tyne 80-81
South Queensferry 75, 80
Castle Terrace 11-12, 46-49, 51
Cheviot House 12, 47-49
Dirleton
Cistercian Order of Nuns 51
Trinitarians 26
Dissolution of the Monasteries 11, 13, 15, 16, 25-26, 29, 36, 39, 44, 59, 67, 76, 79, 83
Dominicans
Bamburgh 37-38
Berwick 10-11, 13, 22, 28-31, 32-40, 58,
Edinburgh 34, 36
Newcastle 19, 36-38
St Dominic de Guzman 32
Domus Dei (See Maison Dieu)
Domus Pontis (See Bridge House)
Dryburgh Abbey 50-51, 54
Dunbar
Trinitarians 19, 26
Edinburgh
Dominicans 34, 36
Franciscans 59
Franciscans
Berwick 13, 34, 56-63
Edinburgh 59
Haddington 56, 59
John Duns Scotus 59-60, 62
Newcastle-upon-Tyne 59-60
Friars of Berwick, The 38, 44, 79
Friars of the Sack 10-11, 27-31
Friars Minor (See Franciscans)
Governor's House & Gardens 15, 75, 77
Grey (Gray), Sir John 74
Grey Friars (See Franciscans)
Holy Trinity School 13, 34-35
Holy Trinity with St Mary, Church of 11, 14, 28, 47, 66, 68-70, 72, 75
Hospitals 10-11, 14, 16, 19-23, 26, 41-45, 48, 64-67, 82-83, 86-87, 90-91
House of God Hospital (See Maison Dieu)
Houston
Trinitarians 26
Hulne, [nr Alnwick]
Carmelites 73, 75-76, 80
John Duns Scotus 59-60, 62
Kettins, Church at 21
Kings of England
Henry III (1216-1272) 22, 38, 47
Edward I (1272-1307) 18, 34-36, 41,47,51,57,64,70,75, 85, 91
Edward II (1307-1327) 78-79
Edward III (1327-1377) 22, 38, 40, 53, 60-61, 65-66, 78, 86-87
Richard II (1377-1399) 67, 83
Henry VIII (1509-1547) 71
Kings of Scotland
David I (1124-1153) 47, 50-51, 54
Malcolm IV (1153-1165) 48
William I, the Lion(1165-1214) 19
Alexander II (1214-1249) 34
Alexander III (1249-1286) 41

Kings of Scotland continued
Robert I, the Bruce (1306-1329) 23, 61
Robert III (1390-1406) 54
James I (1406-1437) 44, 69
James III (1460-1488) 25, 39
Leper hospitals/houses 16, 19-20, 45, 64, 82-83, 90-91
Leper House 90-91 Linlithgow
Augustinians 74
Carmelites 75, 80
Lord's Mount 59
Love Lane 10-13, 22-23, 29, 31, 35-36
Maison Dieu hospital 11, 22-23, 41-45
Matha, St John de 17
Ness, The 15, 29, 55, 75, 79
Newcastle
Carmelites 80-81
Dominicans 19, 36-38
Franciscans 59-60
Friars of the Sack 30
Trinitarians 17, 26
Northumberland Avenue 14, 34, 58, 64
Nunneries
Berwick/Bondington 12-13, 50-55
Coldstream 53
Elbottle 53
Gullane 53
Haddington 53
North Berwick 53
St. Bothan's 53
St Leonard's, Bondington 12-13, 50-55
Order of Preachers (See Dominicans)
Peebles, Cross Kirk 10, 18, 24-25
Popes
Innocent III (1198-1216) 17
Honorius III (1216-1227) 32, 56
Gregory IX (1227-1241) 62
Innocent IV (1243-1254) 55
Boniface VIII (1294-1303) 60, 74
Urban V (1362-1370) 87
Sixtus IV (1471-1484) 40
Preachers, Order of (See Dominicans)
Queensferry, South
Carmelites 75-76, 80
Ravensdale, Chapel of 10, 22, 29-30, 36, 39
Red Friars (See Trinitarians)
Rye, Sussex
Friars of the Sack 31
Rydale, Philip de 41
Sack Friars, (See Friars of the Sack)
St Bartholomew, Church of 15
St Bartholomew's Leper Hospital, Spittal 16, 82-83
St Edward's Hospital 10, 19-22
St Felix of Valois 17
St Francis of Assisi 56
St John de Matha 17
St Lawrence, Church of 12, 46-49
St Leonard, Hospital of 90-91
St Leonards Nunnery 12-13, 50-55
St Mary, Churches of 11-13, 14, 46-50, 68-70
St Mary Magdalene Hospital 14, 20, 38, 64-67
St Nicholas, Church of 71-72
Scotus, John Duns 59-60, 62
Segden 14, 66-67, 85-88, 90 Spittal 16, 82-83
Tintagel House 11, 23, 29-30, 36
Trinitarian Order
Ancrum 26 Berwick 10, 17-26
Bridge House, Berwick 10-11, 19, 22-23
Dirleton 25-26
Dunbar 19, 26
Houston 26
Newcastle 17, 26
Seal, Berwick 18-19
True Description...Plan of c 1580 10, 14-15, 22, 33, 35, 42, 58, 68, 70, 75
Walkergate, unknown building 91
White Friars (See Carmelites)